D1072399

*Springtime
in Paris*

Books by ELLIOT PAUL

Items on the Grand Account

SPRINGTIME IN PARIS
MY OLD KENTUCKY HOME
A GHOST TOWN ON THE YELLOWSTONE
LINDEN ON THE SAUGUS BRANCH
THE LAST TIME I SAW PARIS
THE LIFE AND DEATH OF A SPANISH TOWN

Fiction

THE STARS AND STRIPES FOREVER
CONCERT PITCH
THE GOVERNOR OF MASSACHUSETTS
LAVA ROCK
LOW RUN TIDE
THE AMAZON
IMPERTURBE
IMPROMPTU
INDELIBLE

Homer Evans Murder Mysteries

THE MYSTERIOUS MICKEY FINN
HUGGER-MUGGER IN THE LOUVRE
MAYHEM IN B-FLAT
FRACAS IN THE FOOTHILLS
I'LL HATE MYSELF IN THE MORNING

Springtime
IN Paris

BY ELLIOT PAUL

Harold

Random House · New York

I wish to acknowledge with gratitude the invaluable aid and co-operation of Nancy McMahan in gathering material, conducting independent research, and preparing the text of this book.

E. P.

Copyright, 1950, by Elliot Paul

All rights reserved under International and Pan-American Copyright Conventions.

Published in New York by Random House, Inc., and simultaneously in Toronto, Canada, by Random House of Canada, Limited.

Second Printing

MANUFACTURED IN THE UNITED STATES OF AMERICA

U C
737
P4
1950
914436
P3 2 4s

My. 2050

Os 19 Sep 50 SUS 2.80 (Readers)

407169

To Saxe Commins

Contents

List of Characters

HOTEL AND CAFÉ KEEPERS

Hotel de Mont Souris

Gilles Wilf	Proprietor
Hubert Wilf	Proprietor
Armand Busse	Manager
Aristide Riboulet	Desk clerk
Lola	Chambermaid
Emile	Bellboy

Hotel Normandie

Madame Fontaine	Proprietress
Louis	One-armed garçon

Hotel de la Huchette

Monsieur Mercanton	Proprietor
Thérèse	Cook

Hotel du Caveau

Monsieur Oudin	Proprietor

Café St. Michel

Monsieur Trevise	Proprietor
Big Leonie	Waitress

Rahab (Oriental Night Club)

Aran Hatounian	Proprietor
Helen Hatounian	His wife
David Hatounian	Their son

SHOPKEEPERS AND STOREKEEPERS

Amiard	Orthopedic devices
Monsieur and Madame Salmon	Beef and lamb butchers
Fabian	Their son
Widow Villières	Paint shop, odds and ends
Raoul and Katya Roubait	Stationery and morning newspapers
Madame de Gran' Chemin	Afternoon newspapers
Noel	Taxidermist and market clerk
Monge	Horse butcher
St. Cricq	Shoemaker
Vignon	Grocer
Monsieur and Madame Gillotte	Bakers
Julian	Barber
Madame Fremont	Hand laundry
Hortense Berthelot	Florist
Mlle. Dunette (Swallow-tail)	Antiques
Monsieur Nathaniel	Oriental pastry
Cabat	Druggist
Simone	Registered nurse
Mlles. Pigotte	Cleaners and dyers
Monsieur and Madame Morizot	Corset makers
Madame Pendeleur	Vegetables and fruit
Monsieur Rintel	Vegetables and fruit
L'Oursin	Chestnut man

PROFESSIONAL MEN

Dr. Thiouville	Physician
The Satyr	Chef

PROFESSIONAL WOMEN

Irma	Street walker
Mado	
Consuela	
Daisy	Formerly of "Panier Fleuri"
Armandine	
Dora	

PUBLIC EMPLOYEES

Monsieur Mainguet	Statistician
E. Saillens and Sons	Government contractors
Adolphe	Plasterer
Jacques	Helper
Chouette	Truck driver
Le Taupier	Plumber
Monsieur Dehaupas	Schoolteacher

PRIVATE EMPLOYEES

Be-Bop	Clerk and musician
Maive Callahan	Nautch dancer
Lucien Violet, Aîné	Book dealer
Anatole Pillods	Book clerk
Achille Ithier	Clerk, anti-alcoholic society
The Jonquil	Concierge
Berthe Latouche	Teacher of shorthand

PRIESTS

The Very Reverend Leon d'Alexis, S.J.
Père F. M. Taillepied, O.P.

RUE XAVIER PRIVAS

Germaine Lefavrais	Restaurant worker
Victor	Her son
Messidor	Locksmith
Mignon	His niece
Doc Robinet	Herbalist
Prins	Printer
Madame Cirage	Concierge, No. 10

MISCELLANEOUS

Hermann Pflantz	Refugee
Miriam Pflantz	Refugee
Justin Dassary	Speculator
Carmen (Dassary) Orey	His daughter
Guy Orey	Carmen's husband
Pierre Vautier (Treves de la Berlière)	Painter
Bernard Kahnweiler	Art dealer and critic
Jeanne Piot	The Navet's wife
Eugene Piot	Their son
André de Poitevin	President of "The Friends of the Tree"
Antoinette de Poitevin	His daughter
Christophe	Pushcart man
Xavier	Great Dane
Monsieur Temeraire (Stemwinder)	The last Bonapartist
Monsieur Essling	Reporter
Comrade Rappaport	Subeditor of *L'Humanité*
The American Delegate	U.S. Communist
Garry Davis	First Citizen of the World

Springtime
in Paris

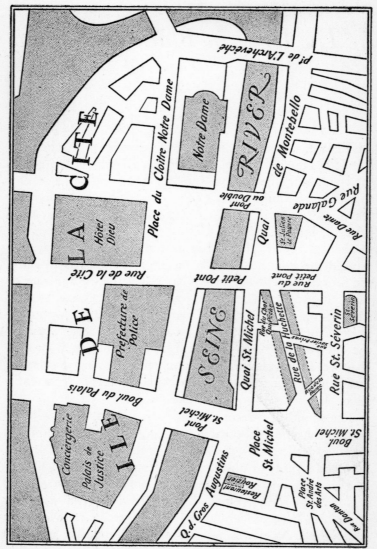

THE QUARTIER

1. *The Dove in Black and White*

AFTER an absence of nearly ten years, I approached the rue de la Huchette from the east, with Notre Dame across the river, at my back, just as the hour of noon was releasing so many working Parisians from their shops and offices. It was a raw, chilly day early in April. The sky was heavy and gray, the buildings and rooftops were moist. The pavements, in need of repair, gleamed in an uneven, desultory way. I crossed the Pont au Double, faced right, and passed along the foot of the churchyard of St. Julien the Poor, aware of early tulips, somewhat bent, inside the iron fence, shabby students on the benches like water birds waiting for an impulse, a few black-robed priests wearing berets instead of the old-time disc-like clerical hats, and children with bare chapped knees playing or idling with varying degrees of listlessness. The plants and the people were persistently alive.

The sound of a resonant bass voice startled me with its familiarity, and I noticed a group of men, about eight in number, gathered around another, younger than the others, who had a sheaf of posters under his arm. Suddenly I realized that the tall, gaunt man whose voice I had recognized was my old friend, Noel, the taxidermist of the *place* St. André des Arts, and a regular at the Caveau bar the last time I saw Paris. Noel was wearing what might have been the same beige linen duster and black felt hat, with limp string

3

tie, that he had bought in Clemenceau's time. He was older, and his clothes hung looser over his bony frame, but he seemed to have lost neither his dignity nor his serenity.

At Noel's left was Monge, the horse butcher of No. 13 rue de la Huchette, who as an avocation had played some kind of antique French horn. Monge had aged more visibly than his taller companion, but the way they stood there, side by side, glancing at each other from time to time as the discussion about the posters progressed, I felt sure that they were still close friends.

Among the others present, I remembered Monsieur Mainguet, a small neatly-dressed man with spectacles, a starched collar, detachable cuffs, with a small gold cross in his black four-in-hand. He had worked as a statistician in one of the numerous government ministries, changing jobs when prime ministers fell. Monsieur Mainguet had not aged or changed at all.

The strangers of the group around the posters included a gnome-like man with a large head and high-domed forehead, whose arms and body were long, and whose legs were short. His hands were large and expressive, and he used them constantly, gesturing. The others addressed him as Monsieur Amiard, and because he was taking the discussion more to heart and reacting more vehemently than anyone else, I suspected that Noel, a born joker, and Monsieur Mainguet, a shy but sly wit, were egging him on. It was certain that, although I had not known Monsieur Amiard, the men from the rue de la Huchette knew him quite well, as was the case with the young man in the center whom they called "Raoul."

From where I stood, it was easy to see the posters, other copies of which I already had noticed on billboards and walls from one end of Paris to the other in the few days just preceding. On each was a reproduction of a lithograph of a dove, in black and white, drawn in profile facing toward the right. Each bore the facsimile signature of Picasso. Above the picture of the symbolic bird was a lettered announcement of a "World Congress of the Partisans of Peace," to be held within a few weeks in the Salle Pleyel, the best of the Paris concert and assembly halls, in the Faubourg St. Honoré.

"Now there's a fine proletarian quarter for the Commies from all over the world!" said the taxidermist.

The gnome, Amiard, began to hop and almost to crackle.

"Who pays?" he demanded.

He turned to two men, both in working clothes, who were allied in some way, and openly in favor of the Dove and all it implied.

"Who pays?" Amiard repeated. "Not Russia!"

"The workers," said one of the men.

"What workers?"

"Union workers. . . . Their dues," suggested a mild man with a round face and a trace of flour in his hair. In spite of the cold, he wore no cap. It was another of my old friends, Gillotte, the baker, from No. 16, who had always deplored the existence of unions, in a mild, good-natured way.

"Not the Americans?" asked Noel. "They pay for practically everything in the end."

Raoul, who was proud of his posters, made haste to defend them, and the cause for which they stood. He was a healthy and engaging young man with alert gray eyes, a shock of wavy dark brown hair, and a russet outdoor complexion. Because at his feet there were a pot of paste, a brush, and a step-ladder, I concluded that he was posting the Dove bills noontimes, on a volunteer basis, and most likely was a member of the Communist Party. What he said left no doubt of that, but he was naturally enthusiastic, completely convinced, and not overzealous.

"Lots of American workers want peace," Raoul said, with no intention of making a humorous understatement.

Noel stepped in again. He would not let the subject rest.

"It seems to me," he said, appraising Picasso's artistry with unconcealed appreciation, "that the peace pigeon is one of those who can tumble and do flipflops in the air."

Mainguet smiled. "That will be indispensable for a bird who wishes to follow the Party line," he suggested.

"You ought to be ashamed, Monsieur Mainguet," Raoul said. "No one should make fun of peace."

"Peace, just lately, has become Communist property. The Kremlin's taken it over," Noel explained to Mainguet.

The latter nodded, and added, gently: "Without the Prince of Peace, of course."

Raoul was not to be diverted. "In my opinion the Congress can do a lot of good, not only for Communists—for everyone. Two thousand delegates are coming, from more than sixty different countries," he said.

"And who elected them?" Monsieur Amiard demanded. "Who says they're not Soviet spies?"

"They're men and women of reputation, internationally known," said Raoul. "Men of talent and ideas."

"And all against the Atlantic Pact and the Marshall Plan," said Amiard. "Why can't you fellows ever come out straight and say what you mean?"

"American aid has its dangers," insisted Raoul.

Forgetting myself, I suggested that the United States was not sending articles or equipment which could be manufactured in France.

"Arms are being sent," said one of the men in working

clothes. "Against whom is the United States arming Western Europe, if not against Russia?" he continued.

"Against no one," I said.

The man shrugged, mirthlessly. "That's a new item in history—arming against no one."

"And who is Stalin arming against?" asked Amiard, hotly.

"The Soviet Union menaces no one," Raoul said, calmly. "Peace is international. The Congress will demonstrate that." He made an expressive gesture toward the posters.

"Whoever pays the bills, someone must have printed a billion of these pigeons," said the horse butcher, Monge.

"Doves," I corrected him, through the iron fence.

Noel suddenly looked straight at me. He clutched Monge's sleeve, to turn him half around, and said, incredulously to me: "You're back again. Where did you come from? It's the American!"

Relieved by the warmth of their greetings, I hurried around to the gate, entered the churchyard and shook hands all around, with Noel, Monge, Gillotte, Mainguet and those I had not previously known. Raoul, it developed, had been in his teens, still in school, when I had left France in early 1940, but he remembered me and was pleased when I praised the art work on his posters, and the thoroughness with which he and his colleagues had spread them throughout Paris.

"There's a blank wall," I said, pointing across to the side of No. 1, rue de la Huchette, which had a rough, crumbling, plain surface up as far as the single second-story window. The battered little building had been sold to Monsieur Amiard, who was a trussmaker and dealer in orthopedic devices.

The two men in working clothes, both Communists, had rented from Amiard the second-floor room above the truss shop. It was the blank wall space below their window which I had indicated as an ideal place for Picasso dove posters.

Hotly Amiard declared that no Communist propaganda would be displayed on any wall belonging to him, not if world peace was hanging in the balance and depended on his decision. Amiard cared for no politicians, statesmen, or even for the Pope. He was a militant Free Thinker, and opposed to practically everything.

Raoul, anxious to dispose of his posters to the best advantage, was disappointed, but did not press the matter just then.

Shortly after lunch, Anatole, the book clerk, who was certainly the most sedentary young man ever to live in the neighborhood, wandered as far from the *place* St. Michel as No. 1 rue de la Huchette, a matter of 180 yards or so, but Monsieur Amiard noticed nothing unusual. He was still fuming from the discussion of the Peace Congress.

"Picasso! Ah, there's an artist!" Anatole began.

"It can't be hard to draw a bird—especially in black and white," the trussmaker insisted.

"In black and white, if you'll excuse me, such an effect is harder to obtain—the form, the tenderness. What shall I say? The plastic eloquence . . ."

"You're wasting your breath," grunted Amiard. "A bird is a bird, and any artist, great or small, who bothers with one, or sells a picture of one to the Reds, to flimflam humanity . . ."

"You've never sold a truss to a painter, I suppose?" asked Anatole.

"Not likely," Amiard said. "Only men who do men's work get ruptured and come into my shop."

"And women?" Anatole asked.

"They stretch too easily," the trussmaker said. "They seldom need repairs, in my line."

Try as he might, Anatole found difficulty in making an opening. At last, he said:

"If I had a wall, I'd be proud to have Picasso's work on it, no matter what the printing said."

"Stick them up in your windows, if you like, and your employer's fool enough to let you," said Amiard. Then he caught on that Anatole was behaving self-consciously and almost exploded. "Who put you up to this? Those scheming Reds? Those traitors? Not one of those posters will go on my walls, if I have to guard the premises with a shotgun, night and day. Tell that to whoever sent you! I'm disillusioned. I thought you were my friend!"

"Alas," Anatole said, when he returned to the Normandie bar. "My old father was right. I've little force, and still I'm no diplomat."

It was l'Oursin, the Chestnut Man, who had survived the toughest kind of guerrilla service on and off the coast of Finisterre, who came up with the next suggestion to the Communist tenants of Amiard's room.

"After all. If you want to put one of those posters in your window, your landlord can't stop you, can he?"

So, the next noon, when the group, somewhat enlarged, took a stroll over to the churchyard of St. Julien, the entire window space on the eastern side of Amiard's building, second floor, was occupied by two of the largest-sized Dove posters, in full view of all passers-by.

When twelve o'clock sounded on his elaborate Swiss clock that struck the quarter hours, the trussmaker, blinking like a dissatisfied owl, put aside the pad he was making, removed his apron, slipped on a jacket, stepped out to the narrow sidewalk, turned, and locked his door from the outside, with a large iron key. He felt relatively tranquil that morning, since the Dove distribution in the street seemed to have been accomplished to the satisfaction of Raoul and everyone concerned. Those who were foolish enough to permit propaganda displays inimical to France were punishing themselves by so doing, he thought.

Actually, considering that the number of active Communists in the rue de la Huchette was only twelve, from a voting population of three hundred, Raoul had done rather well in publicizing his World Congress. The Dove appeared in the windows of the new drugstore at No. 12, on the corner of the tiny rue du Chat qui Pêche.

Katya, the zealous young Lithuanian woman who had married Raoul and kept him up to scratch in ideological and tactical matters, had taken it upon herself to appropriate the front and side walls of the Panier Fleuri, the former bordel run by Madame Mariette. The four-story building, a few years ago so neat, had been closed "in order that France might live" and vacated in 1945, on the wave of reform.

On the front and side of the old police station at No. 14, the Doves of Peace occupied prominent places. Those premises, with an adjacent junkyard, were occupied by a wholesale steamfitters' supply concern, as a supplementary warehouse.

There were, then, two Picasso doves in the drugstore windows, three on the walls of the old disorderly house, and two more on the converted police station. Amiard did not take much stock in the efficacy of drugs, was not fond of women, either fallen or respectable, and distrusted cops on principle, as well as those who occupied the former haunts of the police. The posters did not trouble him. He felt that they were appropriately placed.

The trussmaker might have suspected something, if he had observed that so many of the men, and a few women, of the quarter, had decided to take an airing in the church-yard that noon, and that all of them must have started slightly ahead of the hour. Preoccupied as he was, he did not even notice that everyone was watching him, covertly, and casting upward glances at the Dove posters in the windows. When he saw some of the neighborhood boys grinning and glancing behind him, Amiard looked back over his shoulder, truculently, and saw what was wrong. Instead of exploding, as the others had expected, he was shaken with a quick involuntary shudder as he registered the shock, bent his oversized head forward and downward, and crossed the rue du Petit Pont with such disregard of the noontime traffic that he narrowly escaped being run down.

Where formerly there had been a French style delicatessen, or *charcuterie*, at No. 6, a forceful and jovial old maid, Mademoiselle Dunette, nicknamed "Queue de Morue" (or Swallowtail), kept an antique shop called "Au Temps Difficiles," which means, translated, "At the Sign of Hard Times." The title conveyed a gentle hint that householders with good furniture, and in need of ready cash, might tide themselves over by selling their period pieces to Mademoiselle, who herself had seen more prosperous days and understood such predicaments.

Mademoiselle was known locally as "Queue de Morue" (literally, Cod's Tail), because she wore indoors and out a strictly tailored swallowtail coat, the kind American Negroes call a "Jimswinger." Her hair was spun silver, her pince-nez were cocked at a rakish angle, her eyes were mocking, or melting, as the case might be. Her voice was deep, but well-modulated. She spoke correct and eloquent French.

It chanced that Mademoiselle Dunette was in the church-yard across from the eastern portal of the rue de la Huchette when the neighborhood jokers had gathered to watch truss-maker Amiard when he spotted the Picasso Doves in the second-floor window of his dilapidated corner building. There were too many against one for her taste, and so she started thinking. Whenever Mademoiselle Dunette started thinking, something came to pass.

Mademoiselle, herself, whether it was a pose or not, was an avowed Existentialist, which, because so many of the second-string leaders of the cult were disciples of the late Leon Trotsky, was anathema to the Communists and the Partisans of Peace. That did not blind her to the marvels of Picasso's art, or the remarkable opportunity for profit offered by the peace posters. She had accepted one from Raoul, framed it well, and it leaned among the question-able oil paintings, Lautrec posters, and other wall decorations displayed in her window at No. 6. She caught herself looking at that Dove and wondering how an artist could shape objects in black and white and paint the space around them as if he held it in his hands. Then, very tactfully, and being sure that Katya, who thought of her as a female Demon, should not get wind of the project, she ordered five hundred Dove posters at cost, and stored them away in her already overstuffed back room, as an investment. That later she could sell them, one by one, for 15,000 francs apiece, she thought was certain.

In the large, or western end of the rue de la Huchette, near the *place* St. Michel, a garage had been established at No. 30, since Liberation. This, because of the auto school attached, had become known as the Garage de la Terreur, and in it, among such a weird assortment of vehicles, large and small, as could only be found in France, Mademoiselle Dunette kept her "delivery truck," which she drove herself. It had some of the aspects of a station wagon, others of a baker's cart, and its wheelbase was such that it fitted almost exactly into the narrow end of the street in front of her shop, so that pedestrians could pass with difficulty, single-file, on either side, when it was parked there.

Because, like Amiard the trussmaker, Mademoiselle Dunette lunched regularly and nearly always dined at Thérèse's special round table in the Restaurant de la Huchette, she enjoyed as much of Amiard's confidence as he extended to anyone. He fumed and ranted against the Existentialist movement, from Jean-Paul Sartre down to the raggedest chin whisker on a pale student's face.

On the day the Doves appeared on the side of his building, Amiard did not show up for lunch, and Thérèse the cook, who had no patience with his anti-revolutionary attitude, threatened to slit his throat with a bread knife if he came in late. He did not appear at all, although he opened up his shop promptly at two o'clock and started working doggedly on a truss. When he was angry or brooding, one of Monsieur Amiard's eyebrows went up and the other down, involving a shifting of the eyelids so that one owl-like eye appeared larger than the other. It was not always the same one.

In mid-afternoon, Mademoiselle Dunette strolled across from her shop at No. 6 and into Monsieur Amiard's doorway at No. 1. It was raining, as usual, not a downpour and not exactly a mist, but an indefinable dampness that moistened and molded the walls, made footing uncertain and slippery and visibility low. The temperature was around fifty, and seemed much colder. That kind of weather had persisted, day after day, week after week, throughout March and into April. People had stopped cursing and grumbling, because the comments had become as annoying and monotonous as the weather itself. All Paris, except the black and white peace posters spread helter-skelter, was in terms of gray, slate, oyster and bitumen.

"*Bon soir, monsieur*," said Mademoiselle, as Amiard looked up, eyes rimmed and smoldering.

He grunted. She got right down to cases. She was going to make a trip in her truck through the rue Jean-Jacques Rousseau, near the Bourse de Commerce. If he could spare the time to go with her, she thought she could show him something of interest to them both.

"And what, mademoiselle, could possibly interest us both?" the trussmaker inquired, turning his head in profile to glower at her more effectively with a single eye.

She did not tell him, outright, but she let him understand that whatever she had in mind might help him circumvent his Red lodgers who had shown a willingness to sacrifice to the cause of World Peace their window with the eastern exposure, and the view of Notre Dame.

As Mademoiselle recrossed the street, Katya Roubait, from the newsstand at No. 7, who had seen the Swallowtail enter Amiard's shop, did not fail to make a mental note. Katya was not a busybody, exactly, but she had been trained in the Slavic tradition of party activities and tried to overlook nothing that might later prove helpful to the eventual triumph of the proletariat. That the comrades were given so much leeway in France and that, consequently, so much of the work which could just as well have been done in secret could be performed openly had troubled Katya, vaguely.

The fact was that Katya was not outstandingly popular, although nearly everyone more or less accepted her on account of Raoul, whom nobody could distrust or dislike. He loved Katya dearly and at times she was deferent to him, but when political or ideological questions were in consideration she had a way of becoming positive, if not patronizing or dictatorial. It was more a question of a contrast of manners, Slavic and French, but Katya antagonized many of the neighbors as naturally as Raoul ingratiated himself with one and all.

Their retail newspaper business was confined to the morning dailies, of which there were many, at least one for each political party, sect or movement. It was the post-war practice in Paris to license certain dealers to sell morning papers, and others to sell afternoon papers, so that the meager livings involved could be shared by a larger number of individuals and families.

Since by noon almost everyone who wanted a morning paper had already bought one, and the early afternoon editions they were not permitted to handle were appearing, Raoul and Katya had more leisure in the afternoons than in the mornings. Infrequently someone, an adult or a child, dropped in for stationery or school supplies late in the day, but one person could easily tend the shop, and either Raoul or Katya was left free for a few hours of party work. Just then Raoul was spending all his free time with the peace posters and Katya stayed at home. When the roles were reversed, and Katya was on the loose, no one knew precisely what she was about. Raoul realized that Katya got an enormous lift from secrecy and mystery, and helped her enjoy it. The more curious of the neighbors strained their faculties to keep tabs on Katya, and got nowhere at all. She relished direct questioning, because it gave her practice in replying evasively without disclosing anything.

Katya had seen Mademoiselle Dunette dart into the trussmaker's place, and, after time had elapsed for a short or cryptic conversation, go back to the antique shop. It was out of the question to imagine that the active, healthy Swallowtail needed orthopedic reinforcement. What, then, had been the object of the visit? Because the matter of the Dove posters was foremost in so many minds just then, Katya's instincts told her that something subversive was afoot. A little later she watched Swallowtail walk up to the garage, and in due time emerge driving the truck which bore the legend "Au Temps Difficiles." She observed that Mademoiselle, instead of heading eastward and parking in front of her antique shop across from the newsstand, crossed the wide end of the rue de la Huchette and disappeared into the rue de la Harpe. But in the meantime Monsieur Amiard had closed his shop, leaving on the inside of the window the usual placard "Will Return in ―――― Minutes," and, dressed for the street but not for Sunday, had left the rue de la Huchette by the eastern portal and turned southward. That he and Swallowtail would meet somewhere along the rue St. Séverin, out of sight of their immediate neighbors, Katya was sure, but she had to be certain. Leaving the shop in care of little Fabien Salmon, the butcher's sensitive son, aged 10, Katya slipped through the four-foot passage between Nos. 1 and 5, saw the Hard Times truck pull up at the corner near St. Séverin, and Amiard get in beside Mademoiselle the driver.

It was impracticable for Katya to follow them, much as she would have enjoyed it. All she could do was glance at the window placard on the truss shop. The space for the number of minutes before the proprietor's return was, as always, blank. Then she took a moment to step out into the rue du Petit Pont, between the swift relentless flurries of traffic, to look up at the second-story window and make sure that the emblems of World Peace were still in place. There they were, dove over dove, in pure black and white, and no one in the street had suggested that honest union workers did not have the right to use their windows as they liked, within the limits of decency, from the inside.

While Katya had been gone, little Fabien had made two sales for her, a notebook and an ink eraser, which he reported dutifully and counted out the change. The cash drawer had been locked, so he had completed the transactions from his own pocket, in order that Katya might not lose the trade. He was a boy who liked to please, and was intelligent.

Fabien's nerves were tuned to war concert pitch, what with the underground danger, the barricade at his own family doorstep, and the death of three patriots in the sight of his eyes, at the age of five. I am sure that he realized that Katya had been spying on Monsieur Amiard and that it was best to say nothing about it, not one word. Fabien knew that the trussmaker was an infidel and that Katya was a Commie, and that his father, supporting "the government," sometimes said that all Reds should be hanged. Also he knew that his father, stained *cap à pie* with Blood of Beef and Lamb, would really hang no one, least of all Katya and Raoul.

To reach her objective from the rue du Petit Pont, into which she turned, sharp right, after taking Monsieur Amiard aboard, Mademoiselle Dunette had to double back, via the boulevard St. Germain and the boulevard St.

Michel, cross the *place* within a few feet of the garage from which she had started, go over the bridge of St. Michel, cross the Ile de la Cité, take the busy rue de Rivoli as far as the rue du Louvre, speed west a few blocks, and turn left sharply at the place des Deux Ecus, to the rue Jean-Jacques Rousseau, which enters at a jaunty angle. It would be hard to decide, under the chaotic conditions prevailing in those times of Black Market cars, illicit gasoline and the post-occupation disrespect for law and order, which of the many sections of that short journey, at the most a mile and a half as the crow flies, is the most perilous—especially on a dim and slippery afternoon, when the rush hour is impending. Each yard of the trip had to be made in the knowledge that getting back to the St. Michel quarter would be ten times more hazardous.

For a moment or two, after he and the Swallowtail had stepped free from the truck, which was parked, in a manner of speaking, in the rue Jean-Jacques Rousseau, Monsieur Amiard did not catch on. But when what at first had appeared to be a second-story corner window revealed its true nature to him, his eyes popped, he clenched his fists, pawed or shifted his feet like a ram, and slapped the jovial Mademoiselle on the shoulder, a most unusual liberty for him.

"*Pas possible!*" he said, and exhaled like an overblown tube.

"A client of mine, who wants an object very much that I have, a lawyer so unscrupulous that he's seldom proven wrong, explained some things to me this afternoon," Mademoiselle said. "While a window exists, as such, a lodger has certain rights pertaining to it. But a landlord, for reasonable cause, may alter or modify an aperture plan," said Mademoiselle.

Mademoiselle did not think of the risk or laws of chance, but Monsieur Amiard did and once he got out of the Hard Times truck, he never got in again, and made his way home on foot, beating Mademoiselle's time by more than an hour. But what the trussmaker found on the corner of the rue Jean-Jacques Rousseau made him grateful to Mademoiselle, and set his baffled mind spinning again with plans of self-assertion and revenge.

Almost everyone at the narrow end of the street was surprised because the high-tempered Monsier Amiard seemed to take his defeat in the Dove poster controversy so easily. To Noel and the more observant ones the trussmaker's complacent attitude almost gave the show away. I knew what was afoot, through Mademoiselle Dunette and Anatole, the book clerk, and consequently was able to bear more philosophically the realization each morning that we were in for another drizzly day.

One noon not more than a week after the Doves had been placed in their window, an extra large group had assembled between showers in the churchyard. Suddenly Katya let out a yell and pointed to the bedroom window. The black and white peace posters were being withdrawn, quickly, from the inside, and a moment later the entire window disappeared, leaving only the casing and an oblong opening. Everyone was watching by that time. The crowd saw what seemed to be another window inserted in the old frame. In it appeared to be Monsieur Amiard sitting, in Sunday black, his hair slicked back the way Julian, the barber, habitually left it on Saturday nights. The dressed-up trussmaker was seated in some kind of easy chair, indistinguishable at that distance, and held in one hand a large pink flower, presumably a rose.

The chorus of comments and guffaws that greeted the

strange apparition was interrupted by the entrance, very quietly, of Monsieur Amiard himself, who came in through the side gate of the churchyard to join his neighbors in surveying the effect of his civic improvement. It was only then that most of them caught on that the figure in the window was painted, and so was the window and the glass, for that matter.

In the days of the Bourbon kings, when windows were heavily taxed, sometimes, landlords substituted false painted windows and some of the vain proprietors had their portraits painted in them. Monsieur Amiard had got the idea in the rue Jean-Jacques Rousseau, where an example of the old false-window art still existed. Mademoiselle Dunette had bought it, and Anatole had painted over the original face and figure that of Monsieur Amiard with polite disregard of much of his bodily distortion.

The lodgers had lost their window. The Communists had suffered a propaganda setback. The landlord, Monsieur Amiard, had scored a local triumph, rare for Paris landlords these days.

2. *Rosemary for Remembrance*

THE little lop-sided corner by the river of the 5th arrondissement known as the St. Michel quarter, of which the rue de la Huchette is the center of animation, suffered more on account of lighting restrictions than most sections of Paris. In the best days there had not been enough street lamps and those that existed were not too carefully tended. In Paris, lights were dimmed, reduced in number and shaded throughout ten dismal years, and in the early spring of 1949 were still inadequate, because of the shortage of electric power.

In the rue de la Huchette, from September, 1939, until mid-April, 1949, except for a few jubilant days when the lid was off following Liberation, the evenings which before the war had been so long, diversified and merry, had been abbreviated, uniform and dreary, by necessity. Dinner, as a rule, did not begin later than 7 o'clock, and in the cold season little was done in the stores or shops after the meal was over. For years in winter and in spring, heating facilities had been even more meager than the lights. There were only two neon signs, both small and modest—one over the main entrance of the Hotel de Mont Souris, in a faint raspberry shade, and another for the "Rahab," at No. 29, on the corner of the rue de la Harpe, in a luminous tone of white.

The Rahab had caught the fancy of tourists, or tourist

agencies. It was listed in some of the periodicals advertising night spots of Paris, and brought to the neighborhood considerable numbers of visitors in season. This was unheard of in the rue de la Huchette, but the newcomers liked the North-African and Near-Eastern cuisine, and the supposedly clandestine belly dance, accompanied by Moroccan hautboy, which took place in an interior room and supplemented the floor show which ranged from U. S. Negro, through up-to-date French, and modified Indo-Chinese or Algerian. The name of the place was Egyptian. The proprietor, a timid and at the same time enterprising and expansive man, was an Armenian named Aran Hatounian, cut down by all non-Orientals to "Monsieur Aran." The hautch dance was performed by a lithe Irish girl named Maive Callahan. The members of the band were mostly French. The waiters were French-Algerian or Turks with false passports. The cook was a shrunken Armenian so old he had lost count of years. His face was lined and criss-crossed like a pickled walnut. His helper was a Belgian bleached blonde, energetic but not very bright.

In the brown-out, the Rahab's scrolled windows were only faintly discernible, but the sound of the band and the hautboy filtered through the western end of the street, and those who had to go to bed early were grateful, when they stirred in their sleep, for the reminder that something presumably gay was in progress.

Cafés in the *place* St. Michel and all along the streets were dim, the customers were few, and those who patronized them could not afford to drink as much as they had in the past. A few big cafés, like Dupont's, six blocks along the boulevard St. Michel, flaunted restrictions brazenly and sent forth a blaze of light. No one seemed to mind, or think of making an effective protest. Parisians were inured to the fact that some men had special privileges and cared little about national economy.

As well as I knew those little streets, I had some difficulty in finding my way as I wandered through them at night. What few brown shadows were cast by the street lamps looked amorphous and deceptive. Curbs and hazards were obscured, distances falsified, conventional shapes distorted. Shop windows and doorways were blank. Headlights of prowling automobiles and the lamps of bicycles, in passing, left the area darker. Pedestrians hunched their shoulders, or, if they were young and defiant, moved in groups or columns and sang songs, many of them political.

On the first evening I headed down the boulevard toward the rue de la Huchette, I met a crowd who must have been attending a meeting. They were marching, raggedly, four or five abreast, along the broad sidewalk, beneath the budding plane trees, the trunks of which could barely be seen. There must have been a couple of hundred of them, and they were singing in French the *Internationale:*

"C'est la lutte finale . . ."

The final combat. I wondered. None of them seemed to be thinking about combat, or finality. They had met together, heard some speeches, and were going to have cheap glasses of coffee, with insufficient sugar, and eventually walk home. They were accustomed to the brownout, and aware that preceding generations had placed so great a load on their shoulders that each of them was a modern Atlas. A sextet of police officers, four on foot and two leaning on bicycles, chanced to be chatting on the corner of the rue St. Séverin.

As I approached the head of the column, the marchers

and singers in behalf of the prisoners of starvation parted to make way for me. The six policemen, without interrupting their conversation, shifted over a yard or two to make room for the singers. It was all very casual and sociable. I supposed that elsewhere in France there might be as many young enthusiasts whooping it up for De Gaulle. Nobody sings for the Middle-of-the-Road Government.

I had thought, when I was in France in the 1920's and 1930's, that French bureaucracy had reached a low level which could not be further demoralized. It was not long after my return when I was willing to admit that I had been wrong. The public services have deteriorated. Not that the systems on which they operate are any worse. That really would be impossible. And public servants, as individuals, atrociously underpaid, are not more inefficient. There are, simply, more of them to the square yard, and they get in one another's way. One third of the population works for the Government.

The French who work for themselves, for relatives, or for small private employers, apply themselves in a way the citizens of no other Latin countries could approximate. Hardships have toughened them and those who have survived are unusually energetic and active. The élan is lower in the Government services and large industrial concerns. Public employees and industrial workers seldom do a real day's work, and the Communist leaders try to indoctrinate them night and day against overexertion in behalf of a hostile government or rich capitalists.

Concerning the tourists, the Middle-of-the-Road coalition and the Communists are sharply divided. The government leaders want Americans to come and spend dollars. The Reds slander Americans, collectively and individually, in their newspapers every day, and by exerting pressure on the members of the public employees' unions within their sphere of influence, try everything possible to make a tourist's life insupportable. Communist writers refer to Americans as a drunken "master race," the members of which want to reduce French citizens to a colonial status. No minor news item that reaches the offices of *L'Humanité* or *Ce Soir,* the Communist organs, is too trivial to be falsified in order to make Americans appear barbarous, degenerate, greedy or vile.

Of course, the relatively friendly French newspapers seldom get anything about America or Americans straight, and unintentionally, sometimes, cause as much damage or confusion in the Paris public mind as the sworn enemies of the United States. Of whatever shade of public opinion, Paris newspapers have an utter disregard of people's names and plain facts.

The following is not extreme, but typical. A tragic accident occurred this summer and was reported in the Paris edition of the New York *Herald Tribune* as follows:

PARIS ECA GUARD KILLED
BY ACCIDENTAL PISTOL SHOT

John R. Brady of Omaha, Neb., a security guard at the Economic Co-operation Administration's headquarters in Paris, was shot and killed Wednesday night when a .45 caliber automatic being cleaned by a fellow guardsman, Colin M. Mechlin, of Columbus, Ohio, accidentally went off.

Brady, a former Marine and holder of the Purple Heart, was the son of Lieutenant Colonel R. R. Brady, of the Medical Corps of the American Graves Registration Command headquarters in Paris.

Brady was driven to the American Hospital in Neuilly by a French police ambulance, but died early yesterday morning following an operation. The bullet had entered his left side and gone completely through his body. Mechlin was released in the charge of Seabrook Foster, ECA Security officer, pending an investigation.

The Communist *L'Humanité* (circulation 252,000) printed the following variation for the indoctrination of its readers:

REVOLVER SHOTS

AT THE EMBASSY

OF THE UNITED STATES

A Brawl after Drinking Causes Death

A violent brawl broke out last night at the United States Embassy, under conditions about which the police, under orders, maintain the most complete discretion.

What is certain is that the Americans who fought each other with revolver shots had drunk much more than was reasonable.

The one named Rechlin Colin wounded mortally John Bradly, who died a little later at the hospital of Neuilly.

The subordinates at the Embassy were ordered to give out no information concerning the presence of several attachés of the Embassy at this quarrel, worthy of the films of the gangsters of Chicago.

Figaro, the most conservative morning paper, and one which follows the Center Government's policies whenever possible, interpreted the incident as follows:

A FRENCH CHAUFFEUR
KILLS A GUARD EMPLOYEE
IN THE SERVICES OF
THE MARSHALL PLAN

Saint-Florentin Street, in the Hotel Talleyrand, where the American personnel of the Marshall Plan have installed certain of their offices, an American guard, M. John R. Brady, was killed with a revolver bullet by a French chauffeur, M. Collin.

The circumstances of the drama rest somewhat mysterious. John R. Brady, of the "Security Guards," came on duty at the moment when M. Collin took up his. The latter entered the guard room and a few seconds later a shot sounded.

M. Brady, hit by a bullet in the stomach, was then transported to the American Hospital where he succumbed a little later.

It was in manipulating his revolver that M. Collin mortally wounded M. Brady.

The De Gaullist *Aurore* did not suggest that a drunken orgy had taken place, that facts had been concealed by United States officials, found no mystery, but was contemptuous about the way American veterans handle firearms. The *Aurore* account read like this:

A DEAD MAN
AT THE HOTEL TALLEYRAND

The "Security Guard" in the offices of the
Marshall Plan thought that his
revolver was empty

The drama that took place at the Hotel Talleyrand, No. 2 rue Saint-Florentin, where are installed the offices of the E.C.A. (Marshall Plan) and which cost the life of a young American guard, has nothing mysterious about it. It is all simply stupid.

John R. Brady, 23 years old, veteran of the Pacific war, and Colin M. Mechlin, 28 years old, both "security guards" at the Hotel Talleyrand, were checking their revolvers, Colt .45. Mechlin emptied his weapon of cartridges to clean it, when the entrance bell sounded. The two men placed their revolvers on the same table and went to open the door. When they came back, Mechlin took hold of the one of the Colts he believed was his own and maneuvered it to load it again. But he was mistaken in the weapon. He had taken that of Brady which contained still some cartridges. The shot departed. Brady slumped, his lungs perforated. He was transported immediately to the American Hospital at Neuilly where, in spite of surgical intervention and several blood transfusions, he succumbed four hours later.

Parisians are in no way disturbed because their newspapers are corrupt, biased, sloppy, venal, inaccurate and contradictory. To them, after three and a fraction Republics, such journalism is a part of the ordinance of nature.

Other public services are no better than the French Fourth Estate. One Monday morning, I decided to change some American money into francs. I had a hundred-dollar bill, a crisp new Federal Reserve Note, No. B13590775A, with a grayish picture of Benjamin Franklin on one side and a green front view of Independence Hall on the other. According to the Paris *Herald Tribune*, the official rate of exchange that morning was 319.20. Innocently enough, I expected, therefore, to get 31,920 francs for my century note.

I took a bus to the Opera, a few yards from the office of the American Express in the rue Scribe. The lobby was already overcrowded. There were a few North Americans, hordes of English, many South Americans, and a few Near-Easterners, Italians and other voyagers from Mediterranean lands, Dutchmen, Norwegians, Swedes, Danes and several Irish.

Before each counter, or grilled window in the rue Scribe office was a ragged queue, which was truly more like braid than an Indian file. Visitors from countries where war had been seen, first hand, fell into place philosophically, but there were always others, natural chiselers, who pretended not to understand language or even signs, so at the head of each line there was much disputing, shoving, and often abusive repartee. The jaded clerks seemed to expect that, and paid little attention.

After I had waited in line about fifteen minutes at the American Express, during which time I had progressed, inch by inch, a distance of about ten feet toward the cashier's window, I asked the sinister-looking floor walker, a hold-over from pre-war days, what rate the company was paying for dollars that morning.

"Three hundred and ten," he said.

"It says in the paper that the franc is worth 319.20," I protested.

"Here it's 310, and may go lower," the villainous-looking major-domo said.

That meant I would get for my one-hundred-dollar bill only 31,000 francs, or 920 francs less than the sum to which I was entitled. With 920 francs I could buy almost four pounds of steak, a copy of the King James Bible, and the works of Rabelais, or four packages of black-market American cigarettes.

"If you want to do better," the floorwalker said, "try the Bank of France."

There was a huge branch of the Bank of France not too far from my quarter, in the Boulevard Raspail. So I took the bus back in that direction. The bank, when I reached it, proved to be enormous inside, with dozens of caged windows in rows, and rimmed with anterooms, private offices of executives, and refuges for clerks who were spared direct contact with the public. In that spacious, cavernous setting, the few customers in front of the various windows seemed practically lonesome. A polite uniformed functionary informed me that, if I wished to convert dollars into francs, I would be accommodated at a window fifty yards or so from the main entrance, well to the rear. In finding my proper window, I passed at least twenty others, where various kinds of banking business were proceeding unhurriedly, in dimness and almost absolute silence. Compared with the American Express lobby, that of the large branch of the Bank of France was like a sanctuary.

Another polite, well-built, middle-aged man in uniform intercepted me. I repeated to him that I wanted to exchange American dollars for French francs. After glancing at my passport, he smiled and handed me a card on which was written in blue pencil the figure "9." I counted those who were standing in front of me and they added up to eight. All seemed to be in order in the best of worlds.

"What rate are you paying today?" I asked the uniformed man who had numbered me.

"Three hundred and fifteen," he said.

"But in the newspapers . . ." I began.

He smiled indulgently. "There has to be a margin for service and overhead," he explained.

I could not be churlish enough to object to that. If I got 31,500 for my $100, I would be doing 500 francs better than I could have done at the American Express. That meant a pound of lamb, plus a bouquet of *fines herbes*, my afternoon newspaper (the staid *Le Monde*), Cooper's *Le dernier Mohican*, and about four small boxes of what the French Government puts out as "safety" matches.

Still holding the No. 9 ticket, I had become actually No. 3. Also I had become aware that all the applicants who had been in front of me were not getting exactly what they had come for. No. 7, for instance, a barbered Englishman who smelled of the products of Ed. Pinaud, had a letter of credit which entitled him to twenty pounds, changed into francs, each week on Monday. The day was Monday, the bank had the money, and all was in order, except that when he had collected his allowance the last time, someone had neglected to stamp his letter of credit in all the appropriate places. He was sent, emptyhanded, to see a certain Monsieur So-and-so, who had the kind of rubber stamps that could be used retroactively.

It was then that I looked carefully at the clerks of the Bank of France who were behind my window. Both were boys, not old enough to vote. One was blond, slight, very smart and sure of himself. The other was darker, an athletic type, who looked to his companion for guidance. They were well-bred, self-possessed, the kind of young men who, in the United States, would get into the diplomatic service when they were older.

They were dealing with No. 8 in our line, an American woman who had brought with her, besides her own passport, her son-in-law's passport and three twenty-dollar American Express checks, signed and countersigned presumably by him.

The blond boy in the cage sighed, clucked and shook his head. He explained, softly and patiently, that the absent son-in-law would have to present himself in person, to verify his signature, identify himself and accept the francs to which his traveler's checks entitled him. With that he stepped aside to give his alternate a chance to deal with me. I faced the dark-haired, clean-cut youth and extended to him my pristine $100 bill. He looked at it reverently and was about to count out my francs from a cash-drawer of the type in use in American grocery stores in the early 1900's.

"Ah, but no," said the blond youth, restraining his impetuous colleague. "Here we cannot change $100 bills. We have no experts who can determine whether or not they are authentic."

I let out an exclamation that was inelegant, but not directed at either of the young clerks. It expressed my surprise and disappointment.

"Sorry," the dark-haired clerk said. "You must go to the main office of the Bank of France, at No. 29 rue Croix de Petits Champs."

He wrote the address for me on a slip of paper and also the name of the appropriate Métro station, the "Palais Royal." So I took the Métro, and after changing lines twice, and walking a few yards, I found myself in the main *siège* of the Bank of France. There the line in front of the exchange window was so long that I could not possibly hope to reach the cage before the bank closed at 12 o'clock noon, for the two-hour lunch recess. I went to lunch in a small but select restaurant in the rue Montpensier, one I had known in the 1930's. The food was still very good but the prices had gone up, so that what I paid, beyond what the meal would have cost me in the quarter St. Michel, more than consumed the amount I thought I had saved by passing up the American Express in favor of the national banking institution of the Fourth Republic.

Soon after two o'clock I went back to the bank and stood in line, with a ticket numbered 32. When finally I got to the head of the queue and showed the three clerks my new $100 bill one of them made inquiries and found that of the two experts attached to the main bank, one was in court testifying in a counterfeit case and the other was at home, in Passy, incapacitated by lumbago.

Exasperated, I taxied over to Thomas Cook and Sons in the *place* de la Madeleine, another extravagance, and took what they gave me without cavil. The total was 30,800 francs, or 200 francs less than the American Express Company had offered me early that morning.

Since Hyacinthe Goujon, with whom I had shared so much while she was developing from a precocious child of six to a gifted actress, was dead by her own hand, the woman I wanted most to see, on returning to Paris, was Hortense Berthelot. I was not sure what had happened to Hortense, or even whether she had survived.

For some years before World War II broke out, Hortense had been a clerk in the department of the Paris prefecture where foreigners applied for renewal of their identity cards. I was anxious to talk with Hortense, if that were still possible, before I went back to the rue de la Huchette at all. So with that in mind I went directly from Thomas Cook and Sons to the prefecture, where the paving of the bleak courtyard was more worn and treacherous than ever, and the ungainly doors were rotting on their hinges.

Inside the gloomy building, the unlighted stone corridors smelled of creosote. Rain was falling outside and streaking the unwashed window panes, of which there were too few.

With difficulty, but without asking for directions, I found the office where years before I had infrequently called for Hortense. No improvements were discernible. The line of nervous outlanders who were permitted to stay and work in France, and their apologetic dependents, looked about as they had in the 20's and 30's. As I passed them they glanced at me, furtively, as if they were afraid that, somehow, I would make things more difficult for them.

As I touched the shaky knob of the door I thought of the gloves Hortense used to wear, always neat, and even in the unventilated prefecture retaining their fragrance of fine leather and mild toilet water. Unable to afford *chic* suits, hats or dresses, Hortense, between the ages of thirty and forty, had economized in order to wear gloves and shoes of distinction. She never had many francs at her disposal, just what she could salvage, over and above her food and lodging expenses, from her paltry municipal wages, nothing more. Being extra sensitive to cold and chill, she had spent small sums for firewood and kindling, delivered up three flights of stairs to her room by the huge slow-thinking Auvergnat who had been the neighborhood coal man. He had died in a prison camp in Upper Silesia, before the Russians got there, having rebelled against the Nazis as a labor deportee. I reminded myself that I must ask about the coal man's blue-eyed wife, Alice, whom he had called "his heart."

I peered into the dimness of the barren room, behind the counter where Hortense should be. She was not there, and neither was the evil old woman, her colleague, who had hated her, along with the rest of the human race. That was a shock to me, and I was further demoralized when I asked the bald-headed man who seemed to be sitting in Hortense's old place if he knew where I might find Madame

Berthelot. He had difficulty in understanding me because, somewhere in North Africa, he had stumbled on a road mine and the force of the explosion had smashed one of his eardrums and damaged the other. That would be the kind of man any *gouvernement français* would be likely to select for a job where all kinds of foreign dialects and accents would be encountered.

The bald-headed man looked like a villain, the kind who play Nazi roles in the movies. He had a scar across his partly bald head; one of his pale blue eyes had a cast while the other stared straight ahead, as if it were of glass. He seemed willing to help me, however, if only because it enabled him to drop his regular work and keep the long line of applicants waiting. Leisurely he consulted the other three employees in the room, one a veteran with a metal larynx, and a brace of widows whose breadwinners had died for France. In front of the counter a couple of Englishmen drifted in and started clamoring for service. The four functionaries formed a small hollow square and started arguing at the tops of their voices about women who had worked there before. The hubbub attracted the attention of their immediate chief, who had a small dark office off the main room.

"Alors, quoi!" the chief said, sticking his head out of his doorway like a character in a Molière play whose ill-nature should produce a laugh. "What is it that comes to pass here?"

The two widows scattered like hens before a lawn-mower. But my bald-headed man held his ground, gestured with his thumb toward me, and tried to explain. His boss waved him away and plodded over to the counter across from where I stood. Evidently he had been fast asleep, when the din of voices had disturbed him, and he had not regained full wakeful clarity.

I told him that a certain Madame Hortense Berthelot had worked several years at the counter now guarded by the bald monsieur.

"Poor woman," the chief said, with feeling. Then he looked severely at the bald-headed man, the veteran with the metal larynx and the two baleful widows, in turn. "There is no longer anyone by that name employed here," he said. He leaned closer and stared searchingly at me.

"You are English?" he asked.

"American," I said so emphatically that the two Englishmen in the line drew themselves up and bristled.

"You are not, for example, a lawyer from New York?" the chief persisted. All work had stopped from one end of the room to the other. The under-functionaries were listening, avidly, while pretending to study documents and rubber stamps on their desks.

"No," I answered, "I'm a writer from Boston."

"*Merde* . . . pardon," said the chief. "I read just this morning that a lawyer in New York had left some lucky camel of a Frenchman in the Midi 50,000,000 francs."

In his excitement about the legacy from the dead New York lawyer, my errand slipped his mind. The chief beckoned the bald-headed-man to join us.

"What is it, exactly, that this *numéro* is after?" the chief inquired of the mild Nazi type.

"A Madame Bertrand, Berthaud, something like that," said the subordinate.

"Berthelot. Hortense Berthelot," I corrected him.

The chief then explained that no one in the department had been there very long. He advised me to go to the Jeu de Paume Museum, where one of the guards named Gobert, or Godot, was stationed. The party, Gobert or Godot, had been in the chief's present office, some years before, and might know the woman for whom I was searching, the chief said.

I thanked him, and the other, and decided to go on to the rue de la Huchette, at the risk of being disappointed. There, after witnessing the beginning of the dove-poster incident, I learned from Noel that Hortense was safe and well. He led me to the door of a flower shop at No. 23, and tactfully retired. A moment later I caught sight of Hortense inside. She was hatless and gloveless, and had draped over her slender shoulders a soft-colored loosely knitted shawl. Her face was averted, but she stood erect and self-possessed, and seemingly in much better health than she had enjoyed just before the debacle.

Opening the door quietly, I asked, "Aren't you in the wrong end of the street, Madame?"

She turned, her face lighted with spontaneous astonishment, tears moistened her eyes, and she stepped forward offering one cheek, then the other, as she clung, trembling, to my coat lapels. I was so deeply moved that the whole scene was blurred, and I was not quite sure what I was doing, or what I could find to say. With her unfailing instinct, she refrained from asking questions until after I had got accustomed to her presence again. We had been through too much, as friends, to plunge into the purely personal, and, as witnesses, to reopen what already had become a historical process.

"How do you like it?" she asked, with a gesture embracing the flower shop, in which was mingled the spicy fragrance of carnations, yellow roses, pink roses, forget-me-nots and some lilies of the valley which had been picked just too soon.

I had not come out of the daze of sudden encounter. Meeting so many good men I had known had given me a sense of continuity. Hortense brought me color and warmth.

"I looked for you in the prefecture," I managed to say.

She passed over my remark, and moved her expressive hands, palms upward, toward the counters, pots and vases, again.

"You don't understand. This is mine," she said.

Actually I heard the words, but understood less than ever. She opened a rear door, brought in a chair which I made haste to take from her hands. Before I had placed it, she brought in another. Ten years had passed, and if she had been in her thirties in 1939, she must be over forty, I knew. Still, her movements were more vigorous than they had been when she had been steeped in fatigue because of her work in the prefecture, and her forebodings about the future of France.

We dined together at the Balzar that evening. The wind had changed direction, slightly, and there was no rain but only a different kind of chill and a sulphur-colored mist around the hooded street lamps. The brown-out had not been lifted. Its dinginess, however, and the damp war the weather waged against nerves, did not tarnish the comfort I was deriving from Hortense's company, or the contagious mood of gladness she was quietly enjoying. Outward circumstances were against us. The plane trees dripped along the sidewalk. No lights were showing in the windows of the stores in the boulevard St. Michel. Traffic was sluggish and sparse in the dimness. None of the drivers who were out were not wishing they were indoors. The outmoded makeshift ill-assorted vehicles skidded on the slippery pavements. Horns, raucous and inadequate, squawked in a desultory fashion like disgruntled marsh birds in the wrong swamp.

The Café Cluny was closing before eight in the evening. We did not comment on the fact. The yard and walls of the old Cluny Museum, in former centuries a prison and torture house, were dug up, partly demolished and littered because of repairs that had been started about the time of Munich and then abandoned. As a vulgar reminder that common hardships had not scotched special privilege, the enormous Dupont café was ablaze with electric light. The vast *terrasses* were practically devoid of customers, displaying what looked like half an acre of wet metal tables and chairs. At intervals, inside and grouped around the long curved bar, were clients, mostly young and disreputable, or old and gone to seed. Most of the young men were Orientals, from Siam, Malay, Tonkin, Annam and a few from the ancient central kingdom of Cathay, with a few East Indians and North Africans to boot. Conspicuous among the others because of their soot-black skins and kinky hair were French colonials, some in badly worn and ill-fitting army uniforms, from Martinique, Madagascar and Senegal. Add to those a few white boys with orang-utan whiskers, open flannel shirts, baggy corduroys and no hats, examples of what had become known, with the growth of the Existentialist movement, as "The Zazous of St. Germain." Most of the young colored men, yellow, brown, snuff, mustard or ginger in hue, had white girls with them. A few of the latter were students from the Sorbonne near by, taking extra-curricular courses in broad-mindedness. Others were female Apaches who liked students or tough guys with money and knew that the colored boys for a while spent more freely when white women lent them prestige.

No flood of contraband electric light could make that

notorious corner of the Latin Quarter appear gay that evening, and still Hortense ignored its sordid implications,
pressed my arm a little closer and smiled. Just inside the
window two men, Siamese or Filipinos, sat on a bench opposite two ratty-looking girls, not prostitutes but obviously
tramps. The men were dour and scowling; the girls looked
bored. One of the Filipinos, or whatever he was, took from
his side coat pocket a small automatic and laid it on the
table, looking sullenly at his girl the while. A waiter came
into the scene with a tray of drinks, some colored, sticky,
bottled appetizer. He placed the drinks on the table, and
while he stood there, the girl across from the gun boy got
up, fussed with her tight skirt, patted her backside, and
started for the toilet. The other girl, uninvited, got up and
followed, at a distance of three or four yards. One of the
Filipinos paid the waiter; the other put the gun back in his
side coat pocket. As the waiter turned away, the two brown
men looked at each other and suddenly smiled all over their
flat round faces.

Hortense saw it all, as we walked past, slowly. She might
have been watching a spider descending from the ceiling
on a self-spun thread or a ball zigzagging in a pinball game.
As always, she was uncritical of human behavior and objective as could be. We both could visualize the Dupont's of
the pre-war era, on a mild spring night, with the Boul' Mich'
and the quarter alive and teeming. That particular café had
not been a favorite with students, because the prices had
been high. Men from all parts of Paris and many countries
used to go there to pick up small-size women. Dozens of the
tiniest women in Paris, with normal need for francs, used
to congregate on Dupont's *terrasse*. Some were under age,
others had grown children, but they dressed in so far as
possible like schoolgirls, to furnish a provocative and stimu-

lating illusion. Now the corner seems to be an informal world center for miscegenation. One sees occasional mixed couples that seem radiantly happy, but they are the exceptions. For the most part, the contrastingly colored couples looked like exhibitionists on a rampage or ordinary folk who are bored or are victims of slipshod mistakes. That part of the Latin Quarter has its share of baby carriages and small children, little half-breeds, quarter-breeds, and all conceivable hybrids. Those who are old enough, and not too old, seem to get along without consciousness of race or pigmentation.

Around the corner of the rue des Ecoles, a few doors down on the right-hand side, Hortense and I reached our objective, the Balzar, where we had spent many hours in the past, when we could afford it. The beer was and is the best in Paris (served also at Lipp's in the *place* St. Germain des Prés), and the cuisine is sound Alsatian. It formerly had a solid neighborhood middle-class clientèle, supplemented by the more discriminating foreign residents and intellectuals, some of the most companionable of the professors and teachers from the Sorbonne, and, afternoons and late at night, French columnists and newspapermen. That when Hortense and I entered, it was dimly lighted, and there were only four other customers, did not depress our spirits. In our honor, two more lights were turned on.

"You find it strange that I'm happy, and in better health, when all around me others are finding life so difficult," Hortense said.

"I didn't think anyone or anything could get the best of you, if your strength held out," I said. The fears I had felt with regard to her physical stamina came through the timbre of my voice, like the tones from an out-of-tune string on an instrument.

"I'm more durable than you expected—or I expected, either. For a while, beginning in those months when the war, as far as we French were concerned, was at a standstill, and we all knew that the only time we were likely to have for effective action was being wasted away, I went down and down. My skin turned yellow. I was so thin my bones stuck out. When the Nazis came, and I saw and heard them in our street, and, worse than that, saw men who called themselves Frenchmen tasting boot polish, I realized—and I was not glad—that I had reached my lowest level. I endured, in a state of suspended animation, until faint hope began to stir, and I resisted, lacking courage to revive. Then the message from De Gaulle—and men began to fight, women, too. You know what happened after that. Let's not talk about it now. . . . Must there be another war?" she asked.

"No," I said, so positively that I startled her, and myself.

"*Will* there be another one?"

"We must assume that there will not," I said. She nodded.

The old head waiter was glad to see us, and so was Conrad, who had spent three years in a German prison camp. The third waiter was new, raw-boned, young and clumsy. I looked toward the high desk, beside the taps from which the beer was drawn. The head waiter told me that the proprietor I had known had been killed in action, and that his widow and her sister had gone back to Colmar.

The Balzar used to make a specialty of shellfish, mussels steamed in sailor style, shrimps, prawns and crevettes, oysters, clams, langouste and homard. Under the conditions prevailing in early April, none of the foregoing could be served. Neither could the delicious fish and shellfish combinations baked, cheese-crusted, in shells. Those required cream, which was forbidden restaurants by law and decree.

The proprietor of the Balzar was not one of those who could ignore regulations, it seemed. Already he had been caught by a middle-of-the-road inspector with a half-pint of cream in his icebox, for family use, and had been heavily fined. That had reinforced his feeling for De Gaulle.

Hortense and I, side by side on the bench, in a corner we had occupied many an evening, were not ruffled by the absence of the delicacies of yesteryear. A high plateau of our friendship had been attained, and before us a new vista extended. Not all the most prodigious brains, combined, or the most complicated computing machines can add up details and trifles of recovery, and lay a total on the line. The turning point has to be felt, as human brotherhood has to be felt, by each individual in his own specific moment.

We made out all right, with a hare paté, onion soup, a rare sirloin steak with French fried potatoes and watercress, a slice of Port Salut that came from some little corner inspectors had left inviolate, and a tart of those small sweet Alsatian white plums called *mirabelles*—a lovely word, most happily applied. The coffee was not bad, and the liqueur was clear and burned as if it were white hot, with an aftertaste which implied that when the distiller's man had driven around, all the raspberries in eastern France had been set out for him on front doorsteps.

Hortense seldom forgot or overlooked anything which might have a bearing on the pleasure or comfort of a companion, so she suggested, after we had finished at the table, that we sit a while on the *terrasse*, diagonally across from the little *place* Paul Painlevé in which, among other trees, stood a linden. She had astonished me several times that day, but never more than when, on a damp chilly evening, she proposed sitting outdoors.

"Of all women, you used to be the one who dreaded cold the most," I said.

She was very pleased, and beamed. "I overcame that," she said. "There was no heat, in any season, for so long . . ."

I realized that most of the Parisians had done likewise. At best, in Paris, provisions for combating cold and dampness had been inadequate. When, because of war, they became non-existent, the French steeled themselves and built up the necessary resistance. Today most of them are quite indifferent to extremes of temperature and humidity. In autumn, winter and the wrong kind of spring they dress as warmly as they can, with little regard for aesthetic effect. If they look shabby, on the streets, nobody cares because that has become a part of the national adjustment.

Descriptions in print of meals such as I have just set forth reinforce the false impression current throughout the United States that food is plentiful in France and that Paris "is just the same." The dinner check that evening added up to 2,110 francs, plus the tip, 320 francs. That amounted, just then, in terms of American dollars to $8.10, but a good French mechanic, the kind who in the United States would earn about $12 for eight hours' work, would have to work two and one half days to earn 2,430 francs, which on account of taxes and social security contributions would not be all velvet. My dinner with Hortense, from the viewpoint of a French skilled mechanic, cost the equivalent of thirty dollars. Not many Parisians can afford to pay thirty dollars for a meal for two. The housewives in moderate circumstances would figure about that amount for a week's supply of food for a family of four. As for clothes, the working Parisians take care of them the way the expert custodians preserve art treasures in the Louvre.

Hortense, I was amazed to observe from the first moment I found her, was taking new interest in her clothes and spending whatever was required to dress becomingly and in style. No more shiny thin dark suits and plain skirts, with practical shirtwaists and hats which might have come from the property room of the Odéon reserved for the costumes of character actresses playing roles of poor relations. She would have looked well in the dining room of the Ritz or Hotel Georges V. I could remember when she had so little patience with her face that any kind of makeup would have seemed absurd to her. Under the lights of the Balzar, her complexion looked clear, her skin soft and smooth, her cheeks were flushed with rouge that harmonized with her lipstick, her hair was artistically styled, and she wore delicate pendant earrings.

As soon as we were comfortably seated in the corner of the *terrasse*, with an after-dinner seidel of Alsatian beer (Hatt de Cronenbourg) it was time to ask her how she got into the flower business, and I did.

"Things were worst for me," Hortense began, "while the Boches were here. Up to that time, I kept my job at the prefecture. After the surrender, Cousin Arsène (the Navet)—I am sure it was he—had me discharged. I had no savings, and no other place to work that did not mean helping the enemy. Madame Absalom (the aged virago who had had a wool and thread shop on the quai near by) took me in, fed me until she died, and left me her stock which she had hidden from the Boches. It was the case of an oral will, but no one questioned the arrangement."

"You were able to sell the stuff?" I asked.

Hortense flushed and lowered her eyes. "None of us is without shame," she said, simply. "I didn't sell it, myself. Or rather, I sold it to Hubert . . . No questions asked."

"Hubert?" I repeated. She colored again, but looked straight into my eyes.

"The junior Wilf," she said. "I forget that you have not met him. He is the junior partner in the new Hotel Mont Souris. He . . . Well, for quite some time he has been—helpful to me."

Hortense was so embarrassed that I chuckled aloud.

"I realized that Mainguet was still faithful and hopeful," I said.

"You must believe," Hortense said, trying to recover her poise, "that in the case of Hubert Wilf, I've not been the aggressor."

"He sold the hanks of wool and spools of thread to the Boches, I suppose," I suggested, to make it easy for her.

"He never told me what he did with the goods. I'm sure he overpaid me. At any rate, the proceeds kept me in food and shelter until the Nazis were chased out. Thank God I had a hand in that, with Madame Sarthe, our district leader of the Resistance. There was so little I could do, but that little I accomplished—at little risk, of course. No one suspected me."

"Not the Navet? He was the worst on the street."

"He was too busy saving his own skin," she said. "It wasn't my fault that he got away."

When she talked about the Navet, the loathing she felt, so unlike her normal kindliness toward all, made her ill.

"The flower shop," I prompted her.

"Imagine," she said. "Another bequest. My late husband's brother, whom I had not seen or heard from for years, died and left me a small house with some land and a garden at Clermont-Ferrand."

Again she hesitated, diffidently. "I didn't want to live in

the Midi," she said. "After so many years in Paris, without a day in the country, I should have died of boredom."

"So?"

"If you must press me . . . It was Hubert, again. Clermont-Ferrand, as you know, is a remarkably fine place for Collabos, what with the old artillery school and its clique of staff officers, the bishopric loyal to Pétain . . ."

"Clermont-Ferrand's always been a jolly rendezvous for that kind," I agreed.

"Monsieur Wilf found some purchaser who needed quiet shelter in a backward province, quickly. He got an amazingly good price—unless again he tampered with the accounts, and overpaid me. It seems next to impossible for Hubert to complete a transaction in the ordinary way. When no one else is cheated, he swindles himself. . . . Do I sound ungrateful? I don't mean to be. With the money I got from the sale of the property down in the Midi, I took a long lease on the shop, where there are also living quarters —one bedroom, that is to say. And I went over to the flower market, on the Ile de la Cité, with a dissolute porter, and bought flowers."

"Why flowers?" I asked.

"I've never seen enough of them," she said. "I wanted to deal in something lovely and fragrant, not too heavy, not seasonal. Something is always blooming. I wanted a commodity that was perishable, so I would not have to keep looking at slow-moving items on shelves day after day. More than anything else, I wanted a luxury article. Starving people have no great longing for flowers, and, in hard times, flower merchants are not torn with impulses to give their wares away."

So at the time when France was struggling hardest to regain her footing and repair the ravages of total war, Madame

Berthelot, who had spent so many years in poverty, while France was dancing a devil's minuet to the tune of false security, was running a small business of her own.

"At first I sold few flowers," Hortense told me. "Then, one day, Armand came in. . . ."

"Not Hubert?"

"Armand Busse, the manager of the Hotel Mont Souris. He gave me a standing order to supply flowers for the lobby and the dining room. I can make a fair living on that commission alone. . . . And M. Mercanton, of the Hotel de la Huchette, gave me a similar daily order, much smaller, of course, soon afterward. It all seems like a dream. Not too much work. No risk. No worry. What do you think? Do you see any flaw?"

I remembered suddenly that while I had been in Hortense's shop, I had seen Monsieur Busse, so well-groomed and frock-coated, come tripping across the rue de la Huchette, singing softly to himself. He had come as far as the doorway of the flower shop, and brought up with a start when he had seen Hortense and me, heads together, in rapt conversation. With a pouting, injured expression like that of a willful, disappointed child, the plump, elegant hotel manager had, without saluting Hortense, pretended that he had made a mistake or forgotten something. He had turned on his heel and walked away, toward the *place* St. Michel. Great snakes, I said to myself, as at the Balzar I recalled the incident. Is Monsieur Busse another one who is courting Hortense, in addition to Mainguet and the junior Black Marketeer, Hubert Wilf?

I asked the question rather bluntly. "Did Hubert put Monsieur Busse up to placing that order, which practically guarantees you a fair profit, day in day out?"

Hortense looked at me ruefully. "How can one account for such developments?" she asked. "When I was young, and passably good-looking, no one, least of all my husband, paid much attention to me—as a woman, I mean. Now that I'm old, and merely a bad cold might transform me into a scarecrow . . ." She completed the thought with an expressive gesture. "And it can't be my income . . . Although some weeks I've doubled my earnings through tips on the stock market. . . . Again Hubert, who gets them from his brother. . . . What I mean is, both Hubert and Armand Busse have means of their own and have preserved their liberty all through the years. I might have married Mainguet, perhaps, long ago, if he were not such an ideal Christian. His character's so saintly that he frightens me. At every turning in my life when I've had to do right, because of my limitations, I've longed to be wanton. Laugh if you must, but that's the truth."

"Every word you've said has made me happier," I said.

We left off talking for a while to contemplate the linden tree. I used to watch it in the late afternoons when the light was slowly changing, and in the evenings by street lamp and moonlight. When a breeze stirred, the leaves responded, and soon the twigs that moved the leaves in clusters. The smaller branches took up the symphony of concerted motion, and communicated a basic rhythm to the larger branches, then the boughs, while the trunk, firmly grafted to the stump of a sturdier tree, held firm.

The linden tree swayed, shifted its contours and outlines, redistributed its form, and seemed to pirouette, responding to the universal whirl, absorbing light and shadow that it needed, refracting or reflecting the rest.

It must have been placed in that small quiet square just opposite the Sorbonne a year or two before the *place* had

been given the name of Painlevé, mathematician and statesman. That would be a quarter of a century ago. In another
twenty-five years, if Paris does not fare too badly, the
linden will be replaced by another, on the same oak stump,
roots wider outspread.

3. *In Pursuit of the Spiritual*

WHEN I crossed from New York to Le Havre in late March, the old *De Grasse* was the only liner still afloat of what had formerly been the world's most magnificent passenger fleet, the French Line. The *Normandie* had been destroyed through criminal negligence. The *Paris* had sunk. The *Ile de France* had long been out of commission. My voyage had been trying, but it had afforded a reminder of the France that had been and a foretaste of the France of today. Those of us to whom France is a refuge and a second home could travel no other way.

At a table next to mine in the dining salon a group of three were placed, and between them they spanned the two eras, yesterday and today. The father's name was Justin Dassary, a speculator in commodities and proprietor of a fine old market restaurant in Les Halles of Paris. With him was Carmen, his spoiled and nervous daughter, and her husband, Guy Orey, who seemed to maintain their difficult relationship with a minimum of strain or fuss. I got acquainted with father and daughter, separately, in the course of the voyage, and both of them were quite frank in discussing Guy, from their own points of view.

Carmen was a svelte brunette young woman, rich, restless and essentially lonely. I found her sympathetic because of her unusual candor, and the nature of her problems, which involved no lack of money or restraint of her free-

51

dom of action. Her father adored her; her husband was correct and tolerant. She simply did not know what to do with herself.

First I was attracted to the trio because of Monsieur Dassary, an outstanding *gourmet*. He had no need for the usual trumped-up shipboard entertainment. He could relax like a tomcat, in an easy chair in the smoking lounge, after a meal beginning with eggs in Russian style, sliced sausages from Troyes and Chambéry, *lingots* in French dressing, sardines in olive oil, and calves' head, vinaigrette, followed by guinea hen consommé, *dorade* with sauce *béarnaise*, rare sirloin sliced thin with wine sauce, braised endives with toasted Gruyère cheese, French peas, and a lettuce salad with a dressing he himself prepared, with oil, vinegar, the yolk of a hard-boiled egg, dry mustard, salt and pepper. That he would top off with a portion of ripe brie, an iced dessert, a large glass of Armagnac, black coffee, and a Havana cigar. He had traveled on the French Line frequently in the course of twenty-five years, had been fairly rich in the beginning and, in spite of world disasters, was richer in 1949.

According to Denis, the wine steward, who had known Monsieur Dassary on shipboard and ashore over three decades, Dassary felt a special responsibility on account of his only child, Carmen, because her mother, who had died when she was born, had been unhappy, and had never complained. During the eleven months of each year when he had been immersed in business, he had spent little time in their apartment. Madame Dassary had always wanted her husband to take a month off, in the slack summer season, and travel with her through Spain. He had resolved each year to please her, but instead, when August came, he had left her with an aunt and gone fishing with some business acquaintances.

His dead wife's unhappiness Monsieur Dassary had always attributed to the fact that he had been so busy and preoccupied. Therefore he had made up his mind to secure a husband for Carmen who would be free to amuse her when she was in the mood. He had made it perfectly clear from the start that he would furnish ample funds, so that his son-in-law would never have to think about earning money. As a matter of fact, Guy Orey had met Carmen and they had been mildly attracted to each other before Guy knew of the conditions under which Monsieur Dassary wanted Carmen to get married. When the proposition was put to him, bluntly, he saw no reason to object. Guy liked to design wallpaper and fabrics, and had never found a market for his work because it fell somewhere between the conventional and modern, and pleased neither faction.

When I met Carmen and Guy they had been married six years and, to Monsieur Dassary's unspoken disappointment, had had no children. Carmen was aware, I felt sure, that her chronic discontent sprung from her own temperament or character, and she tried to control herself, so that her father would not be worried and Guy would not think she was reproaching him. Without meaning to be, she was difficult enough. If a porthole was open, she wanted it closed, and if it was bolted shut she felt the need of fresh air. When she did not like the shoes or wrap she was wearing, she would send Guy to their suite for others. What was listed on the menu seldom tempted her, so she would order something special, and before her order could be served would see something from the regular bill of fare on someone else's plate and change her mind again. The ship's personnel, the members of which had known Carmen's father long and favorably, for his generosity, could not do enough for her. She danced well, and had no lack of partners, although her heart was not in it.

"You've been observing me," she said, asking permission with her expressive eyes to sit beside me at a wall table in the smoking salon.

"I sit facing your way all through mealtimes . . ." I began.

"Please don't apologize. I'm glad," she said. "I'm at a loss about myself, and if you've drawn any conclusions . . ."

"You're young, rich, good to look at, with all the leisure there is, and no one or nothing to prevent you from doing as you please. You're sensitive, intelligent. What more could anyone want?" I asked, not unkindly.

"One could envy your magnificent detachment. You sit here alone, drinking brandy, hour by hour. I've longed to share your thoughts, so many times," she said, and hesitated quite tremulously. "Tell me honestly," she implored. "Do you think I'm destructive to the nerves of those around me?"

"What do you think about?" I asked.

"Myself, most of the time," she answered, ruefully. "Uncertainties, quite meaningless. Shall I go down to breakfast or have it brought to me in bed? What to wear? What to buy? Where to go?"

Early one morning I blundered into the hideous brown assembly room called the Salon des Conversations and nearly tripped over a nun who was kneeling near the port entrance. Bewildered, I saw that two or three dozen men and women were on their knees and that a Mass was in progress. Carmen was well up in front, as demure and saint-like as could be. Religion, I learned, had never touched her deeply, but she observed its forms and ceremonies with Gallic detachment. Guy, it developed, was a Free Thinker, and her father sel-

dom entered church more than twice a year. I asked Carmen
if her mother had been pious. She looked surprised, somewhat taken aback.

"I don't know," she said. Then she paused and reflected.
"I know nothing about my mother, really," she said. She
told me that she disliked confessions. "I simply will not
concoct imaginary sins, in order to dramatize them. Should
I be ashamed of being so empty?" she asked.

She was always catching me off base, like that.

We did not get far along the road to a mutual understanding, but since she believed that my inner life was rich
and knew that I had found Paris inexhaustibly interesting,
she urged me to call on her, in her apartment in the Ile St.
Louis, and I promised. She was a person whose qualities did
not show through her spoken personality, or the inconse-
quential things she did. Considering her resources and op-
portunities, she had acquired little that was satisfactory to
her, but she had kept away from false substitutes. I was
anxious to see her again and to know her better.

When the opening of the annual Independent art show
was announced, I thought of Carmen, telephoned to invite
her to go to the exhibition with me, and she seemed delighted. She asked me to spend the evening with her, the
day before the *vernissage*.

The Ile St. Louis has always been one of the most tightly
self-contained quarters in Paris, set apart from the rest of
the city because the Seine, having flowed from the direction of Charenton and Ivry to a point a little downstream
from the Pont d'Austerlitz, divides itself in two and forms
a snug little island which bears the name of France's sainted
king. Having accomplished that, the historical old river

veers, splits and forms another island which was the site of the old fortified city of Paris and today is called "l'Ile de la Cité."

On the Ile St. Louis, even the poorest inhabitants have always been smug and exclusive. A floating "city hall" was once established on a houseboat moored to one of the quais, and several times the residents of the island have tried to "secede" from the rest of Paris, and of France, in order to establish a "republic" of their own.

Every square foot of the island, except those occupied by the narrow stone-paved quais, the slits called streets, and a triangular park at each extremity, is covered with buildings from four to six stories high. Trees standing along the rim, with their roots in the water, grow tall and in prosperous times are trimmed to spare the view from upper windows. Large high-ceilinged apartments, reached by means of long flights of stairs from a central courtyard, have been occupied by discerning men, large numbers of them bachelors; by women of means or careers who live alone, or with other women; by eccentrics or recluses who seek the ultimate in remoteness and privacy; a few rich merchants from the Temple quarter who keep expensive mistresses; high-grade courtesans with powerful protectors; and aesthetes, some of them neurotic, who might have stepped from the pages of Huysmans.

The rich or privileged have sat for centuries behind the high windows which command the most extensive views, of the immense Halles aux Vins, of the Jardin des Plantes and the zoo in the middle distance, of the back and side of Notre Dame de Paris on what is scornfully called "the other island." Of course, the "other island" (l'Ile de la Cité) has the great Cathedral, the prefecture, the gaunt Hotel Dieu, or city hospital, the Palais de la Justice, La Sainte Chapelle, the famous Horloge, the central flower market, the forbidding old Conciergerie, the quaint *place* Dauphine, and the intimate river-level park of Henry IV. That has never prevented the people of the Ile St. Louis—from the hardest-working washerwoman or tugboat hand to the members of the obsolete aristocracy or the *bistro* keepers, library owners, collectors of blown glass, bric-a-brac, fruit wrappers, miniatures, fans, manuscripts, costumes or pressed sea plants—from calling the citadel of ancient Paris "the other island" and feeling superior to the dwellers thereon.

Before War II what few Americans lived on the Ile St. Louis were cosmopolitans in outlook and closer to European culture than that of the United States. And very few Ile St. Louis Frenchmen had absorbed any sartorial or cultural influences from the United States. The poor on the island had felt the influence of the Seine, which is seasonal, of hard times which are periodical, of wars, which drained away the young men, and of inflation, which harassed and confused them. They have not been able to afford changes or improvements. What with the unsanitary conditions prevailing around the bottoms of the buildings and the dank river mists that settle in the narrow streets, those who live there with no margin have done well to survive. From the lodges of concierges and the dark ground-floor lodgings may be heard, day and night, the sound of chronic coughing, or retching, spitting, sneezing, snorting and loud blowing of noses. Infants gurgle, children snuffle, grown folks wheeze. That is considered normal.

In sunlight the Ile St. Louis is like a crudely cut gem with a dull finish, one that glows on its outer surfaces and hints of murky depths within, from which come occasional glints of inner facets which smolder behind the outer sheen. In lunar light, the old plaster walls and velvet shadows form an ungainly carved moonstone. The myriads of chimney pots and vents are like runted gargoyles which look up toward scudding clouds and mackerel skies instead of downward, like the stone demons escaping from Gothic churches. And, indeed, there is a crust of opulent, unique and, in its way, abundant life going on around the musty kernel of that island, with free walls to catch the shadows of tall trees, with fortunate men and women, some separate and solitary, going about their days and ways with a minimum of regard for contemporaneous events, main currents of history, political trends, economic determinism, or those pachyderms, the centuries.

In cellars, basements, cisterns, hallways, dens off courtyards, there are darknesses in cells and patiences in eyes. On the higher stories, front, with river and space in the foreground, there is breathing room, with vistas of the wine market's compact acres, the Latin Quarter, roofs and acres, the zoo and cultivated plants, with cages and acres, domes of learning, domes and towers of worship, domes of commerce, angles, streaks of streets—the stuff that maps are made of.

Monsieur Dassary had bought for Carmen and her husband, soon after they were married, a fine apartment six feet above the level of the parapet, at No. 20 quai de Béthune. The building, five stories in height, and near the water's edge, had been built in the early eighteenth century and thus, as such things are reckoned in Paris, was neither old nor new. To me it seemed ancient. There was little through traffic along the quai, which curved around the downstream end of the island. The trees along the river were very tall and reached high toward the thin gibbous moon before branching out to hold aloft spring foliage.

Carmen was standing in the doorway of her apartment,

waiting, when I entered the courtyard. There was a button near the main doorway which caused the latch to click and the door to open, but once one was inside, and the heavy door closed behind him, it was impossible to get out again without the co-operation of the concierge. She asked me a few questions that bewildered me at first. Carmen had suspected that her father, who would go to any lengths to please her, might have taken matters into his own hands and sought me out.

I sensed before I had stepped into the hallway that she was alone. Guy, she said, seldom stayed at home evenings. The cook lived a few blocks away, and she had dismissed the maid, who had a dormer room in the attic.

"Is Guy at all jealous?" I asked, when she told me about an acquaintanceship which had developed in America between her and a lieutenant from Arizona, and that had come to nothing because he wanted, principally, to learn French and she found it tiring to speak French with him because he failed to grasp the nuances of the language. I could readily understand that French without nuances would be as bare and thin as a Butterick pattern of a fine garment without material or artistry.

My question caused Carmen's dark eyes to open wide.

"Jealous?" she repeated. "I had no thought of making Guy jealous. If only I were as self-sufficient as he is. He makes no demands."

"He understands that you're lonely?" I asked.

"He thinks I'm constituted that way, I suppose," Carmen said. "It's Father who can't give up the idea that life, for me, must be wonderful."

"And you?"

She sighed. "Either I'm finished with living, or haven't yet started. Who knows?"

There was no mistaking that she had hoped for helpful suggestions from me, and I was inclined to believe that her troubles, being negative, were resulting from her scattered education. She knew how to behave, socially, and about the choice of clothes and the use of cosmetics. History was a blur to her, and so were current events. No one had taught her anything she could accept about the arts or literature. Her languages—French, English, German, Italian and Spanish—were fluent, on the surface, but her French and English had depth.

Science meant nothing to her. Enough had been spent on her schooling and private instruction to give France another Madame Curie, if her teachers had that kind of orientation. Actually she was as ignorant of mathematics or physics, biology, or other branches of scientific learning as any young African tribeswoman in the jungle. But because she was so sure that I had the secrets of wisdom, time, tide and tranquility, I did not have the heart to impress on her that I had almost no formal education. Had I told her the truth about that, she would have thought that I was bored with her and did not wish to make any effort at all. That was not true, because I found her so amazingly untainted with misinformation.

What bewildered me most was the apartment, its location, its ideal plan, the furnishings which had been selected with so much discrimination and assembled in such good taste. Carmen seemed anxious to show me everything, and I could not help being aware that she was observing my reactions to each room, object, or set of furnishings. Most certainly she could not have chosen many of the things, or determined their arrangement and disposition. And after glancing through one portfolio of Guy's wallpaper designs I was even surer that he had had no hand in furnishing the place. Guy had an attic room, like that of the maid, only larger, for a studio and did all of what they called "his work" up there. There was no communicating tube or telephone.

A long narrow hallway extended from the front entrance all the way through the apartment, terminating in the fine old-fashioned kitchen, which had a separate door in an alley, for deliveries. On the walls, between the doorways and above the seats and benches, were paintings and drawings, Vlaminck, Utrillo, Matisse, Dufy and other contemporary French artists whose work was colorful, light and free from extraneous non-aesthetic qualities. There was a small table with a tray for calling cards (and no cards) near the courtyard entrance, an umbrella rack with a porcelain tray for rubbers, and, toward the rear, a wall telephone. Other modern telephone instruments were distributed in some of the other rooms, but for those who preferred to stand, the wall telephone was there. Like several other articles, it seemed to be a holdover from the previous tenant.

On the side toward the river, was the grand salon, a music room, and the library. The furniture of the salons was Louis XIV, with Gobelin tapestries on the walls and old French rugs on the floors, each one worth a small fortune. The full-size grand piano, a Pleyel, had a case in the style of Louis XIV, too, although in those days there had been no pianos. Its tone was big enough for Carnegie Hall.

Across the hall, toward the center of the island, was the reception room, a small study (in which there was an Underwood typewriter, Model No. 5, on an antique mahogany table with chair to match), and the dining room. The paintings on the dining-room walls were by Chardin.

The kitchen, with its sets of copper and bronzed kettles, pots and casseroles, the immense stone hearth with wrought-iron fire tools, Dutch oven and vertical grill, besides a battery of iron ranges, reflected more beauty than one could reasonably expect to find in an entire house. There the floor was of tiles, and in the other rooms of fine woods, inlaid in parquetry style.

The bedrooms had a corridor of their own, and were comfortably distant from the living rooms. Two guest rooms were fitted up in combinations of antiques and early twentieth century, corresponding with the rest of the apartment. But when Carmen hesitantly opened the door of the one she shared with Guy, I was a little startled to see that the furniture and decorations were banal and perfunctory. Evidently the whole outfit had been bought, as a unit, in some second-rate department store like the Samaritaine.

My outraged reaction caused Carmen to laugh, and I realized that I had not heard her laugh heartily before. It was a bell-like musical laugh that seemed to indicate a zest for life and sensory enjoyment such as her father undoubtedly had, and sometimes caused him to feel vaguely ashamed, not on account of any Puritanical notion that what he liked was wrong. Monsieur Dassary was regretful that others, and especially his own flesh and blood, had less pleasure. At the same time, it would have horrified him if anyone had recommended similar indulgence for Carmen.

After the chilly and barren effect of the store bedroom, the library almost floored me. Like the other rooms it had a high ceiling, but it was narrow, and at right angles with the hallway. One end had a soothing river view. The walls were lined with shelves. There was a long table, and ranged on both sides, good reading chairs. The books included a remarkable selection of contemporary French poetry, plays, novels, essays, wit and humor, criticism and philosophy. Also there was the best of the standard fiction, and many unusual items, in French, Dutch, German, Italian and Spanish. English and American writers were well represented.

"I don't know what to say," I stammered, as I glanced along the shelves. Carmen, standing near the door, saw that I was deeply impressed, and she laughed again, but softly.

"Nothing here has anything to do with me, except that awful bedroom. I bought that myself, in a temper, after trying to do better and failing," she said.

Then she relaxed, and began talking, naturally and easily. The apartment had belonged to a wealthy, cultured Dutchman who had lived with a woman of Belgian and English parentage who now was Monsieur Dassary's mistress. The Dutchman had had to go to California for his health, and unselfishly had left Elizabeth in Europe. During the war, Monsieur Dassary had met Elizabeth in Barcelona and she had broken with a Catalan manufacturer who had superseded the ailing Dutchman. Elizabeth, at the time of which I am writing, was in Paris but preferred Montmartre to the quiet Ile St. Louis. Monsieur Dassary, according to Carmen, gave Elizabeth whatever she wanted and let her do as she pleased, within reason. Carmen discussed her father's mistresses as casually as she would have spoken of his investments or automobiles. In matters like that she was utterly without self-consciousness.

So it had been the Dutchman who had selected the period furniture, seventeenth-century tapestries, Post-Impressionist paintings and that marvelous international collection of books. But Elizabeth, who was a capricious, extravagant young heroine, had insisted on having the master bedroom to her taste. Carmen's description of it made me laugh and shudder. There had been a bed about four feet longer and wider than it seemed a bed could be, with an ornate headboard and provocative footboard, and lamps of parchment in opaque red. The lace-trimmed pillows had been like foam, and at the foot had been stuffed cushions, with frills and ruffles, and buxom dolls in negligee, as Boucher might have painted them. There had actually been a painted metal boot-jack in the shape of a woman wearing only black hose, flat on her back, with legs outspread. Boudoir scenes from Fragonard had graced the walls, in the form of colored engravings. There had been a huge loveseat shaped like the letter "S", a pouf, and lace-trimmed hassocks. The large dressing table mirror, and other mirrors in the panels of the doors had been so placed that anyone lying on the bed could see himself reflected at various angles, and when he moved, the images moved in unison, like participants in a Swedish gymnastic drill. When Elizabeth had learned that Carmen did not want the bedroom that way, and had no use for anything in it, the Belgo-English phenomenon had moved all her treasures with her to Montmartre, where they remained intact.

That explained why Carmen had been obliged to try to furnish the room, and her dismay because she found the selection and composition of household objects so difficult still was with her.

"I found that I knew nothing at all," she said.

"Your standards are high," I said. "That makes anything hard."

My eyes kept wandering back to the shelves of books.

"Don't think I've read all these. I haven't," she said. Then she turned to me appealingly. "You'll help me, won't you? I won't take up your time. . . . Just tell me what I should do—for instance—what I should start reading."

By some malicious chance my eyes were resting on a copy of Franz Kafka's *The Castle*, translated into English. I cast about quickly and guiltily for another, and found Monther-lant's *Les Célibataires* in French.

"That's a good one for a start," I said. "It will make you understand what money means, to certain individuals."

She looked at me reproachfully, and touched the back of Kafka's *The Castle*.

"This was the one you saw first," she said. "Am I unfit for it, or it for me?"

Rather impatiently I said: "Carmen, I know more good writers than competent readers. Reading—creative reading—is as hard to learn as playing the violin the way Kreisler does. Try Kafka, if you like, and you'll soon see what I mean."

"I'm really a fool," she said, disconsolately.

I reassured her, and she brightened.

Some time later, after she had served cool Alsatian wine, small cakes from La Poire Blanche, and Turkish cigarettes, we said good night. The wine had come from a vineyard that sloped toward the sun, in a year when the sun was kind to Alsace. The cakes had been mixed and baked with an art that antedated the Cubists, Impressionists and the Romanticists. The tobacco would have been rare and precious in peacetime in Ankara. The books, the Seine, the legendary island, the incredible products of an incredible civilization, wistful Carmen, Elizabeth who had the secret sought by Ponce de Leon, the periods and values, all mingled in my "tobacco trance." How could I remind myself that the rue de la Huchette was less than a half mile away, with its people and its problems, that the rue de la Paix (of the dear old Peace) was peacefully resting in the shadow of the Opéra on the expensive Right Bank, that the sidewalks of New York were hours behind us, by the clocks, that the moon was not yet due to shine upon the Wabash, that the Queen of Odi-eye-dee might have lost her way, that wars were fought one thousand nine hundred and ninety-six years out of every two thousand, somewhere on the planet, and that, however slowly, there will be some changes made.

Paris is a bill poster's town. Its walls and kiosks display a continually changing variety of sheets and placards advertising theatrical shows, plays, concerts, recitals, circuses, political or scientific meetings, lectures, soirées, fairs and all kinds of exhibitions, from the historical to the ultra-modern. The announcement of the spring show of the Independent Artists, their sixtieth in Paris, indicated that the exhibition was being held in the Palais de New Yo (*sic*). Naturally the Parisians would not take the trouble to spell correctly the name of a rival capital. In the press and elsewhere "New York" comes out "New Pork," "New Cork," "New Fork," and in some cases "New Work" and thus is confused with Newark.

But search my memory as I could, I was unable to remember any large building in Paris, suitable for exposing three or four thousand paintings to view, that was called the Palace of New York. From a newspaper I got the information that the Palace of "New York" was in the avenue de New York, which before World War II had not existed, either. I had a little black book which listed the streets of Paris and in it was a record of the streets the names of which had recently been changed. The avenue de New York proved to be the spacious and beauteous riverside thoroughfare that skirts the Right Bank from the *place* de l'Alma to the Trocadéro, as far as the Passy line, and formerly had been called the avenue de Tokyo.

That is a district in which one is likely to find streets with American names. The avenue President Wilson is a block to the west. The avenue Franklin D. Roosevelt is not far to the north. The rue Franklin (Benjamin) is just over the Passy line. The rue Washington (George) is more or less parallel with the avenue Franklin D. Roosevelt and farther south.

Because Japan had cast her lot with the Axis, Tokyo had had to give way to New York as a street name, but few of the Parisians and almost none of the taxi drivers have got used to the change. I had to direct the veteran chauffeur who drove Carmen and me from the *place* St. Michel to the Independent Show. I asked her to lunch in the Restaurant de la Huchette, so she could see my quarter, and afterward we had liqueurs on the *terrasse* of the Café St. Michel. I do not know how much Carmen observed during that first visit, but my friends there got a good look at her. She was dressed in a neat jacket of earth green with a garnet skirt. Her hat, shoes, gloves and handbag were of suede, trimmed with silver, and she carried a slender new umbrella in a green sheath which matched her jacket.

We reached the Palace of New York just as the great doors were opening and anxious painters, sculptors, critics, dealers and amateurs of modern art were shuffling in. I bought two catalogues, for 100 francs apiece, thinking of the days when 200 francs would have purchased a small painting or creditable drawing from the walls. Today about 3,000 francs, a little less than ten dollars, is about the bottom figure, and medium-sized Renoirs go for 2,000,000 francs sometimes at the Hotel Drouot.

The days when the paintings in the Independent Show were so shocking to the public that riots broke out have departed, and will return again only when an adventurous group like the Impressionists (circa 1900) see the world around them in fresh terms and find new ways of interpreting their own times. Or when an iconoclast like Picasso places bombshells under the accepted art of his period and paints the explosions. But the 1949 show was not uneventful, and to Carmen, utterly unprepared for what she was about to see and hear, was baffling and exciting.

The Independent Show consists of paintings, for the most part recent, some scarcely dry. There is no jury. Anyone who has the urge to paint and the small fee required of exhibitors may show his work, and be ignored, ridiculed, accepted or discovered. Many established painters, who believe in freedom of self-expression, send canvases to the Independent exhibition, and among the novices—this year the total number of exhibits was 2,984—nearly always there are a few whose talents the dealers and collectors cannot afford to pass by. Of course, most of the paintings are imitations of other paintings, either conscious or unconscious, ranging from primitives and false primitives to the latest lunatic fringe. Some exhibitors are deadly serious, and others are consummate practical jokers. Sophisticates who come to scoff are likely to miss a valuable item in disguise, and unwary experts can make blunders that will keep their faces red throughout the year.

Carmen was dazed. The modern paintings the Dutchman had bought for the apartment were all relatively mild and essentially decorative. They were the kind that are pleasing, in the sense that fine millinery can be. What surprised her most at the Show was the wide range of emotional reactions. Enthusiasm, repressed, became tense. Indifference, feigned, seemed almost hysterical. Quarrels broke out, some staged for publicity purposes, others spontaneous.

In one of the connecting galleries, so placed that there was not enough distance in front for a painting eighteen feet by twelve to be regarded as a whole, was a lugubrious caricature of a cafe *terrasse* and its occupants watching with contempt and fear something taking place off-scene. Probably it had to do with Nazi occupation, and the mural monstrosity was not without terrifying impact. As usual, most of the crowd found something to laugh at, although the laughs were nervous, and anything but merry. Carmen, sensitive in the extreme, felt the disturbing vibrations and clutched my arm, without being aware of what she was doing. Her posture was no longer listless. She was breathing. Her blood was circulating. If her head was in a whirl, she seemed to be glad that something inside it was stirring.

We were in the middle of a shifting group of spectators, most of whom were staring, sneering, laughing or chattering. Reyberolle's big mural was one of the outstanding sensations of the show. When I was about to turn and lead Carmen to the rear gallery, I was arrested by a feeling that someone was looking intensely at the back of my head. The sensation was a disconcerting one. I must have made a movement, because when I hesitated and changed my mind, Carmen already had started away. She worked her way back to my side and waited. As I faced about, I glanced at the men and women behind us, and saw no one I recognized or who seemed to be interested in Carmen or me.

"You're nervous," Carmen said. "Does it tire you, seeing so many strange paintings, in such a mixed crowd?"

"I'm enjoying myself," I said.

"Did you think someone was watching us?" she asked. I raised my eyebrows, surprised.

"Yes," I admitted. "Have you seen anyone you know?"

"Not yet," she said.

"It doesn't matter," I said. We passed along into the transverse gallery farthest from the main entrance and which, since the war, has been reserved mostly for posthumous exhibits. Six of the painters represented had died within the past year, some of old age, and others in the service of France or because of its consequences. We stepped into the alcove devoted to the works of the late Luc-Albert Moreau, who once had been a vice-president of the Society of Independents, although he had been a successful and rather conservative painter.

An elderly woman dressed plainly in black approached one of the paintings and placed three yellow tulips with the stems behind the frame. She was accompanied by a small man in black who wore a black satin hat with a stiff brim and an artist's flowing tie. The woman cried softly. The man took her hand, reassuringly. She controlled herself, and he led her away. The tribute was simple and touching, entirely personal in character.

Again, as the woman and her escort walked away, arm in arm, I felt sure that someone was watching me. Screening myself as best I could behind Carmen and a group of sightseers who were gaping at an indigo African mask, I glanced over my shoulder. The tall spare figure of a man in blue serge seemed vaguely familiar to me. He was leaving a little hastily, it seemed to me, and the longer I looked the less I could find in his carriage or stature that helped me place him. It would be futile, I realized, to try to recall tall spare men I had known, who might be wearing blue serge suits ready-made.

"That man who's leaving. He was behind us in the other room," Carmen said.

"No friend of yours?" I asked.

She shook her head, ruefully. "I haven't many friends," she said.

I saw that Carmen was tired, and I was, too. Nothing is more fatiguing than looking at a rapid succession of assorted paintings, mostly atrocious. On our way out, a painting in one of the larger salons where the committee in charge had grouped a number of the works most difficult to classify, caught the corner of my eye. I paused, detained Carmen, turned and stepped closer.

"Ah," she said. At once she had grasped that I had found something that held me.

It was true that I had sensed at first glance that the painter and I had something in common, if only uncertainty about ourselves.

The medium was oil paint, thinned, I thought, with kerosene, which gave it a dull, smooth surface without distracting reflections. As a composition, the painting was simple but nicely balanced, with a compelling, piquant rhythm, mostly implied. Whatever motion was suggested, the eye instinctively continued, to complete the lines and curves. Below what passed for a wavy horizon was an expanse of some earth color like sienna, modified with brick rose, and representing desert or plain—unbroken solitude. The sky, or upper spaces, was an indeterminate gray. I could not decide at first whether either of the principal colors was warm or cold. In any event, they were not flat or opaque. Somehow they seemed transparent, and three-dimensional, with indeterminate depth.

On the desert was a figure not more than two inches tall, shaped unlike man or beast, monster or symbol, seed, atom, insect, fish or fowl. But it was masculine, and how that quality was conveyed I was at a loss to understand. The he-creature or essence, whatever he was, was bound more or less to earth. At least he could not fly. His gesture showed such complete despair that the effect was Olympian, not agonizing.

The sky or space above was unbroken except for an object ascending, trailing a tendril or twine, severed and unanchored—a kite, a bubble, a balloon, an aspiration. Whatever it was, it was lost to the entity below and was abandoning any ties which might have kept it near or available.

Those two objects or creatures—I think the lower one was a creature and the escaping one some kind of value— had been traced with the point of a brush handle or some kind of sharp stick, so that their outlines, which bent forward and backward as well as from side to side, were in a faded parchment hue. There must have been an underpainting of that tone, because it showed also around the edges of the canvas. The three dominant colors, brick rose, misty gray and the wheat or mushroom tint, were so harmonious that they looked as if they must have aged or ripened together. I knew all too well that no such tones can be squeezed directly from bought tubes of paint. The artist had first achieved and opposed them in his mind or imagination, then had mixed them from crude primaries and pigments on his palette, then had spread them, with fine regard for textures, in exact proportions. The color distribution would be perfect, whether the painting were right-side up, upside down, or resting on either side.

Again that nagging sensation that I was being followed and watched. I stiffened with annoyance, faced about deliberately, and the timing was such that the man in blue serge was already turned with his back to me. He strode away without knowing that I had seen him. Unquestionably he had been stalking me from hall to hall in the exhibition palace and had observed my intense interest in the painting that had caught my fancy. I was convinced that some time, somewhere, I had known the man, that he had recognized me and had considered renewing our acquaintance, had been held back by a strong reluctance to do so, and had decided, in somewhat of a temper, against it. Violence of emotion and inner turmoil were written all across his narrow back.

Carmen was standing by, meekly and patiently, not missing a detail of the strange by-play, pathetically anxious not to seem overcurious or to be troublesome in any way. She had gazed at the painting before us as long and as intently as I had, and was not far from where she had started. The subtle color harmonies, the balance, the implications of frustration and despair, in microcosm, were lost on her, as far as definitions were concerned. Whether she felt sympathetic vibrations because of my own reaction to the work, or had dim responses of her own, she could not be sure, and neither could I.

"Who did it?" she asked, feeling obliged eventually to say something. The tone that escaped her when she pronounced the word "did" suggested a misdemeanor. I had not read the painter's name, and could not, the way the signature was scrawled on the canvas to help indicate the hummocks of desert sand in the foreground. Even that was high art, of an intellectual nature. Nothing had been executed carelessly, or left to chance. Before one brushstroke had been placed on the canvas, the painter, whoever he was, had seen the whole in his mind's eye and from then on had made no compromise.

When I consulted the catalogue, I gasped, and said aloud, involuntarily:

"Pierre Vautier!"

Carmen frowned and wondered if the names, as well as the pictures, were in code. Because the name listed, to correspond with the painting, was "Treves de la Berliere." That had completed the train of thought associations I had been waiting for.

"His mother's maiden name," I said.

She caught on, with a quick intake of breath.

"The man in blue serge who's been trailing us?" she asked.

Carmen, peering back into the catalogue, murmured the title of the painting, almost with asperity.

"La Chasse Spirituelle."

"Oh, God," I muttered. "He hasn't shed his old Surrealist tricks. Imagine . . . Pierre Vautier, who all his life has been chasing lost causes, is now in pursuit of the spiritual."

"Paul, may I buy that painting? I want to very much," Carmen said.

The idea pleased me, too. It might drive Pierre into a rage, or flatter his erratic ego. We went to the committee's office upstairs, made inquiries, and were told, after some delay and regretful consultations, that "La Chasse Spirituelle" was not for sale.

"But why?" I asked, annoyed. I had wanted Carmen to clinch the deal before Vautier could know about it.

"A few of our exhibits are offered on that condition," the committee member said. But he was puzzled, too. "Most of those," he added, "are by established artists whose dealers are holding their works as investments. . . . 'Treves de la Berliere.' I don't remember having heard of him." He checked a card index. "He's never exhibited before."

"How long ago was the exhibit entered?" I asked, but there was no exact record of the date.

Carmen, who so seldom was denied anything she wanted, was disappointed, but not ready to give up.

"You'll have to see the painter, himself," I told her, and she said she would do so without delay.

"I've known him off and on, for twenty-six years. At times he's unbearable," I warned her. Something like a faint gong was sounding at the back of my brain, warning me that the meeting of Carmen and Pierre, unless he was mightily changed, had hazardous possibilities.

As we were drinking *apéritifs* Chez Francis, indoors, because the rain was falling again, I told Carmen as much as I thought was best about Pierre Vautier. Nothing I said was maliciously intended, because at times I had been deeply fond of Pierre, and had sympathized with him in his perplexities.

It had taken Pierre a long time, several years in fact, to break down his almost hysterical reserve sufficiently to confide in me. He had only done so when his most agonizing failures to adjust himself or find a foothold in life had reduced him to a desperate state, or when he had seemed to achieve something temporarily satisfactory to him, and which he believed I had thought he would not accomplish. Whenever he had come to me in those bygone years because of his despair, I realized that he had done so because there was no one else with whom he could speak frankly. In his moments of elation, which were few and far between, he had enjoyed showing me that he was not completely a failure. I had admired his talents, his wit and his fine contempt for the smugness of the society from which he had tried to emancipate himself, but Pierre always clung to the idea that I secretly disdained him.

His mother had been a gentle, rather vapid daughter of the fading aristocracy, and his father came from a family that was old enough and had enjoyed some renown before Napoleon's time. Pierre's father, however, had a practical streak in him, had gone into the manufacturing business as a young man, and had made a modest fortune. Vautier, *père*, had had a factory in which French door and window accessories were made. At the time I was talking with Carmen, I did not know whether either or both of Pierre's parents were dead or alive, but when I counted the years, and established that Pierre, who I still thought of as a boy in his early twenties, was forty-five years old, I was disconcerted and thrown off my calculations. That he was a painter, and, to my mind, such a talented one, did not surprise me much. I only wondered why he had not turned to painting earlier in life, and skipped much of his frustration.

I told Carmen, experimentally at first and with more frankness when I found that she understood more than I had expected, how Pierre had suffered a crisis of nerves and chagrin when he had found, just after he had broken with his father in 1923, that he had got into a veritable nest of homosexuals, all of whom were agog about him, and some of whom were quarrelling violently between themselves on his account. Of course, he had assumed then and there that I had suspected him of sharing tastes of which he had been naively ignorant.

When, later, he had had to give up his mistress, Mary the Greek, to whom he had turned in a panic, trying to overlook the fact that she was a hopeless alcoholic, with her mind unhinged by her own grief, he had been vibrant with resentment against me, because he thought, truly enough, that I had foreseen when first they got together how the affair would end.

In the middle 1930's when he had taken up the cause of Republican Spain and fought there, bravely, and had seen the brave betrayed and martyrized by men and nations, Fascist, and nations supposedly democratic, he had written me passionately from the battlefields, but when he returned to France had avoided seeing me, most probably because we both felt the defeat so keenly that talk between us could only be painful. When last I had heard from him, he had joined the Communist Party outright, and was a lieutenant in the French Army, and an undercover worker for the Party, then the second largest in France, and which Daladier, the stooge of Munich, had outlawed for political ends.

"It isn't likely that he's a Communist now," I said to Carmen.

"But why?"

"The painting. It's nowhere near the Party line for art," I said.

"He's a most unhappy man," she said, pensively, and I knew, in the few moments of silence which followed, that Carmen would try again to buy the painting and meet the artist, face to face.

4. The More Things Change...

I DID not notice until I had been back in Paris several days that the old rue Zacharie, which cuts across the mid-section of the rue de la Huchette, extending all told about 120 yards between the rue St. Séverin and the river, had been renamed rue Xavier Privas. The change had been voted officially by the Paris Municipal Council some time in 1945, but the city employees whose job it was to take down obsolete name-plates and put up new ones had switched only two of them. The third plaque, where the little street touched the quai, had been overlooked and, in 1949, four years after the post-war rechristening, still read "rue Zacharie."

Xavier Privas quite evidently was a man's name, and it is not the custom to name Paris streets for men until after they are dead. Usually, unless the street's namesake is a saint, the honor is bestowed because the party in question had distinguished himself in one of the sciences or arts or had served France in some important civil or military capacity. So, when I noticed the two new and strange street signs on the short southern stretch of the tiny cross street, I asked my old friends and new acquaintances who Xavier Privas was, and what he had done to deserve a memorial in our quarter. Nobody could answer me, or had thought much about the subject.

St. Cricq, the shoemaker at No. 9, had the idea that Xavier

Privas had been a poet, and not a particularly good one. The Satyr, a professional cook, was of the opinion that Privas had been a composer of music. I consulted Anatole, the clerk in the large bookstore on the quai, who knew the names and works of nearly all the French poets. He had never heard of Xavier Privas, and could find no record of any of his writings. There were two fairly well-stocked music stores between the *place* St. Michel and the rue du Petit Pont, one of them situated on a corner of the rue Xavier Privas. None of the clerks could find on the shelves any published music attributed to a Xavier Privas, or give me any information about him.

In such cases, the final resort was always the amiable little statistician, Mainguet. When I put the question to him he was so astonished at finding his memory a blank that he blushed with chagrin. Mainguet knew a lot about the history of the quarter, far more than anyone else, and the quarter had had a long and varied history. A few years back, when Monsieur Mainguet had been working for the Ministry of Justice, he had looked up nearly everything reprehensible that had happened in the old rue Zacharie. Nothing he could recall off-hand from his findings shed any light on the life of our forgotten man.

All the old residents were consulted, and the matter was discussed in the stores and cafés. It was generally assumed that, in order to rate having his name attached to one of the neighborhood streets, Privas must have been born, lived a while or died somewhere near by. Furthermore, most of the new street names, bestowed since Liberation, had belonged to heroes of the Resistance Movement. The local heroes all were known, except two passing strangers who had lent a hand at the barricade and died anonymously. No Privas was on the honor roll.

Actually, no one got much excited about Privas. If Main-guet did not dig up an obituary of the missing celebrity, an explanation of the Council's action would probably come to light in due time.

On the southeast corner of the rue Xavier Privas and the rue de la Huchette, two floors above Monsieur Vignon's grocery store, lived a widow, aged thirty-two, Germaine Lefevrais, and her eleven-year-old son, Victor, whom many of the neighbors liked especially well, while as many others thought of him as a problem child.

That spring of 1949 was a terrible period for Victor, who had known a few others before—as an infant when his father had been called into the army; later when, after the debacle his father had been framed by the No. 1 local Collabo, the hated Navet who was a lieutenant of Pierre Laval, and sent to work in Germany. Still later—Victor had then been six—when his father, on account of mistreatment in the Reich, had died on a train bound for Paris and home and been taken off in a crude wooden box, and a change had come over Victor's mother, his playmates, the flat and everything in it. Hatred of the traitors, of the Boches, and a thirst for revenge had started like a ringing in his ears and remained with him always. The agitation for the release of Pétain, favored by so many of the parents of the boys with whom Victor went to school, had got Victor into a dangerous state. He would fight at the slightest suggestion that the Vichy chief should be let out of his solitary cell for any purpose except guillotining. Victor's teachers tried to discipline him. Parents of boys he injured complained. Victor's mother, who had to work herself up to an hysterical pitch in order to punish him at all, beat him quite brutally. To cause his mother anxiety and pain was torture to Victor, but he could not do otherwise.

One afternoon Mme Lefevrais had to take a bus ride over toward the Gare de l'Est on her free day, in order to pick up a suit which had been outgrown by the son of one of her co-workers in the restaurant. The suit could be made over for Victor in such a way that it would look practically new. She had asked Victor if he would like to go with her.

Victor had gone on the bus ride with his mother and had behaved fairly well, from his own standpoint. But before they had been able to get into the No. 38 bus in the *place* St. Michel, someone along the street had let it drop that it was Fabien Salmon's saint's day (which is celebrated in Europe, generally, instead of birthdays) and Germaine had decided that it would be nice for Victor to give his friend a present.

"I think he'd like some kind of pet," Germaine said.

Puppies were too expensive. Kittens, in the crowded popular quarters, led miserable lives, unless they happened to be tough and smart enough. In one of the booths along the sidewalk, between the church of St. Laurens and the big railroad station serving the eastern lines, were some goldfish in a large tank with pebbles and water plants. The moment Victor saw his mother's eyes light up, at the sight of those goldfish, he knew that one of them would be bought, and that he, who had no feeling for exotic fishes, restrained and uncommunicative as they were, would have to take the creature over to the butcher's apartment and present it to his mild, admiring schoolmate with such grace as he could command. Germaine was sure that Fabien would like the fish. Victor had no hunch about that. If Fabien were touched and pleased, he would give Victor credit for having made the choice of present, and Victor would have to spoil the party by denying that he had anything to do with the selection. Or else, Victor would have to hedge and pretend, again.

None of the foregoing was mentioned in the tale Madame Lefevrais was telling the crowd in Les Halles de la Huchette.

The goldfish, which in its jar was being held up as Exhibit "A," had cost 100 francs, and for 30 francs more the sidewalk dealer had furnished the glass jar, a few pebbles and a small sample envelope of fish food.

On the bus bound for home, the conductor had come around to collect fares. Germaine had offered tickets enough for herself and Victor, at the reduced rates to which she was entitled as the widow of a war victim. The conductor had spotted the goldfish in the jar, which she held balanced on one knee and steadied with her free hand.

"You have a live animal there, madame," the conductor said.

"A small inedible fish, enclosed in a jar and carried in my hand," Germaine said, defensively. "It can incommode no one, monsieur."

"As an animal, he or she must pay a fare," said the conductor. "A fish is a live animal, while it is living. If it had died, and was wrapped in a package from which no offensive odors escaped, you would be entitled to transport it free of charge."

"Kill it, Mother," Victor suggested, glaring at the conductor scornfully.

Germaine got angry, too. "See what you've done," she said to the conductor. "You've agitated my son."

"That does not repeal the regulations under which I oversee the operation of this public conveyance," the conductor retorted.

"Most likely you don't know how to drive it," Victor said.

"Victor! French politeness!" his mother cautioned him.

Rather than make a scene, Germaine offered for the gold-fish's fare the same number of tickets she had paid for herself and Victor, respectively. She was afraid Victor might attack the conductor and that they would be put off the bus, goldfish and all. He had sailed into more than one adult who had seemed to be annoying her.

When the conductor counted the number of tickets in Madame Lefevrais' hand, he drew himself up.

"That won't do, madame. The fish is not entitled to ride at the reduced rate the Republic extends to the relicts of war victims. For the fish you must pay the full rate of fare," the conductor said.

In a corner of the second-class compartment, a ragged old man was scratching himself.

"I suppose," Victor said, "that the old type there who has fleas will pay a million francs. Aren't fleas live animals?"

"Victor! The poor old man might hear you! French politeness!" Germaine said.

The conductor, exasperated, pulled the rope to stop the bus between corners, so Germaine, under protest, paid a full fare for the goldfish. The cost of the ride, one way, was 15 francs for Germaine, 15 francs for Victor, and 20 francs for the living goldfish.

There always has been quite a lot of horsemeat eaten, and often with relish, by Parisians who were obliged, or felt they were obliged, to economize. Under the current scale of inflated prices and debased currency, horsemeat costs the retail buyer 15 or 16 percent less than steer beef. In the days of 40 francs to the dollar, horsemeat was cheaper in proportion, because times were not so hard and there was less demand for it. Probably, in the late 1930's, a pound of horsemeat could be purchased for 80 percent of the amount that would buy a pound of beef.

What are the differences, aside from the price? Horsemeat is somewhat drier, coarser in fiber, inclined to be stringy, and the fat has a yellower tinge. There is not much fat. Horse steaks are not satisfactory. Roasts are passable. Stews, ragouts and hashes can be very tasty, depending on the seasoning and cooking.

Ever since the times of the Bourbons, and perhaps before, the French, by and large, have believed that horsemeat hamburg, cooked lightly in bouillon, is good for invalids and convalescents. So the rich have eaten horsemeat by prescription, and hospitals have bought and served large quantities in normal times. In madhouses, jails and various public institutions what has appeared as "beef" on the menus and accounts has nearly always been horse beef, and most of the lamb is goatmeat.

But notwithstanding that the use of horsemeat is widespread in France, and has a long respectable history, there are those who prefer not to talk about it, or to buy it, openly, where their neighbors can see them. All the horse butcher shops, like the one at No. 13 rue de la Huchette, have a gilded horse's head, carved in wood, above the front entrance, and no other kind of meat is sold on the premises.

We had a talk with Monge at the Normandie bar about the horsemeat trade, while the April rains were still falling. The war, he explained, had given his business an unprecedented boom, which had been prolonged by government regulations, food rationing, price fixing, inflation and postwar increases of the cost of living.

In pre-war years Monge had not done badly in his shop. He had supplied small restaurants and boarding-houses, and housewives who had to pinch pennies, but most of the latter came to him from a distance of two blocks or farther. The dwellers in the rue de la Huchette who ate horsemeat were shy about buying it from an intimate acquaintance, in plain sight of those who lived around them. So they walked a block or two, and got theirs in the Buci or St. Germain markets, or across the river, in the 4th arrondissement.

Sharing the hardships of war made the folks of the quarter less wary and self-conscious, and Monge did plenty of business with the people near by who formerly had avoided his shop. In fact, there had been months at a stretch when Parisians from any quarter would buy all the edible meat they could find, and the demand for horsemeat had exceeded the supply. All the régimes, from that of the Third Republic through the Nazi occupation and the Vichy-controlled collaborators, clamped a ceiling on retail prices, and since Liberation the ceilings had been frescoed with rules upon rules, with penalties, warnings, supplements, appendices and contradictions. That did not mean that Monge could not save the best cuts from the horse carcasses which looked soundest to his practiced eye for his old friends and favorites, like Thérèse the cook and Monsieur Trevise's big Léonie, who did the buying for the Café St. Michel.

"I never used to know what was happening around here," Monge said, after remarking that his immediate neighbors were no longer too proud to foregather and swap gossip in his place.

"Had anyone had the foresight, he might have made a fortune with a horsemeat ranch," Monge said. Then he sighed. "It's too late, now."

"Nonsense," said Madame Gillotte. "Your prices are higher than ever, and going up every month."

"And where shall I be when rationing ends, and beef begins flooding the market?" Monge asked. He had asked the same question of himself, many times lately.

Some were of the opinion that the end of rationing and government price fixing would bring about more inflation and a severer depression. A few of the Communists insisted that the United States would swamp France with surplus American beef, mostly diseased. Hubert Wilf assured Monge that the rich would be richer and the poor poorer, and that the percentage of families with "feeble economy" would increase. Hubert had thought his words would be comforting to Monge, as indicating that there would be no slump in the horsemeat business. Monge did not agree.

"The poor, at best, can afford only to buy the tail, the tongue, the bones, the scraps, the shanks, kidneys, lungs, liver and lights," Monge said. "I shall be stuck with the expensive cuts, the filets, roasts and round."

"You sell the brains, I suppose," Madame Gillotte said. She had never, to her knowledge, tasted horsemeat. "A wise old horse, who had dodged traffic in Paris fifteen or twenty years, should have developed better brains than a bovine eunuch in the pasture."

"The use of thinking apparatus does not make it more tender and edible, perhaps," suggested Noel. "You know how tough a chicken is, who has run pell mell around a yard all his life. His muscles are like thongs. So it might be with a smart old horse's brains."

Monge looked at his best friend reproachfully.

"You've never eaten horse brains, most likely . . . In fact, I haven't, myself," Monge said.

But he told Noel and me later that, if the horsemeat trade got bad again, as it had been in the late thirties, he was not going to dribble away his savings which he had defended against extortion, taxes and inflation, by converting them into Swiss francs.

"I'll get a job nights in a factory," Monge said. "My lease runs ten years more. That I can sell, perhaps."

"You've never worked for anyone else in your life. You couldn't do it," Noel said. "Supposing, on your first night, the union boss came around and ordered a slow-down. You'd forget you weren't on your own, start working like a beaver, and get beaten up, or fined. Maybe both."

"Sell your stuff to the Jesuits for bastards, delinquents and orphans," suggested the trussmaker, Amiard.

The war, which had stimulated the horse butcher's business, had knocked the bottom from under the taxidermist's trade. For years Noel had been unable to obtain the necessary wire and chemicals for mounting birds and beasts. Hunting had been at a standstill, for lack of guns and ammunition. Sportsmen caught no remarkable fish, in war time, to be displayed on plaques. Noel's shop was closed, most of the time. The stuffed foxes, heads of stags, wild boars, pet cats, canary birds and parrots were on display in the windows.

During the occupation the only stuffed creatures the Nazi troopers had wanted were the vipers which Noel had in stock. The practical jokers among the Boches had liked to chill stuffed snakes in a company ice-plant and place them in the beds of their comrades, or female prisoners. Noel could have sold any number of stuffed snakes to the Germans, but no German officer would give him permission to make the thirty-mile trip into the Oise, to catch vipers. Neither would the Germans in the country let amateur snake-catchers ship dead snakes to Paris. No rules or precedents had any bearing on reptile transactions.

Everyone who had lived in the rue de la Huchette even half as long as I did knew who the enemies of the Republic were and could have listed the Collabos in advance. The outstanding Fascist, the only one who took an active part in the Vichy régime and its extensions in occupied France, was Arsène Piot, locally known as the "Navet" (Turnip). He was the one who had arranged for the deportation into Germany, as a laborer, of Victor Lefevrais' father.

Before War II had broken out, the Navet had been an official under Chiappe in the prefecture, and an active organizer of the black-hooded Cagoulards. He had made a scene one night which had echoed all up and down the street, screaming accusations of infidelity and insubordination at his gentle deaf wife, Jeanne, and attempting to beat Jeanne and their son, Eugene, who then was about seventeen years old, with a heavily-buckled leather belt. Eugene had floored his father with an umbrella stand, knocking the Navet senseless and wounding his scalp.

At the time of the great exodus from Paris, just before the Nazis motored in, the Navet commandeered a large bus, and forced Jeanne to flee southward with him. Already he had placed himself under the protection of Pierre Laval, who had use for the Navet at Vichy. Along the way, before they got far out of Paris, Jeanne saw some of her neighbors by the wayside, appealed to them and was rescued forcibly from the Navet. Before Pétain's surrender and the subsequent arrangements for the suppression of the Republic could be completed, Jeanne had taken refuge with her Persian lover and gone with him to Turkey.

The Navet, as soon as the Vichy Government was set up, was sent back to Paris, to purge his former quarter of dangerous characters. Before the Nazi debacle in 1944, he escaped to the Argentine, with his wife's inheritance converted into cash. No one knows his address, but several are determined to obtain it, some day—among them his son, Eugene. Of the Navet's wife and son, there will be much to say later, since both are living in the street, in an apartment directly above the one they once occupied with him.

The residents of the rue de la Huchette who took such an heroic part in the August uprising against the Nazis, making a fortress of their little street by means of barricades, cleaned out the local Collabos with a thoroughness that has left the present population of the St. Michel quarter about 100 percent pure, as far as patriotism is concerned. Actually, those who had accepted the Pétain-Laval régime, and had believed for a short while that liberty, equality and fraternity had been suppressed, permanently, as a slogan for France, got out of their own accord, in time to save their lives. They lost their businesses, their jobs, their real estate and leases, and today most of them are scattered throughout France, in localities where their war behavior is not known, or where they have relatives, friends or anti-Republican fixers who shield them.

St. Aulaire, the custom tailor, had been an outspoken Royalist and bitter anti-Semite all through the years he had had his tailor shop in the street. He had never believed the quarter was worthy of him and his clients, many of whom had been French military officers more stuffy than he was. The Navet, when he made his getaway, fled without a thought of protecting those who had shared his treachery. So St. Aulaire had been left, high and dry, when Paris was liberated. Mostly because the stiff-necked old tailor had always ranted against everything liberal, long years before the Cagoulards or Germans came, his neighbors made no attempt to detain him when he packed his belongings, sold his bolts of imported English tweeds, cheviots and worsteds, and his high-grade French fabrics, at a most advantageous price, and departed. His lease was taken over, unofficially, by the widow and daughter of a follower of De Gaulle who was listed as "missing." Their story, too, will follow later.

The proprietor of the music shop, so many years at No. 26, was too chicken-hearted to risk anything but secret flight. Gion left behind his stock of music, including a few violins, and his mistress, Bernice. He had hired Bernice as a clerk, while she had been a relatively young girl, and seduced her in order to secure her services free of charge. Nobody blamed Bernice on account of Gion's fervor for dictatorship. Everybody knew she had lived in terror of him. Noel and the others helped Bernice dispose of the music and the violins, find a room above the Auto School offices at No. 30, get a job as cashier in the Samaritaine department store within easy walking distance. Not many days passed before she was enjoying the jam sessions held by the antique-shop clerk, Be-Bop, and his jazz companions, drinking herself into a state of passive contentment over the week-ends, and living in terms of hand-to-mouth. She was like a tree that had seemed to be withering, had been jolted and bruised by a Juggernaut, and afterward started flourishing again.

Had not Madame Durand, the former florist, been warned by her confederates and cleared out ahead of Leclerc's and the American advance, she would have been mobbed, or thrown into jail, and tried by one of the kangaroo courts that sent so many Collabos, and, unhappily, a few mere political enemies, to forced labor or death. Madame Durand had denounced to the French Gestapo and the Nazis some of the best men and women of the street, with a kind of maniacal zeal, as if she had been waiting all her life for such a chance to strike. Her building, No. 23, was confiscated, and later released to be sold. She is living somewhere in the south of France, waiting frantically for the Fourth Republic to disintegrate.

The old doctor, Clouet, was so senile and ineffectual that nobody bothered about him at all. He left his office more or less as it was, without running water or sanitary equipment, and went back to his native village in the Ain, where there are plenty of unregenerate Pétainists to this day, quite solid with the bishop and the anti-Jewish provincial administration.

Of the small fry, there was Panaché, a former floorwalker who had lived at my hotel, the Caveau. I could find no one who knew what had become of Panaché, or who remembered why or when he had dropped from sight.

So the rue de la Huchette had purged itself, without recourse to the courts. Where formerly a conflict had smoldered between the believers in republican government and those who favored a monarchy or a French version of Mussolini's and Hitler's "new order," today the struggle continues between a minority of Communists and Soviet sympathizers, on the one hand, and the remainder of the population on the other—the majority, or remainder, being split into factions and so-called political parties like pieces of a mosaic which fit into a pattern, but lack cement.

After World War I, when I was in the Ruhr and the Rhineland while the French were occupying Essen and Düsseldorf, the British were in Köln, and the Americans were in Coblenz, the mark skyrocketed from 100 to the dollar to 3,000,000 or more. A seidel of beer in June, 1923, was 10 marks, then 100 marks, then 1,000 marks in July, and within a few weeks, 10,000 marks. I paid 9,000,000 marks at the factory for an inferior pair of shoes in Burg-bei-Magdeburg. I spent one week-end in Köln when British soldiers and German factory workers were paid in 1,000,000-mark notes, the first ever printed. The men were wandering all over the city, unable to buy as much as a box of matches because the supply of small bills had been exhausted and no one could change a 1,000,000-mark note.

At the Hotel Furstenhof, on the Rhine, I tipped a chambermaid two American dollars, after she had tidied my room and brought me my breakfast for ten days. She sank to her knees, dissolved in tears, and gave me a shock of shame from which I have never fully recovered. I found that I had given her the equivalent of two years' wages.

"Now I can get a dress," she said. It was evident that she had not had a new one for several years.

In France today, inflation has not distorted the pattern of affairs or the general outlook to the extent that Germany was affected in the early 1920's. But the situation is confusing, disheartening, quite maddening, and week after week, month after month, year after year, becomes steadily worse. French courage and determination help, but they are not enough. American aid is a Godsend, but no permanent cure. The nation is not self-supporting. Since World War I, it has been insolvent. Words and figures may be dyed, marcelled or maneuvered like veils around a dancer. Behind them, the nakedness is there. Others may deal with French finances on a scholarly or international basis, and a long-term view. What is frightening to me is the effect of the glorified nonsense on individuals.

I cannot forget the bewildered, injured and, oh so weary look on the face of the veteran head waiter at the Balzar when on the occasion of my first revisit he made out my check and tried to add the figures. He had been a waiter all his adult life, and a busboy in his teens, and had written and totaled many thousands of meal checks. Professional waiters in France cannot afford to make many mistakes, because shortages in their accounts are charged to them.

Auguste's eyes blurred, his fingers trembled. He was uncertain of himself and mistrustful of his brain. A slice of plum tart he had sold for five francs, year on year, was listed at 100 francs. His monthly pay, which had been 1,000 francs plus tips, had become 14,000 francs, plus tips which amounted to little in the off-season for tourists. The main dish, veal with white sauce, was 275 francs. He could not remember what the price had been in normal times.

Multiply this perplexity by the active population of France, by the minutes of the day, the cities, towns and provinces, the pencils, slips of paper, fumbling fingers and groping minds, and you have one destructive phase of inflation.

How can I make such a situation clear to an untraveled American on a sheltered continent? How can he share the feelings of a Frenchman from a corresponding walk of life? The self-same coins and bank notes the Frenchman has been using all his life have depreciated 12, then 25, and now 60 times in value, with prices ballooning, food, clothing, supplies and transportation being rationed, scarcities developing and persisting, and wages deteriorating in buying power much faster than they seem to mount in figures.

Let the American imagine how, if the United States had lain in the path of total war and suffered as France has, an ordinary day would begin. The breakfast milk would be available only for registered invalids and children, for whom special ration cards had been secured from the local police station. Whoever bought it had to stand in line more than an hour, having brought her own container. Cream would be out of the question. Butter would be scarce, and most severely rationed, and require more standing in line, or an appeal to a Black Market dealer who had it hidden under the counter and charged $2.00 a pound. It would be used only for cooking.

A drugstore breakfast of coffee and two doughnuts would cost $2.50; the coffee would be diluted and bitter, the doughnuts inadequately sweetened, if at all. The morning newspaper would cost $1.00, the same old dollar bill which in 1915 would have bought 50 newspapers. The bus fare to work would amount to $1.20. Already there would be nothing left of a five-dollar bill. If the American should buy a pair of shoes for one of his children, he would have to count out $48, all soiled and torn but once worth their face value, in silver or gold. A store suit for the American, himself, would cost $480, to be handed out in terms of the same fives and tens he had always used and formerly respected. A pair of theatre tickets would come to $120.

The bank notes would become worn, torn, soiled and dog-eared, and those which had come to pieces would have been mended with scotch tape, so that the numbers on the corners would not always correspond. New issues of fifties and hundreds would be put into circulation weekly, and when the rent was due and the American had to give his landlord about $1,200, the use of unfamiliar five-hundred and one-thousand-dollar bills would increase the awful feeling of unreality that stalks a man when money talks irrationally.

Cashiers, clerks, waiters and those who have been adept at ordinary figures are the first to lose their grip. Those frantic souls who have had to defend their existence, franc by franc, and use all their ingenuity to keep afloat, are likely, under storm conditions of inflation, to lose their minds.

Frenzied computations, made necessary time and time again each day, break down mental and physical health. The sensitive collapse. The hardiest survive, and readapt themselves, doggedly. The cunning prey on their countrymen with more abandon.

Raoul Roubait, the morning newsdealer, keeps his bank notes of small denominations in two boxes under the counter. In the left-hand box—Raoul always favors the left—he stores the bills which are still fairly presentable. These he gives in change to his customers who share his Communistic views, and others outside the Red faith who are agreeable, sympathetic, tolerant of Stalinist influence, or just naturally polite. For customers Raoul finds irritating, arrogant or difficult, he reserves the tattered filthy bills, held together precariously by soiled strips of adhesive. The reactionaries, grouches and anti-social clients get those.

A shocking example of the post-war attitude toward the waste of public money and growing tendency toward malingering in the public service unfurled itself day by day at the wide end of the rue de la Huchette. The old-time residents, with standards of morality and behavior which antedated the world wars and the decadent late 1930's, were depressed and disgusted by the spectacle. The younger people took it as a matter of course.

While the Nazis were in Paris, one of their giant tanks which was being driven through the city streets to test its speed and maneuverability—also to serve as a warning to Parisians who might be thinking of sabotage or resistance— veered from the boulevard St. Michel into the rue de la Huchette, took the right turn into the rue de la Harpe too sharply, and crashed through the rear corner of the four-story building, No. 31, knocking out supporting pillars, demolishing the ground-floor shop, and causing the ceiling of the corner room above to crumble and collapse.

No one was in that part of the building at the time, since the corner shop had been for some months vacant and unoccupied. The tenant of the second-floor apartment had not been at home. Without stopping to appraise the consequences of his careless driving, or whether anyone had been killed or hurt, the Nazi tank driver had hurtled on, across the rue St. Séverin, all the way to the boulevard St. Germain, where the tank plunged right again, with utter disregard to the normal traffic, and passed out of sight. None of the Nazi officers stationed in the neighborhood seemed to care. They took the matter as a joke. But the French who lived in the rooms above the lower back corner of the building were not sure that the structure would stand. The only Frenchmen near by who knew anything about building could not answer, one way or the other. Because the tenants had nowhere else to go, one by one they felt obliged to take the chance, and after a week or two had passed, and no further disaster had occurred, they stopped worrying. A few heavy timbers were inserted in the gap, and used as props, and until some months after Liberation not much more was done. The proprietors of the Café du Palais put up a temporary wall of matched boards, lined with beaver board, to keep the draughts out of the back end of their restaurant. Sightseers paused occasionally to look over the damaged premises, as one of the scars of war.

Three years after the end of the war a contract was awarded to Edouard Saillens et Fils, of Paris, Acheres and Bordeaux, to restore No. 31 rue de la Huchette to its former state of utility and safety, the job to be done under the system known in the United States as "cost-plus" or "force account." That is to say, the contractor was to furnish the labor at the prevailing rate of wages, the engineering and other supervision, materials at current prices, and supplies. To the cost of these the contractor was permitted to add an appropriate amount for depreciation of tools and machinery. He was to be paid, monthly, at the rate of cost plus ten per-cent, with a nominal hold-back to insure the completion of the work.

The job at No. 31, progressing at a pace that would have shamed a snail, continued unnoticed by higher authorities throughout the regimes of Ramadier, Bidault, Robert Schuman and Queuille. Cabinet ministers had come and gone and swapped offices like participants in a glorified game of musical chairs. The more or less permanent secretaries, under-secretaries, chief clerks, and functionaries who actually did what work was done remained, and the Saillens contract was passed along without question, each month when the estimates and bills came in.

E. Saillens and Sons had never assigned more than four men at once to the rue de la Huchette repair job. Early that April a union plasterer named Jacques, his helper, Adolphe, and a plumber nicknamed "Le Taupier" (The Mole-Catcher) because he had been pottering around in a shallow trench across the sidewalk day after day, used to show up at the Café St. Michel about 8 o'clock each morning, have coffee spiked with brandy, a piece of gray bread, and a glass of red wine, and saunter across the street to No. 31. What they did there cost them little exertion and the results were hardly perceptible.

About ten o'clock, the repair crew would go back to Trevise's café, have another drink or two of red wine and chat a while with Big Léonie and other customers who happened in.

From noon until two P.M. they took a recess for lunch.

Each one brought a sandwich and some cheese, wrapped in a newspaper. Monsieur Trevise let them eat their lunches at a table in his back room, and furnished the wine at the usual rates by the glass.

Along about five P.M. they began to get ready to knock off and go home at six.

The first day I observed their routine, the truck driver, called Chouette (Screech Owl) because of his habit of driving with his head sticking out of the window, like the engineer of a locomotive going into a station, stopped his large truck at the curb in front of the repair job. The capacity of the truck was several tons. The load consisted of one two-foot length of six-inch terra cotta pipe. Chouette hung around about an hour before the piece of pipe was unloaded, and an hour after it had been placed in a corner of the ground-floor room, against a wall. The job was charged with the truck and driver for half a day, a matter of 3,500 francs.

Two inside walls which had been partly demolished had been replaced and whitewashed. The two outside walls, one facing the rue de la Huchette and the other the rue de la Harpe, were still missing. There was work to be done on the foundation, the cellar, and the second-story room, which also lacked two walls.

The Chestnut Man, Madame Gillotte, Madame Mercanton, St. Cricq the shoemaker, and the sharp-tongued Madame Morizot, of Au Corset d'Art, who were among the stricter spirits of the quarter, narrowed their eyes, muttered and made cutting remarks intended for the ears of the workmen who loafed seven-eighths of the time. Jacques, his helper, the plumber and the truck driver grinned good-naturedly. They thought that only fools worked themselves out of a job, or finished an easy assignment in order to be sent to a harder one.

"To whom do they owe loyalty?" Katya asked. "Surely not to a government hostile to a worker's best interests."

"They'd be shot or sent to Siberia if they tried such tricks in Russia," Amiard said.

"In Russia they would have an incentive to work for the common good," Katya said.

The only vacant building in the rue de la Huchette was Madame Mariette's disorderly house. Throughout Paris, particularly in the poorest quarters, the premises formerly used for establishments of prostitution have not as a rule been remodeled or occupied for other purposes. It looks as if the owners, who must have profited rather handsomely before the reformers got in their work, do not expect the present ban on the exercise of the oldest profession to last forever.

For the present, the public houses are closed and padlocked "That France Might Live." The municipality of Paris stopped issuing licenses to street walkers, of whom many thousands carried official cards. Medical inspection of the women of joy, which never had amounted to much, was discontinued.

In the course of several months of inquiry, I have not been able to find one well-authenticated case of a Magdalen of Paris who has given up her time-worn method of making a living, and settled down to habits of legitimate work. Those who formerly were employed in established houses, where they had a certain amount of security and protection, now are in business for themselves.

Only yesterday police raided an established and ultra-

407169

respectable café, according to long reputation, in the *place* du Chatelet, within golf-ball driving distance from the narrow end of the rue de la Huchette. The café in question is a rendezvous well-known internationally to chess players, and tournaments with games which would make the ordinary player's head swim, are daily in progress—in the front room, that is. Plainclothesmen in that vicinity were first bewildered because so many of the customers of that café wore dark glasses. On investigation, the detectives whose duty it is to harass the girls of easy virtue and established prices, found that the men with colored glasses passed unnoticed between the chess tables and, at the entrance of a back room murmured a password, "Pompom."

"Pompom," it should be explained, is the name of a famous French bull immortalized by the sculptor, Bourdelle. "Pompom" had more offspring than Brigham Young had grandchildren.

The back room, of course, was a well-appointed clandestine bordel.

A number of streetwalkers have been murdered, many others beaten up and robbed. Still others have victimized unwary customers, whom they were never likely to encounter again. Also the pimps, who were almost as numerous as the whores and seemed to be necessary to the comfort and morale of a large percentage of the girls, have suffered cruelly. It has proved even harder for the scarlet men to adjust themselves to bourgeois ways of living and providing than for the women whose earnings they share. While in pre-reform days those idle men with scarves and pinchback suits constituted no menace to the general public, and did much to relieve the abysmal loneliness of the girls who had to serve all comers, impersonally, today the *ex-maquereaux* are being absorbed by the criminal element addicted to theft, mayhem and violence. The tide of crime in France is steadily rising, and so is the venereal disease rate.

From Madame Mariette's "Panier Fleuri" the nymphs have departed and, to paraphrase T. S. Eliot, "their friends, the loitering heirs of city directors" know pretty well where to find them, or the younger practitioners who have elected to keep the torch of Venus burning until reform has spent itself. Mireille, beloved of so many, died, tortured but not broken, in a Nazi prison. Grave Consuela, who used to impersonate the "bride," went back to Barcelona, and worked for a while in a bordel there from the windows of which she could see the tall statue of Christopher Columbus.

Little Daisy, so light-hearted and utterly perverse, married a rich gambler, spent most of the war years in Monte Carlo and slips back to the quarter to romp with her old friends an hour or two whenever she can safely elude her husband for that length of time. She loves him, he is mad about her, and she is grateful on account of the financial security he affords her. But having lived so many years a life so varied, unpredictable and well suited to her unusual talents, Daisy has found any other kind of existence boring and insupportable. In physical appearance she has matured, and she dresses expensively. Her smiles and easy chatter reveal the same sweet childish mentality, completely without guile.

Mado, who after a slow start became runner-up to Mireille in terms of popularity with the clients, carries on more or less as usual in the clandestine, with the ladies' shoe-shop front, in the rue de la Harpe, a block from the scene of her former activities.

Another occasional visitor to the *place* Xavier Privas, where the former sporting girls and their male friends congregate, is Old Armandine, who was fifty in 1935, and still had faithful clients for whom none other would do. Armandine got the concession for a Bureau de Tabac (tobacco shop supplied and O.K'd by the régime) on the outskirts of the city, behind the *place* de l'Italie. And the little niece, Christiane, for whom Armandine used to knit snug garments while waiting for business to stir at old No. 17, has finished her training as a nurse and has a good job in the American Hospital at Neuilly.

When the Panier Fleuri and corresponding havens of pleasure by the thousands were flourishing throughout France, and the women I have just mentioned were in the heyday of their careers, an honest whore knew where she stood. If she did not like the house she was in, there were plenty of others.

Today, the women of that profession take their lives in their hands when they enter strange bedrooms by day or walk the streets by night. There is no fixed scale of prices, no unwritten conventions, no expectation of fair play or common humanity. The men, if they are of that temperament, try to pay as little as possible, and the women are out to get all they can. Formerly, an unusually magnetic girl like Mireille would earn more than a stenographer or school teacher, and less than a motion-picture actress. Dora, the coal-black Negress, earned more than her husband, who read proof on the *Mercure de France*. Girls who for some reason were not steadily in demand—there was usually one of that type in every house—still did better than the female clerks in the large department stores. At present, the tough aggressive ones make a bare living, and keep up with the rising curve of prices. The timid ones suffer and go hungry.

Somehow, I cannot picture the return of the Panier Fleuri to the rue de la Huchette. Such institutions, so uninhibited, frank and at the same time sociable, had a quaint nineteenth-century flavor even between the world wars. Non-professional competition, in Paris, as elsewhere, has gnawed away the foundations of Magdalenism. Bordels need, in order to flourish in a wholesome bawdy style, a society around them that is fairly rigidly bound by conventions and taboos, so that women who place themselves beyond the pale are definitely set apart and can enjoy the advantages as well as the stigma of their demi-mondaine status. Without a robust double standard, the admittedly loose women play a losing game.

5. *Rise to the Sun*

AND lo, after weeks and months of misery, mold, drip
drip, worn tires slipping over old pavements, wet feet,
chills down the spine, before twilight on Good Friday the
skies over Paris bared themselves in terms of blueness. Spring
was in the air. It was a sailor's evening, with cloud battalions
retreating, and stragglers streaked with red—geranium,
salmon, vermilion, magenta. Between them, their comple-
ments of robin's egg, turquoise, and faint bottle green. As
if the display beneath the stratosphere were not enough,
there were reflections in the Seine which shimmered in wine
darkness.

Coincidentally, the air had cleared. Now was the time
for inhaling and deep breathing, imbued with the aroma of
buds and new leaves.

I lay by a wide-open window and rested a few hours,
suspended between sleeping and waking, anticipation and
relief. Not long after midnight, I dressed for mild weather
and walked over to the Central Markets, Les Halles de Paris,
where I wandered through streets on the outskirts half-
blocked by loaded trucks and cumbersome carts drawn by
stallions, with truck farmers and their women dozing or
chatting on the high seats or sidewalks. From those camions
and wagons which had converged on Paris from all points
of the compass, the holiday supply of fresh food would be
set out by the wholesalers, selected by the retailers, hotel

and restaurant men, and distributed to the neighborhood markets in all the arrondissements for housewives to buy.

Queuille, the country doctor, was prime minister then, and his Cabinet had raised a number of restrictions and taken several staple items from the rationed list. The holiday spirit reviving in the capital had spread through the surrounding countryside to the borders of France. Early crops had been plentiful, and if one could disregard the prices, that wide area from which Paris is fed took on some aspects of the carefree days between wars.

I stepped cautiously along the narrow pathways in the *place* St. Eustache, where fruits and berries were spread on the drying pavements, with all the order of a formal garden. Neighboring streets were lined with double files of pyramids of carrots, henna in lamplight and paler in the dawn, cabbages stacked eight feet high, cauliflower in beige and écru. On hooks in the cavernous sheds were hung carcasses of beef and lamb. The final agony of countless pigs was over and on display, shaved pink, they expressed "It is finished" when, for gourmets, the feast had not begun.

Having promised myself a basket of mushrooms for my holiday breakfast, with a duck-egg omelet flavored with *topin-ambours* (the choicest and tenderest examples of small sunflower roots), I worked my way toward the Bourse de Commerce, near the broad rue du Louvre and the rue St. Eustache, just south of that famous market-district church with the wild flying bastions. I wanted to get there just after dawn, so I could buy what I needed and meet my early-rising friends at the counter of the Café St. Michel at the morning coffee hour. The air was refreshing, the grayness of the dawn had given way to cloudless blue before the rim of the sun oriflammed the horizon. It seemed to me that we were cutting deeper than the season of spring and had been dealt a summer's day.

Superficially, almost anyone would say that the Bourse de Commerce, or commodity exchange, built round, squat and flat, like a huge bottom slice of dirty gray snow, with stalagmite pillars, untidy and pigeon-defiled, was the last place in Paris that could be beautiful. And still, in pre-dawn, that circular monstrosity, having the shape of a round-house in Kansas without the brickwork, undergoes a transformation.

In the lush countryside of the provinces known as the Ile de France, the Seine, the Seine-et-Oise—broad valleys, plains, rolling hills and slopes beyond the ring of buttes that shelter Paris—in pastures, in woods under leaves and moss, behind barns and in deserted earth-floor sheds, grow mushrooms, those subtle, aromatic, earthy plants which appear overnight and wilt in the noonday sun. Their colors are subdued. Their shapes have an essential purity, perceptibly distorted. Lonely shepherds and wayfaring tramps stoop to pluck them, cool with dew, specific against the gnawing of hunger.

French women know that mushroom flavors place housewives on a footing with blue-ribbon chefs, and the great gastronomes in distinguished restaurants are aware that, with mushrooms, they can make simple fare a gourmet's delight.

Hundreds upon thousands of mushrooms are gathered in the fields and forests of France, having grown wild. And as many others, or more, are cultivated within trucking distance of Paris. Just how or why were the wholesalers assigned the area around the night-slumbering Bourse de Commerce in which to display their mushrooms, in baskets lined with leaves?

Mushrooms range in color from the dark, threatening

underside of the giant manzanita, blackly nacreous like ooze, to the alabaster white of the *amanita verna*, or destroying angel, three bites of which will kill a man. I have never heard of a case of mushroom poisoning in France, outside of the popular Sascha Guitry film, *The Story of a Cheat*. When ranged side by side, in ranks and files, eloquent backs exposed like nudes by Ingres, mushrooms in a basket assume the properties of surface, form and numbers. Some baskets are of broad plaited wood, shaved thin and bent. Some tops are oblong, bottom corners informally rounded. Shallow baskets in the shape of large saucers with graceful arch handles are of straw or rattan, dyed with elixirs of roots and herbs, cherry brown, mahogany russet, plum-marble violet. And in all the neat containers, pressed reassuringly together, are the flesh-colored mushrooms, the dust-colored mushrooms, the snuff-hued morrels, the garnishings, the essence of bisques, the tang of sauces.

I have not written of the fragrance. I doubt if anyone can. One may hold a fresh mushroom in the palm of one's hand, and inhale the smell of earth, of gifts, of life and love, of hunger heaven-sent to be assuaged, of sweet fatigue to round out debatable achievement. A small basket, dyed with the juice of the root of sassafras, or of the bark of the choke-cherry, nesting place of slow-winged moths, contains, let us say, one hundred and fifty good-sized mushrooms, stems downward like the thumbs of emperors, backs bent like white slaves attending anointment. Raised to the degree of a basketful, the insidious mushroom fragrance vibrates in richer scents of earth and abundances of flaked ambrosia. Once around the rim of the Bourse de Commerce, a single circle of baskets number more than two hundred, involving 30,000 mushrooms, and there are each market morning many rings of baskets, in widening series, bordered with green leaves, with pathways between them.

Mushrooms in the United States, because of the anarchy of private enterprise, are luxuries. They are easy to find, easier to cultivate, and not difficult to ship. Somehow the price has been jacked up to $1.00 a pound. In France, in the most fantastic climaxes of economic improvisation and chronic inflation, mushrooms are relatively cheap, and poor folks know the taste of them.

The main Bourse of Paris and the Bourse de Commerce were much in the news before Easter time, because 2,000 brokers' clerks had been persuaded by the Commies to strike. It cannot be denied that the clerks, who worked long hard hours in an ambience of profit and loss, of fortunes made and wagers forfeited, of francs, pounds, pesetas, zlotys, rupees, lire and Mr. President of currencies, Hon. Dollar, had grievances. They were paid about 22,000 francs per month (a little less than $75). They could seldom, if ever, buy new suits, shoes might as well have been Golden Slippers, and their wives and children, as hungry as any others, could eat meat not oftener than two days in seven, with fish on Friday. But the fish dealers, in France as elsewhere, had got together and run up the ante until the bounty of the sea costs more, by the kilo, than meat, and as much as poultry.

Many strikes were pending that Holy Saturday morning. I recall that the gas workers were about to walk out, and hamstring home cooking to a certain extent; the electrical workers were turning off the lights now and then, for short demonstration periods; the school teachers of the department of the Seine were on the verge of suspending public instruction; metal workers were uneasy, having been stampeded with scareheads against the Marshall Plan; the bleachers and tanners were determined to eat cake. Also the question was to be decided that very day, in a mass meeting (which would be attended by 20,000 according to the police, 50,000 in the New York *Herald Tribune*, and 250,-000 in *L'Humanité*) whether the C.G.T. members employed on the bus system and the subway were to knock off work over the religious holiday week-end and leave 200,000 tourists and 3,500,000 Parisians stranded, in token of class solidarity.

There is no doubt that the Communist leaders and their lieutenants had a finger in each and every one of the labor conflicts above listed, and many more. Neither could anyone deny that most of the incipient strikers had plausible grounds for complaint, and action. The cost of living had soared beyond the range of their means. While a few Black Marketeers, politicians, bankers, top-grade merchants, industrialists, de-luxe hotel and restaurant keepers and speculators were getting fat and rich, squads, regiments and armies of industrial workers and public employees were not much better off, apropos their pocketbooks, than in wartime, or under Nazi occupation. Moreover, the farmers were so resentful of government regulations that they were holding back deliveries of wheat. There was talk of importing wheat from the United States, to circumvent the recalcitrant French agriculturalists, and the Communists were protesting about that, too.

Nothing reds, whites or blacks can do will dull the Parisian sense of humor. The Commies, just before Easter, had used their influence in the street-cleaning department, to the despair of the brokers in the Bourse de Commerce, and the main Stock Exchange farther westward. So the readers in the St. Michel quarter and other parts of Paris had for days been chuckling into their morning papers.

The central market district of Paris is bounded roughly by the rue du Louvre, the rue Etienne-Marcel, the boulevard Sebastopol and the rue de Rivoli. Between midnight and eight in the morning, that area is alive and bustling with sights, sounds and smells of vegetables, greens, meat, fish, fruit and dairy products. The daily food tide inundates the quarter, only to ebb and recede as daylight is intensified. Once the perishable merchandise has been disposed of, and the farmers and produce men have ridden their trucks and stallion-drawn carts back home, the Paris street-cleaning force goes into action. The mushroom market around the Bourse de Commerce has spent itself by seven o'clock and the personnel has started for the suburbs. The Communist tacticians, with a certain amount of reason, detest the operators of stock or commodity exchanges. So in spring the Red chiefs persuaded the drivers of the huge garbage trucks who gather refuse from the streets and gutters of Les Halles to park their loads, exuding multiple quintessences of stink, around the outer walls of the Bourse and the Bourse de Commerce. There they would leave them, as many as it took to fill the available space, until all the rest of the market district garbage had been reloaded into transportation vans and rushed to the city dumps or incinerators.

Each morning the stench around the Bourses was epic, distilled from fumes of fish guts, entrails of beasts and fowls, with intermediate tones of putrid vegetable rubbish. Crowds formed, at a supportable distance, to watch the underpaid clerks come to work, eyes blinking, noses masked by coat-sleeves, plunging into the stink zone. When the supervisors arrived, later, in frock coats and gray trousers, and still later the brokers in derbies and the conventional black, the swill trucks were still parked around the Bourse de Commerce, their mephitic cargoes contaminating the fog and dampness, or, after Easter Saturday, effervescing in the rays of the sun.

The editors of conservative papers, to whose hearts the ideals of tourism were most dear, appealed in vain to the Reds. The Communist propagandists, who loathed investors and tourists, pointed out that offal trucks must park somewhere, and await their turn for unloading. Petitions were addressed to the President of the Republic, the traveling Socialist, Vincent Auriol. He lacked authority to regulate street-cleaning operations. So did the Chamber and the Senate, where resolutions against political stink bombardments were adopted and embalmed in the records.

Pierre de Gaulle, brother of "Le Grand Charlie," was president of the Municipal Council. The Reds sent him an ultimatum. If he interfered, all the street cleaners of Paris would go out on strike, and the city would become a maggots' paradise.

Holy Saturday morning, having bought my basket of wicked little *cèpes*, I did not have time to wait for the stench demonstration. The Commodity Exchange was beautiful, the low gray building was splashed with slanting sunshine, the pale hues of mushrooms responded to the fingers of Aurora and the gay voices of the market folks who were doing a brisk holiday business. I walked back via the rue de Rivoli, crossed the Pont Neuf, and through the quai de l'Horloge to the Marché aux Fleurs. There each spray, bud, plant leaf and blossom was rejoicing in a chorus, with all the colors of the spectrum and many in between. The display for Easter was Gallic and varied.

I still was too early to find Madame Berthelot there.

Before I entered the Café St. Michel I stood for a moment in the wide end of the rue de la Huchette to register the old familiar spectacle on the first fair day of my return.

The sun had cleared the horizon and was aglow behind the Gothic silhouette of Notre Dame. Along the extent of the warped narrow street, the sunlight gilded dank corners long gray, ignited spirit flashes in window panes and signs —the golden horse's head marking Monge's shop, the shining brass ball from which hung a hank of human hair, ancient symbol of the barber's trade, the vermilion emblem of government tobacco, the giant mortar and pestle above the entrance of the new pharmacy. Early-morning Paris, holiday Paris, resurrected Paris bathed in sunshine, after months and weeks and days and nights of clouds, mist, fog and rain.

"Good morning," Monsieur Trevise said to me, when I entered the café and walked up to the zinc counter. He was stroking Olympe, the café cat, who had found a patch of sun and was testing the metal of the bar with velvet paws to find out if the chill was gone. Something in the tableau struck me as incongruous, and then I remembered that when Madame Trevise had been alive, no cats had graced the premises. Since he had become a widower Monsieur Trevise had mellowed considerably, and, perhaps as a gesture of his new independence, not only pampered Olympe, but took an interest in her tortoise-shell kittens.

Monsieur and the late Madame Trevise had kept that corner café twenty-odd years, until she had died in 1944. If any of the male customers, drunk or sober, showed lustful interest in one of the servant girls, no matter how deformed or simple-minded the female drudge might be, Madame discharged her on the spot, and often with hysterical abuse. Madame Trevise had not permitted her husband to play cards, which he enjoyed to the point that a game drove all else from his mind. He never had a franc to spend. She disapproved of the clients he considered his best friends, and favored those he would have preferred to go elsewhere.

The formerly taciturn Monsieur Trevise, who had worn a plaintive hang-dog expression in the days his helpmeet had been at his side, was no longer listless. Whether the transformation had resulted from the demise of Madame Trevise, or the advent of Big Léonie, was not of first importance. In the same measure that it had taken an outstanding shrew to keep Trevise in subjection, it required a lusty uninhibited female like the Catalan girl to restore his self-respect.

"He should have done away with Marguerite years before," whispered Madame de Gran' Chemin, the afternoon news hag, who was so tiny and looked so grandmotherly and beneficent with her wax-like complexion and zinc-white hair. "It can't be so hard. Murdering someone who's always around. In the Métro, he could have given just a little push, in a crowd, and pssssssssewt, she'd be under a train."

There were a few other women, like Madame Gillotte and Madame Morizot, who acted always as if she had alum in her mouth, who defended the memory of Madame Trevise and the way she had kept Trevise in order. They contended, with some justice, that had Madame Trevise relaxed, and not been strict and unpleasant, her husband would have frittered the years away, playing belotte, the maids-of-all-work would have been pregnant half the time, and the Café St. Michel, so well situated for a steady thriving business, from neighbors and transients both, would have gone to seed.

As things stood, Trevise was far from bankrupt when I renewed our acquaintance in 1949. He wore a boyish smile. He hummed, off-key, and addressed, to cats and kittens, remarks intended for the ears of some of the old customers his late wife had admired. He ate only what he liked—tender meat, lobster, cheese and fruit, with plenty of sweet pastry between meals. No vegetables except potatoes had passed his lips since the day before the funeral. In the old days, Madame Trevise had been partial to stewed greens, cooked celery and limp leeks. The hours he spent in the back room, at a card table, outnumbered those he spent on duty behind the bar.

Léonie took care of everything. She helped and bossed the cook, scrubbed the floors, washed the windows, helped the waiters on the *terrasse*, and put on wrestling bouts all over the sidewalk with the giant Chestnut Man, also a Catalan. Her laugh was as deep and infectious as that of her idol on the screen, the hefty French character actress, Marguerite Moreno. Léonie was tall and well-formed, with sturdy arms and legs, resilient breasts, and broad sloping shoulders. As a young girl she had worked with her brothers in a fishing boat, off Colliure, her birthplace. Later, in Perpignan, she had been chambermaid in a rough-and-ready small hotel. She had got in trouble with the police in 1936, for shoving a merchant out of a second-story window while he was praising the Cagoulards, whose automobiles by the hundreds were streaking through the streets toward a Sunday rendezvous outside the city. In Paris, Léonie had drifted from job to job, because she was easily bored by routine.

What did she find so wonderful at the Café St. Michel? A man who liked her as she was, and who told her, when she needed money, to help herself from the cash box and not bother him with accounts. Trevise did likewise.

Quite a few of the neighbors in the St. Michel quarter had been shocked, at first, because Léonie moved into the café so soon after Madame Trevise had been carried out, in a box, and loaded into a third-class black hearse. Actually, the whole thing had happened in a most natural way, which

Monsieur Trevise, when he was feeling his wine and newly acquired complacency, was likely to recount to the old clients he had liked and his wife had snubbed. Trevise had ridden in the first carriage behind the hearse which bore the remains of Marguerite to the Montparnasse Cemetery, and having drunk considerable *marc* had become confused during the brief ceremony at the graveside, and wandered away. Without realizing where he was walking, he had come straight back to the *place* St. Michel and became aware, in the course of the last few blocks, that he seemed to be following a large young woman who brushed off easily the men who accosted or ogled her. The young woman, who proved to be Léonie, turned into the entrance of the Ciné St. Michel, the neighborhood motion-picture theatre on the *place*, which specialized in comedies. In the daze which had been brought on by the events of the several days preceding —the heart attacks, the deathbed scene, with doctors and a priest, the ghastly "arrangements," the undertaker and his solemn men, the café shutters down, the funeral in St. Séverin, the carriage ride, the open grave—Monsieur Trevise, as if he were a sleepwalker, had followed Léonie into the theatre, down one of the aisles, and taken a seat twice removed from hers in the fifth row, so that it seemed to him that they were right up against the screen. There were plenty of other seats all over the narrow sloping auditorium, and Trevise had dimly wondered about those. Later he learned that Léonie was near-sighted. She had not seen, when in Perpignan she had dropped the Cagoulard out of his bedroom window that there were rolls of barbed wire underneath in the hotel yard.

The film that day was *Le Rosier*, with Fernandel in the comedy title role, and before two minutes had passed, the horrid recollections of the circumstances attending his bereavement had slipped from his mind. Léonie laughed until the roof shook and it seemed that her sides would split, and after the third or fourth paroxysm, Trevise and, as a matter of fact, nearly all of the thirty spectators, scattered sparsely through the house, joined in. Trevise and Léonie began wiping their eyes, slapping their knees and commenting across the two empty seats between them. When somebody said "Ssshhhh" from the rear, each one of them had moved over, and they sat side by side, indicating their mutual appreciation of the funny situations in the piece by lusty grunts and pressure.

At that point in his story, Monsieur Trevise would hesitate, diffidently, and Léonie, if she were near by, could do little to help him. They had walked from the theatre about twenty yards to the side entrance of the Café St. Michel. Trevise unlocked the door; they entered.

Two days later they reopened the café. They waited what they considered to be a decent interval—according to the tight-lipped Madame Morizot, about a fortnight—before Léonie had moved into the bedroom which Trevise and the departed had shared. Meanwhile, Léonie had rescued, from the alley beyond the Hotel Mont Souris, the Maltese kitten with a touch of smoke Persian, Olympe.

"They'll be all right, unless the idiots get married," the trussmaker, Amiard, had said. He had been seconded by the street's company of bachelors, Noel, Monge, the Satyr, Anatole, the wheelchair book clerk, and a few married men whose wives had quit them, like Julian the barber and Isaac Prins, who ran the print shop in the rue Xavier Privas.

Not even Trevise knew the reason Léonie's candid mind was never crossed by notions about marriage. In a moment of maidenly weakness, she had taken a husband in Perpignan, and had never seen him after a honeymoon tiff which had ended by her placing her foot in the small of his back and lofting him out of bed, all the way to a cold wall radiator about six feet distant. Léonie, who loathed any contact with officials or police, would not have gone through the fuss and bother of getting a divorce and remarrying for any reason short of redeeming all France, in the style of Jeanne d'Arc.

I talked with Monsieur Trevise about the stink in C-sharp Minor that was getting under way at the Bourse. He admired my basket of *cèpes*, and so did Léonie. The finest and most insidious little *cèpes* grow down near Perpignan, as truffles thrive at Périgord. Léonie put mine safely in the café ice box—an improvement that postdated the era of the late Marguerite Trevise. Trevise bought me a drink of Armagnac, with another for Léonie and one for himself. The sun rose higher, by the moment, and flooded the space above the river and the quais, the *place* streaked with long shadows of familiar trees, the streets that ran east to west, walls, windows, awnings, chimney pots.

The first of the morning regulars to join us was Old Christophe, Hortense's crotchety pushcart man. Actually, Christophe, who smelled like stale carrots and pickle brine, had not earned money with a pushcart until after he had become acquainted with Hortense. Before his help had seemed necessary, in connection with the flower shop, Christophe had preferred being a thoroughgoing *clochard*, or vagrant. He was in no way humble and, under provocation, became self-assertive.

"Make no mistake," he would say, when anyone made fun of him or got beyond himself. "I'm a man of education. Anyone, messieurs, who starts in the gutter, can remain there. I descended from respectability and have brought about my own downfall."

Concerning women, Christophe had more rigid ideas than

the Pharisees of old. Those who took money for their favors, he held to be lower than the unclean beasts. They were, in his mind "untouchables." All others, excepting Madame Berthelot and a very few women of the quarter who treated everyone alike, Christophe ignored but felt no impulse to exterminate. Hortense had learned, she told me, that Christophe had fixed notions about flowers, more violent and arbitrary than his views about women. Carnations, for instance, stirred the old man's deepest loathing. He sulked whenever Hortense bought them, and this was unfortunate because carnations were somewhat in demand for small bouquets and boutonnieres.

Hortense came into the café, radiant and smiling, from one side, as the Chestnut Man entered from another corner. The sun and balmy air had put everyone (except Christophe) in a rare good humor. L'Oursin stopped in his tracks, at the sight of Hortense, and expressed, with the eloquence of his pose, his admiration.

"Happy Easter," Hortense said.

I felt the thrill of refinding her all over again. She had made up her mind, in the solitude of her small bedroom, to dress for her coffee companions and the morning excursion to the flower market as others would for Easter services next day at the Madeleine. Everything she had on was well chosen and beautiful; also the ensemble, as a costume, was tastefully composed. But, probably because of the dowdy headpieces she had worn in lean years, she seemed most anxious about the effect of her hat. The hat had quite a history, which, out of gratitude to Monsieur Busse, she had kept from me. An acquaintance of Busse's, who was in the administration of the Carnavalet Museum, was organizing an exhibition called "Hats of Yesterday and Today" to be held in mid-tourist season in one of the salons of the former residence of Madame de Sévigné. Several of the finest examples of French millinery already had been collected, dating from the middle 1700's to our own year of 1949.

Busse, who took a passionate interest in Hortense's new clothes, had escorted her to the Carnavalet one afternoon and, through the courtesy of his friend of the Union Française des Arts du Costume, had shown her a hat dating back to 1750, and at the same time astonishingly modern. Busse could not rest until Hortense promised to have it copied, with certain modifications worked out by him, and so Hortense's Easter finery had been selected to carry out the motif.

The others reacted, with heartfelt approval. I could only gasp. My sympathy for Busse was tightened several notches. The hat was small, and rested lightly on Hortense's fine brown hair. The crown was in a checkerboard pattern, with components woven not quite square, of filmy metal lace and changeable sea-green silk, trimmed with a few small moonstones. On the right hand side, at a graceful angle, was a cockade of darker ribbon.

Hortense laughed softly, blushing contentedly. The effect of the hat had gone beyond her expectations. Even old Christophe was standing with his mouth open and his old eyes popping.

Actually, it had not been the hat which had struck my fancy so forcibly, but the ensemble. She was wearing a soft gray woolen hip-length jacket, open in front, and underneath it a dove-gray silk dress with full skirt gathered at the waist. Her gloves were of soft gray doeskin, and her handbag and shoes of silvered-gray lizard skin. Three ornamental buttons down the front of the dress echoed the moonstones, the emerald green and the topaz complement of the changeable silk in the hat.

"In effect, madame," growled Old Christophe, "you must

go to the market this morning in a limousine, like the wife of the President of the Republic."

"I'll enjoy the walk, as usual," Hortense said.

Noel came in, with a book under his arm, and made his comment. Raoul Roubait struggled through the doorway with bundles of the morning papers the Hachette delivery truck had left, as usual, on the *terrasse*. They smelled of fresh ink. Monsieur Vignon, the nervous little grocer from No. 15, entered, chewing on a piece of sun-dried cod. He was always ravenously hungry.

Because we were all so glad to see the sunshine, and gladder still to feel it, we took our coffee and fresh *croissants* from the bar and stood on the sidewalk in the rue de la Huchette, side by side. The seats and the tables for the *terrasse* were still stacked, inside, at the front of the café. In a few moments we were aware of a subterranean rumble: an early Métro train far below, for the subway dips profoundly in that sector in order to pass below the bed of the Seine. Next we heard clattering footsteps in the hidden passageway, and up the steep flights of stairs. A few early risers on their way to work came out of the exits of the St. Michel station, a few yards from the side entrance by which we were standing, coffee cups, saucers and crisp crescent rolls in our hands.

When the small flurry had subsided, two figures were left standing near the hooded subway exit. They were uncertain of themselves and mutually dependent, neither physically robust nor stylishly dressed. Both were slim, had pale blue eyes, blond hair, straight and badly cut, and nervous hands and feet. As they stood there staring at the subway map, then exchanging timid glances, I felt sure they were brother and sister. The shape of their hats, both too small and perched too high, indicated that they bought them either in Switzerland or Germany. In no other lands is there such a lack of feeling for hats.

The brother, who might have been the elder of the pair, wore knitted woolen gloves, straw-colored. They both had on dull tweed suits of similar pattern. The girl's skirt was baggy and clumsily divided, while the cutter had skimped the man's trousers. Their shoes were stout, quite evidently for rough walking. The girl carried instead of a handbag a small net sack.

At first, they did not seem to be getting much help from the map, and then, at the same instant, they both had a flash of comprehension, seemed to understand where they were, and the knowledge disconcerted them. When they noticed that we were observing them, with curiosity, they were flustered. Still they felt obliged to look us over, uneasily, from left to right. Hortense, always ready to be helpful, stepped forward. From long practice, she had realized from the first that the pair were refugees.

"May I be of service?" she asked. Her manner and appearance were most reassuring.

The brother looked at the sister, who inclined her head, encouraging him to reply.

"We're from Cologne," the man said, and the girl nodded.

Madame Berthelot could not help showing her astonishment, which was shared by all of us. Natives of Germany had not been traveling in France, of late. There was no German delegation to the Communist World Congress of the Partisans of Peace which would open the following Tuesday. The big Chestnut Man, whose mind worked slowly when he was not in motion, repeated involuntarily in his deep bass voice:

"From Cologne!"

"Since 1935," the girl explained to Hortense.

"The devil. That's fourteen years ago," the Chestnut Man boomed softly.

The man seemed over-eager to explain himself. "Till thirty-nine we stayed on the Balearic Islands," he said.

"Are you familiar with Paris?" Hortense asked, kindly.

We all had moved nearer, step by step, until we formed a semicircle around the strange couple.

"You're lost, perhaps," persisted Hortense.

"In a manner of speaking, no," the man said. "We were advised to ride the Métro to the station St. Michel. That we have done. But the map does not show the street we seek."

"Which one?" asked Hortense.

"The rue Zacharie. Number ten," the man answered. He took from his inside pocket a wallet, very flat, drew off his right glove and brought forth a piece of paper which he extended to Hortense. On it was written, in German script, the address he had mentioned. Hortense could read no German, but she recognized the No. 10 and the capital "Z."

"This must have been written some time ago," Hortense said.

"In Stockholm, since three years," the man said.

By this time I had grasped that the brother and sister were not Aryan Germans. I assumed they were Jewish, and had fled from the Reich.

"The name of the rue Zacharie has been changed to the rue Xavier Privas," Hortense said.

The faces of the wanderers fell. They shifted their postures and looked vague and helpless.

"What's the difference?" asked the Chestnut Man. "The buildings are there, just the same, and the numbers."

Old Christophe, who distrusted foreigners and loathed Germans, became impatient.

"Madame," he said, severely to Hortense, "it's half past six o'clock."

The male refugee, pathetically sensitive to any kind of criticism, thought the old man with the scraggly growth of soiled whiskers was rebuking him.

The stranger said, "It's much too early. At this hour we could not call on Herr Bernstein."

I could see what must have happened. The brother and sister, to whom their errand must mean a great deal, however long it had been delayed, had been unable to sleep after dawn, and without considering all the factors had started out and arrived hours too soon. They both seemed ashamed of their ill-considered behavior.

"My sister and I will take a walk, and return at eight o'clock. No? Our thanks. *Auf wiedersehen*," the man said.

Flustered, he took his sister's arm, looking backward anxiously in our direction, and side by side they stepped off the curb, exactly in the path of an oncoming bicyclist who had turned his handlebars down. The cyclist swerved not an instant too soon and brushed the startled pair.

"Heil Hitler!" the cyclist yelled, derisively, having glimpsed the German hats.

The refugees, both trembling, quickened their steps without again looking over their shoulders.

How can I describe what I felt as I walked in sunshine across the stone bridge of St. Michel that morning? The Seine was moderately high, and not too muddy to contain reflections. Above the sky was clear blue with morning clouds retreating far toward the western horizon. Hortense, in gay clothes, had nothing drab or grim on her mind. We walked side by side, her slender fingers on my coatsleeve and behind us trudged Christophe with his pushcart which bumped and rattled at our heels.

The hour was nearly seven and more of Paris was awakening, seeing sunlight in slits between limp drapes, splashed over crossings, intercepted by roof-pots, walls, vehicles, pedestrians. Nearly everyone knew that the talk of peace, dove posters everywhere, had a double or triple intent. Nevertheless there was a promise of peace on earth, good will to men, larger sandwiches for lunch, padlocks removed from pumps at the garages, the free sale (that is, unrestricted) of butter, the free sale of milk if you could find it, the free sale of cheese if you could afford it, of cotton in the stores and woolens in the windows, of hides, skins and furs regardless of strikes, of metal parts and gadgets, of grinding machines to make meal and flour, electrical mixers and current to run them every day but Friday, of the bounty of French earth, the mystery of seas and their gifts, of liberty, equality, fraternity; and three cheers for the red, white and blue. This was the season of the resurrection and the light, and if one must believe in something, why not peace?

"*Vive la France*," I said. Hortense patted my sleeve.

Could that be the Conciergerie across the street to the left, repository of so much bygone despair and retribution, kings, assassins, nobles, proletarians? The final combat? And next door, almost, the Palace of Justice and the Sainte Chapelle, and at the corner the famous public clock, still keeping time. To us, and Old Christophe, all those were just gray buildings with gold trimmings and paved courtyards, as was the dingy prefecture on our side of the avenue, where Hortense had worked so thanklessly those many years. I thought of her old clothes—*vive la France*—and the talks at the Caveau, and the letters she had sent me in

Republican Spain—*viva la Republica.* And I was reminded
that the graphs of women, men and nations can slant upward as well as dip downward, and France was on the
mend.

We turned—man, woman, pushcart, tramp—into the rue
de Lutèce and entered the domain of flowers in the *place*
Louis Lepine. The Easter week-end is the peak of the year,
floral-fiscal, so that Saturday morning the area of flowers,
plants and blossoms had overflowed the limits of the market
space reserved, along the Quai de Corse, and part way across
the Pont au Change, which seldom changes, and the Pont
Notre Dame which is quite a distance from the great Cathedral.

We were assailed by laurel, rhododendrons, gladioli,
Queen Anne's lace, anemones, daisies, and tulips in pots. In
high cylindrical containers, massed and distributed, were
branches from fruit trees, profuse with blossoms, white,
pink, in every shade and texture. Lilacs "false-blue, white"
straight from the late Amy Lowell. Roses. I wondered who
had had the heart to cut so many roses, from the Jack roses,
red into ebony, through crimsons, scarlets, pinks, yellows
and white. White was a color that morning, the Easter lilies,
white carnations, pear blossoms and the traditional French
flower for the season, guaranteed to bring good luck, wild
lilies of the valley, called *muguets.* The incongruous creak-
ing *gouvernement français,* which was keeping such a tight
rein over the citizens, had agreed, unofficially—Socialists,
Popular Republican Movement, Radical-Socialists and all
who had a say-so—that anyone could sell *muguets,* tiny fif-
teen-franc bunches, without a license that spring, in token
of recovery.

So the extended flower market that morning had more
customers than usual, men, women, boys and girls who

bought only *muguets* to peddle on sidewalks, vacant corners, quais and bridges. They were risking something, in the hope of earning a little extra. Some spent 1,000 francs, in hopes of a 1,000 profit, and many of the kids, unaccustomed to being up so early in the morning, had a beat-up 100-franc note, and thought they might clear 50 francs. I cannot tell you how fervently I wished them well.

Hortense was a favorite with the flower-market people. That was plain. The dealers and their help are an unusual lot, with one foot in the country and the other in the metropolis. They are at the mercy of weather, almost as completely as sailors at sea. Their skin is weather-beaten, their voices hoarse. In slack seasons competition is brutal, but over the Easter week-end they sell their wares about as fast as they can. Those men and women in the *place* Louis Lepine had things to say about Hortense's new hat, 1750-1949, that never had appeared in fashion magazines, and commented freely about the rest of her outfit. Meanwhile, Hortense indicated with easy gestures what was to be placed on Christophe's cart and the rougher and gruffer the vendor, the more gently he or she seemed to handle the roses, pinks, tulips, pansies in baskets, and potted plants which, that year, were extra luxuriant.

Nearly anyone can recognize that light that sparks in the eyes of Frenchmen, of no matter what walk of life, when an attractive woman is near by. I could not help reflecting that if Hortense, as she had said, had often wanted to go wrong, she could have broken several amateur records that morning. She must have sensed what I was thinking because, without context or provocation, she blushed, eyes shining, and said, "Don't be absurd."

I glanced over toward Christophe, and promptly looked away again, so as not to embarrass him. He had never been

openly hostile, but neither was he fond of me. He seemed
to be reserving his judgment. Being French to the core,
and warped by experience and education, Christophe
thought of foreigners in Biblical or classical terms, as if
they should be nomads from Galilee, senators in togas from
ancient Rome, slim potentates of Egypt with the morality
of eels, or animate Greek statues dressed by Fantin Latour
or Solomon Levi. Neither I nor the Armenians lately come
to the quarter, the Black Marketeers, the Communists, Existentialists, or chin-whiskered devotees of Willie the
Weeper, fell into any category understandable or reassuring to Christophe. For him the world had been changing
for the worse, and growing too complicated, since he could
remember. Like so many men in France who absorb what
is taught them, he had picked up quite an accumulation of
items dating back to the time of François I and covering
the period from his reign until after the defeat of 1870.
From that year on, that is, the years covering Christophe's
actual lifetime, history was relatively hazy in his mind and
problems were his own.

When the moment came for us to start back to the rue
de la Huchette, Christophe was leaning against an upright
and scratching himself, suffering from a battery of itches
brought on by non-bathing and reluctance to disrobe, night
or day. He was Polonius without Elsinore, Tiresias without ambivalence; Lot with no wife; Rip with insomnia;
Moses without flock, pursuers or wilderness. Perhaps, on
second thought, Christophe had the wilderness, imperfectly
contained. At any rate, as we got under way, this time with
the pushcart in the lead, I was aware that the bright morning sun, superb for the rest of us, was causing the old man
discomfort far beyond anything rain or dampness could
engender.

In Hortense's presence Christophe, pushing his cart before her, was too much of what was left of a gentleman to stop and grate his ribs, his flanks or the sides of his leathery neck, down which trickled rivulets of sweat. But driven to the extreme, as we approached a reeking *pissoir*, the old man had precipitously to abandon his flower-laden cart, mutter a hasty excuse and duck inside, where the exposed movements of his ankles and feet indicated that he must be engaged in a kind of rigadoon, like Job in days of yore. Eventually he came out into the open, crestfallen but clinging to what remained of his dignity.

There was no other public-convenience station between us and the *place* St. Michel, and it became evident that Christophe would not hold out that long. In spite of his desperate efforts he twitched like a steer which green-heads were biting, his scalp wrinkled and stretched, his ears flapped. Hortense, who understood something of the old man's predicament and was worried about its effect on his none-too-stable spiritual equilibrium, tried to save the situation.

"Christophe," she said. "I've forgotten the mauve tulips for Monsieur Busse. Please go on to the shop, unload what you have, and wait for us there. We'll join you presently."

The old man was desperately grateful and shoved off, mumbling words of thanks. Hortense and I faced about and took a few steps back in the direction of the Marché aux Fleurs. But I heard a rumbling and rattling of wheels and rims, as if the pushcart were rolling more briskly, and I could not refrain from glancing back, and neither could Hortense. Christophe had started walking faster, in the jerky rhythm of St. Vitus dance, and was on a knock-kneed trot between the handles of his pushcart, making for the *bistrot* on the corner of the quai, where he might find privacy for scratching.

We gasped. Hortense clutched my sleeve and held it tight. Old Christophe had got his loaded cart rolling so fast that he could not stop it when he came abreast of the café door. Just as he had to let go and dart like a rabbit into the doorway, two bicycle policemen, wheeling side by side, came in from the quai on the left. There was a complex crashing, frantic yells that came too late, and before we could wink, the multi-colored load of flowers, the rickety pushcart, two officers in uniforms and two bicycles were entangled on the pavement. The heads, legs and arms of the cops were thrashing and bobbing; damp earth from broken pots smeared the capes and uniform trousers, hands and faces. From the *bistro* emerged a group of men, and a larger crowd appeared on the opposite end of the bridge, from the Café du Départ and the Café St. Michel.

The delegation from the *place* St. Michel, headed by the Chestnut Man and Big Léonie, were on the scene of the collision in time to help brush off the cops and right the pushcart. A few pots had been broken, but not many of the plants and none of the cut flowers had been damaged.

"I'm not allowed to lose, these days," Hortense said. "Thanks to Hubert, my stock is overinsured, from the moment it reaches the pushcart until I dispose of it."

As matters rearranged themselves outside, Christophe strode out of the *bistro,* looking neither right nor left. The crowd, even the disgruntled cops, cackled, guffawed and hooted. Christophe drew himself up, like Joseph Jefferson at his best, or the late Paul Fratellini. Erect, he shoved his way through the strangers and acquaintances without seeing who was there or thinking of his destination. In the open, on the bridge, he maintained his deliberate pace, almost to the Left Bank, where he lost all control, clutched the seat of his pants with frantic claws, yanked, was thrown off his balance, and bounced up off the pavement with the ragged seat of his trousers in his hand.

Instead of continuing toward the rue de la Huchette, Christophe hopped and sashayed to the left, quickened his absurd eccentric dance while trying desperately not to do so, along the quai as far as the rue Xavier Privas, into which he vanished like a beetle gone mad.

By eight o'clock, the sun that had given such lavish matutinal promise, in terms of crystal air, pure sky and heightened colors, had warmed the stones and woodblock patterns of the *place* St. Michel, the fronts of the Périgordine, the padlocked hunting-supply shops without shells, cartridges, shotguns, rifles or stout-bladed knives, the *bistros*, and the exposed areas of the *place* St. André des Arts. The glorious outburst of weather had brought to doors and windows all sun worshippers who had been long in seclusion.

While the rains had held sway, indoor bars all up and down the rue de la Huchette had done the best they could for musty shivering customers. Easter Saturday morning the convivial drinkers sought the sidewalk *terrasses* of the Café St. Michel and the Café du Départ. Wives, offspring and relatives joined them, and most of the proprietors and help who could be spared from Rahab, the bar de Mont Souris, and farther down the street, the Hotel Normandie, Ali Baba *buvette*, the Hotel du Caveau, and the Hotel de la Huchette.

Without authority outside of common consent, the café keepers of the rue Xavier Privas barred both ends of the southern section of the narrow street with sawhorses and, dividing the tiny *place* into sections marked with chalk on the pavements, filled the open space with chairs and tables, some of which caught the sun.

The word passed throughout the neighborhood that two foreign strangers, presumably brother and sister, had ascended from the subway station at 6:30 that morning, and behaved rather oddly. They had let out bits about their past meanderings, involving Cologne in Germany, the Balearic Islands belonging to Spain, and Stockholm in Sweden. They had made inquiries about a Herr Bernstein at 10 rue Xavier Privas, whom nobody seemed to remember. They were either Germans or Jews, and surely refugees. They had vague blue eyes, blond hair, and drab tweed clothes to match.

Having breakfasted on my basket of *cèpes*, with duck-egg omelet and sunflower roots, I sat in front of the Café St. Michel, near enough to keep an eye on the Métro exits. Noel was on my left and Monsieur Mainguet on my right, and we were joined by Armand Busse who was in a reproachful state, having heard that Hortense had displayed her new costume without his co-operation or consent.

As soon as Monsieur Mainguet had heard about the refugees, he had consulted his back files of notes, which he kept methodically and was primed to tell us about the rue Xavier Privas, as it figured in the records of the department of justice. Mainguet, his gray eyes sparkling behind his spectacles, cleared his throat, took out a scribbled memorandum, and started giving us the Word. He had always worked in government offices, either in France or Indo-China, and had never taught a class, but his manner was that of a gentle professor who cloaked much erudition beneath his surface modesty.

"If a street were to be named for me, which is most unlikely," he said, "I should prefer almost any other."

"What's so bad about the rue Xavier Privas?" asked Thérèse. "Cooked foods at fair prices are sold at the Petit Vatel, and Messidor, drunk or sober, can still open trunks or closets when the keys have been misplaced."

"Mmmm! Locksmiths. They know all about skeleton keys. I've often wondered if there shouldn't be a law to regulate the sale of those devices that will open any door," said Monsieur Mainguet.

"The Devil forbid," said Noel. "Since the birth of our Fourth Republic, five new laws have been made, at the least, every day. Not even Monsieur Herriot could tell you, off-hand, what's lawful and what's criminal."

"Let's grant that Messidor is honest," Mainguet said. "There are others. Firstly, each end of the rue Xavier Privas is marked by houses of prostitution. Although they seem to be empty, the women who sinned there are somewhere around."

"You wouldn't want a woman shot because her heels are short," said Thérèse. "France would run short of ammunition, and, pssshhhht would go our national defense."

Mainguet sighed.

"The herb doctor at No. 9," began Mainguet, this time blushing and shifting his eyes uncomfortably.

"Leave old Doc Robinet alone. The women around here can't afford illegal operations. Who cares if they stew up a few dried leaves?" asked Thérèse.

"Don't say such things aloud," said Noel. "Our leaders have been telling us for decades that, in order to be safe from Germany, our women should have babies in litters, like the Italians."

"Italy didn't find herself safe from the Germans," Mainguet said.

"Let the Germans have Italy," Noel said. "If only Gamelin had had his way, we'd have knocked Mussolini into his Italian lake before the Boches got through with Poland."

Big Léonie spoke up. "Is anything wrong with Yvette's beauty parlor in the rue Xavier Privas? I'm going there this afternoon—for a permanent. I hope it lasts a week."

Mainguet raised his eyebrows and looked down toward the bottom of his notes. "It's patronized mostly by fugitives who wish to be disguised," he said.

"You haven't told us yet about Privas, himself. Perhaps he was a charlatan like Cagliostro. From what you've said about the little street, it ought to be named for a crook. And why not? The saints, doctors, politicians, soldiers and inventors shouldn't hog the street plaques. France produces criminals who can't be inferior to those of other nations. Why not honor them?" Noel asked.

"You mustn't think the crime rate in Paris is the highest in the world," the little statistician said.

"Where else? Corsica?" asked Noel.

Mainguet shook his head.

"Sicily," suggested the little red-bearded grocer, Vignon. The bandit, Guiliano, a Sicilian, was then much in the news.

"Chicago," I said.

Mainguet beamed. "That's closer," he said. "Do you know a city called Memphis, in the department of Tennessee?"

"You Americans hold all the records. You'll get yourselves disliked for your pre-eminence," exclaimed Noel.

"Bah! Americans cook oysters!" the Chestnut Man said.

Just then some people came out of the Métro exit, and

I caught sight of a familiar old flat felt hat, 100 percent American and reminiscent of a New England college campus. The face beneath it was chubby and round, featuring humorous eyes behind rimless spectacles and a dimpled chin. I was pleasantly surprised, and rose quickly to my feet. Those around me, being on edge expecting the Germans, did likewise involuntarily. In fact, nearly all of the occupants of our crowded *terrasse* stood up.

But the hefty American, who had spotted me at once and whose face was all smiles because of what had seemed to be a spontaneous tribute or reception, stopped in his tracks, his face transfixed with horror. Those of us who were facing toward him turned quickly to see what was happening behind us and to our left, and had startled him so. Coincidently the women screamed, and the men gasped, groaned and swore. Busse, who was standing at my side, cried out like a wounded hedgehog.

What I saw made me faint and dizzy. A cumbersome open truck with sideboards had run part way over the curb across the rue de la Huchette. Hortense Berthelot was lying prone amid the wreckage of an empty pushcart; her new hat, crushed, was upside down on the pavement, two yards ahead.

Those who got into action quickly, notably the Chestnut Man, cut off my view as they ran to the scene. I saw first the wiry little grocer, Vignon, yank the driver from the seat of the truck. It was Chouette, and I realized tardily that the vehicle was labeled "E. Saillens & Fils." A second later, I was aware that the Chestnut Man had lifted Hortense and, with one of her arms behind his neck and shoulders, was carrying her toward our corner of the *terrasse*. Her Easter clothes were torn and in disarray, and her right arm hung limply from her shoulder, but she was alive and, even before she had recovered from the first effects of shock, was trying to reassure us that she was not seriously hurt. Chouette, who was drunk, had a close escape from lynching. Busse, who had picked up the 1750-1949 hat from the middle of the street, was weeping as he pushed his way to Hortense.

6. *Half-Brother, Half-Sister, Half-World*

THE young Dr. Thiouville, who had witnessed the accident from his doorway at No. 23, hesitated to approach Hortense as she was placed in a chair at our table. He was new to the neighborhood and distrusted by some because of his Communist sympathies. Hortense, however, was always thoughtful of others. She understood the doctor's reluctance to seem overanxious, and beckoned him to her side. He quickly ascertained that the injury to her arm was not serious. The elbow had been bruised, perhaps the apex of the bone had been chipped or broken. The doctor rigged up an impromptu sling, and advised Hortense to go to bed. That she was not prepared to do because of her anxiety about Old Christophe.

Slowly, item by item, those of us gathered around Hortense and within hearing of the contrite truck driver, Chouette, at the bar, pieced together what had led up to the mishap. Having arranged the flowers in her shop, Hortense had thought it best to move the unlicensed pushcart away from the front of her shop, so that Christophe would not get into trouble about it. Chouette had figured that he could earn time and a half at the government's expense by transporting a short length of terra-cotta pipe in his truck to the repair job at No. 31 rue de la Huchette. He had had a few drinks before starting out, had rounded the corner on two wheels, and saw the pushcart and Hortense in her Easter finery too late to avoid the crash.

"E. Saillens will pay," said Noel, sagely.

"But I was on the wrong side of the street," objected Hortense. The others urged her not to stress that fact. The contractor had been getting away with plenty, on that job, and would not dare squawk, no matter how high a bill was presented.

As soon as Hortense had been made as comfortable as possible and champagne had been ordered, to be charged to E. Saillens' account, my round-faced American friend, whom I had met in Hollywood, was spotted by Katya. Glowing with pride, she called to the attention of the other Commies on the *terrasse* that their "guest" was an American delegate to the World Congress of the Partisans of Peace. His picture had appeared in *L'Humanité* and *Ce Soir*. The American delegate was introduced, all around, first to the Reds, and then to the others, political and non-political. He was delighted to find such an unusual community spirit and so many drinkers so early in the day. His reception had been cordial and enthusiastic. In response to the inevitable questions about the state of affairs in America, my friend was about to give reassuring answers when Big Léonie let out a whoop and almost dropped her tray. She was staring at the far corner of the *terrasse*. All heads turned in that direction, and there sat the missing pair of refugees, who, somehow, in the general confusion and its aftermath, had reached the café unnoticed and seated themselves in the most inconspicuous place.

As if he hoped no one would take offense, the brother began, "In thinking upon the matter, afterward, it occurred to us that nine o'clock would be a more suitable hour than eight o'clock for presenting ourselves to the party whose address had been given us."

Those who had been waiting for the pair to show up, and were glad they had not failed them, indicated that they bore no resentment.

The two refugees, distressed because Hortense had been injured, nevertheless showed plainly their relief because she was among those present. Hortense, who was in considerable pain which she took trouble to hide, asked Louis of the Normandie to invite the pair to join her at our table. A room had been set aside for her, on the second floor, front, of the Hotel de Mont Souris, so that during her convalescence she could have prompt service and receive callers who would not have found space in her small back bedroom off the courtyard of No. 23. It seemed to her that the brother and sister were pathetically nervous, among strangers, and that already they had started to depend on her for moral support. So over the objections of young Dr. Thiouville, who wanted her to rest while he was making arrangements to send her to an X-ray hospital, she decided to do what she could for the timid wanderers.

At the bar inside, Chouette began to wail and lament so loudly that Big Léonie tore herself away from our group with the stray Germans in the center, lifted the drunken truck driver by the collar, dumped him into the mop closet, stretched him out on the floor, closed the door, locked it from the outside, and slid the key into her pocket.

The American delegate, who understood less than nothing of what was taking place, was so impressed with her technique that he beamed with admiration. Then, turning toward the refugees he said, *sotto voce*, "Anti-Nazis, I presume."

I nodded.

"And the chauffeur who ran down the countess? He's being dealt with informally, I take it. I'm glad that over here motor-vehicle accidents are not reported to the police," he went on. "Everything's chummier that way."

"In this case, there are special considerations," I told him.

"I can see that there might be. When a sequence begins with a lady of elegance dressed for Easter, pushing a two-wheeled cart . . ."

"Democratic," I said.

He beamed more radiantly, blinked, sighed and drank more champagne.

It was time for the refugees to be escorted to No. 10 rue Xavier Privas. The Chestnut Man, Noel, Monge, the American delegate and I, among others, walked along with the brother. Doctor Thiouville urged Hortense once more to lie down in the room that awaited her in the Hotel de Mont Souris, and the girl from Cologne, who understood and spoke English fairly well, begged Hortense not to exert herself. The girl's eyes, however, showed plainly how much she would like to have Hortense at her side. So the young doctor, Louis, the one-armed garçon from the Normandie, Busse and Madame Berthelot formed the nucleus of the group that accompanied the sister.

The escort, which had started out as two small bands of agreeable holiday folk, took on the aspects of a small procession before it had gone very far. All along the rue de la Huchette, others who knew what was afoot were watching from doorways and windows. We turned right, from the pathway of the sun into the shadows. Victor Lefevrais was standing in the doorway of No. 3, and from across the street, not twelve feet away, the aroma of Strasbourg sausages steaming and sliced potatoes in deep fat crept out from the Petit Vatel. Squint-eyed old Prins was setting type, his nose four inches from his stick, his fingers picking letters from the cases with no need of light. A few men in caps and sweaters were at the six-foot bar in the coal and wine shop. One of the chambermaids from the Hotel de la Harpe was in the chair near the window of the beauty parlor, looking at the pictures in an old copy of *La Vie Parisienne*, and looking like Medusa because of the permanent wave clamps attached by wires to her head.

The herb doctor watched from the doorway of No. 9 as we, at the head of the column, turned into No. 10. Farther on, the courtyard was littered with crumpled sheets of torn newspaper in which vegetable and fruit peelings had been wrapped. A couple of fledgling birds had fallen from a nest in a roof gutter and lay dead on the stones. There were a few discarded bus tickets, some losing "tenths" from the recent drawing of the national lottery, and a torn *en-tout-cas* (combination umbrella and sunshade) turned inside out. Puddles of slops and dishwater had run into the low spots where the flagstones had sagged and dog turds reposed where the stones were upended.

The bar to the left was open, but not for business. A lame Negro with bent back, old shoes slit to ease bunions, and St. Bernard's eyes, was mopping the tiles from which arose the sharp scent of Eau de Javel. The Chestnut Man asked him where we could find the concierge. The Negro shook his head and mumbled, and a neighbor from a high window across the courtyard, whose keen ears had heard the question, shouted:

"The old rumpot's never here in the morning, and seldom in the afternoon."

The brother from Cologne, at the sight of No. 10's exterior, had shrunk inside his loose clothes and his face was gray with misery. Hortense took the sister's hand and pressed it to reassure the girl. I beckoned Victor to come over, and offered him twenty francs if he would find the concierge and tell her she was needed, *pronto*. He nodded and set off on a trot.

A few more upper windows opened. With twenty or more people milling around the stone courtyard and asking questions of the residents and of one another, the din was unusual for the hour and the place. Heads protruded aloft, men and women in shirtsleeves, blouses, nightshirts and even silk pyjamas. The lodgers at No. 10 were mostly Negroes or mulattoes. The girls were young, the men middle-aged. The Chestnut Man shouted up in French, inquiring for a party named Bernstein. Vignon added that the man we were after worked in a bank. A third voice said he was an Israelite.

"Moses Bernstein, a banker," I yelled up in English.

"Man, you ain't talkin' to me," was the reply from one of the coffee-colored men in a flashy paisley robe and wearing gold-bowed pince-nez.

"A banker! Please believe me! Nobody comes on this scene wearin' any green," said another taller Negro from a dormer over the eaves. Then, as an afterthought, he added: "How come you parlay the Anglay so solid and free?"

"I'm from Boston," I said.

"Well, all right, then."

Victor came running back and said old Madame Cirage, the concierge, was on her way. A few minutes later, a venomous old woman came hobbling around the corner of the rue St. Séverin. She bristled at the sight of the crowd, and answered all questions with grunts and a negative shake of her head. She had been at No. 10 only five years. There had never been a Jew in the house. She said that in a manner that indicated her aversion to them. No one in the court, she insisted, had ever claimed to be a banker. Neither had her sister-in-law, who had the job before her, ever mentioned Jews, Bernsteins, bankers or any such specimens.

The refugees understood the French, the English, and whatever else was spoken, excepting the American jive talk. They looked increasingly helpless, disappointed and dismayed. Having carried that address from place to place for three years, and known that Moses Bernstein, whom they had never seen, was a distant relative of the girl, they had expected nothing like the rue Xavier Privas.

"A relative of your sister?" I repeated, when the brother told me about the blood kinship.

He nodded, and did not elaborate. If Bernstein was related to the girl, and not the man, I reasoned, they must be half-brother and half-sister, as seemed appropriate for those who moved in a half-world.

By that time, the name of the Jewish banker the German refugees were seeking had spread all up and down the rue de la Huchette, the rue Xavier Privas, the Quai St. Michel, the rue de la Harpe and the rue St. Séverin, not to mention the smallest of them all, the rue du Chat qui Pêche. The question had mounted from the ground level to the attics. Nobody in the quarter knew of a Moses Bernstein, or remembered having heard of such a man before. From time to time the brother took the slip of paper from his pocket and reread the address, 10 rue Zacharie. He did not seem to doubt the accuracy of the source from which he had obtained it, but rather the evidence of his eyes and ears that sunny morning.

The refugees thanked all of us. We accompanied them back to the Café St. Michel. They declined another drink, walked to the curb, paused again to say *"Auf wiedersehen"*

and again, with their heads turned backward, stepped off
into the traffic.

Hortense, just then, forgot her injured arm in her excitement and reached upward to replace a strand of hair. Such a
white-hot spasm of pain shot through her that she fainted,
ever so gracefully. The doctor rushed to her side and this
time insisted that she be carried to the front bedroom in
the Hotel Mont Souris.

7. *A Man Without Britches*

IN THE sunny front corner bedroom on the second floor of the Mont Souris, Hortense had awakened and had found that some person or persons unknown had undressed her and put on her an ornamental rayon nightgown figured with small male birds, fussed and ruffled, and females with their heads under their wings.

It had been Simone, the registered nurse from Cabat's drugstore, and the chambermaid Lola who had disrobed her, and the streetwalker Irma had loaned the nightgown. When Hortense's eyes came open, Hubert Wilf and Armand Busse had been sitting in straight upholstered chairs, regarding each other like rival tomcats. Armand, having arranged the room and sent her damaged new garments to be mended, had believed he had a right to be there. Hubert was resolved that if any other man was to figure in her return to consciousness, he had better be on hand.

Soon after I entered, and found Busse and Hubert still there, one smoking a Chesterfield, the other a Milo Violet, the doctor had appeared at the doorway and indicated that Hortense had something to communicate to me. Hubert rose, philosophically enough. Busse, on the other hand, was piqued.

"Oh, very well," he said, and tried to appear indifferent as he made his exit. At moments like that he expressed too well in pantomime what he spent the rest of his days concealing. I had not noticed before that he wore a fine gold chain around his ankle, under his sock of copenhagen blue. Busse knew as well as I did what was on Hortense's mind, and was as anxious to thwart her as I was to help. Having reached the door and taken two or three steps in the hall-way, he could not resist saying, in an injured tone:

"I trust we've seen the last of that impossible old bum," and he repeated defiantly and pettishly: "OLD BUM!"

Hortense smiled, so weakly that I was reminded that her elbow was giving her considerable pain, notwithstanding the mild opiate the doctor had administered. She had the insight to understand that if anything would restore Christophe's self-possession, and prevent him from running amok, it would be an appeal from her, convincing him that she needed his help. Knowing that the plan involved some risk to her, she had decided to ask the old man to tend the flower shop while she was disabled.

"Could he? With the best of intentions?" I asked. It must have been years since he had handled money in appreciable quantities.

"Nobody has trusted him," she said.

"He'll have to have a bath, shave and haircut, and some clothes, especially britches," I said.

"I'm sure he has but the one pair," she agreed, and shuddered involuntarily.

"Won't he be off the reservation already?" I asked.

"How could he? He has no money. I was to have paid him for the week this morning, and he never has a franc left over. He couldn't go out, as he is. He can't afford to have a bottle brought in," she said.

"You know where he lives?" I asked.

Her face fell. "Not exactly," she said, moving her left arm toward the slums of Montebello.

"Victor can find him," I said, and she nodded.

She told me, trying to be explicit without being severe or critical, that Christophe, since she had known him, cleaned himself up about once in three months. Just before he got into such an abject state that he was goaded to the effort, he hit his lowest depressions, and was morose, despondent, and more obstinate than usual. Just after the ordeal by water, his spirits rose and for a while he was quite a different man—until he began to reek again.

"We can take up a collection to buy him some clothes, but it may be harder to make him take a bath," I said.

"Noel will help. So will L'Oursin. As for the expense, I'll gladly pay," she said. She sighed and looked up at me ruefully.

"He'll be running your shop when you get back from the X-ray," I promised, and set out to find Victor Lefevrais.

Suspecting that he might be helping Louis at the Normandie with the chamber work, I mounted the first flight of stairs without first making inquiries at the bar. I found the one-armed garçon and also Victor in Room No. 8, where, in addition to the crucifix above the bed, framed chromos of Mary with the Infant Jesus, and the Marriage at Cana where the Savior turned water into wine, hung a fascinating print, in colors, consisting of at least two hundred little pictures not much larger than postage stamps illustrating "The Drunkard's Progress," from the happy little family in the rose-embowered cottage, through all the ills and evils of drink and ending at the pauper's grave.

The tenant of Room No. 8, who had lived at the Normandie several years, had a job with the Anti-Alcoholic Society in the boulevard St. Germain, and the fact that Monsieur Ithier kept a bottle of brandy in a pocket of an old coat hung in his dim dresser was revealed by Louis, the garçon, only to intimate friends, and by Victor, his volunteer helper, to no one at all. Victor had the faculty of keeping his mouth shut to an almost alarming degree, which worried his mother because she would have liked to have him confide in her.

I offered Victor fifty francs, and asked him to find out where Old Christophe lived, whether or not he was in his lodgings, wherever they were, and, if not, where he could be found. The boy, pleased with the chance to do anything resembling secret-service work, set out without delay.

"A good kid," I said, after he had gone.

I had known the Hotel Normandie in the days of Guy, the former proprietor, and his patient wife Sara, the Jewess. Also the black dog, Mocha, who was killed defending Guy when Guy was shot defending Sara as the Nazis took her away. Guy had been drunk most of the time, had done practically no work, but he had stood up for Sara and her race whenever she or the Jews had been disparaged. As I saw Louis, sitting on Ithier's double brass bed with a dust mop in his hand, I realized what I might have observed years before. The one-armed garçon, veteran of two wars, who sang ribald songs and took his pleasure where he found it, had been in love with Sara, the former proprietor's wife. Not a word or questionable act had passed between them. Sara had been a faithful and submissive wife. I remembered that years ago, Louis, one night when he was unusually communicative, had said that he had never slept with a Jewish woman. All of us knew well that he had tried almost all other kinds, and none of them had complained.

Just before World War II, when race persecutions were getting under way in the Reich, quite a few Jews from Köln, Elberfeld and Essen had stopped at the Normandie. Some of Sara's relatives who lived in the Ruhr and the Rhineland had given the fugitives her address in the rue de la Huchette.

At the time of the World's Fair of 1937, many German citizens with Jewish blood had obtained special travel permits, at exorbitant rates, and had escaped into France, where entry barriers were down on account of the international exposition.

It was clear to all of us then that Sara, who took the responsibility for the welfare of the displaced Semites much to heart, counted more heavily on Louis than her dissolute husband to help them and escort them around Paris, to make what contacts they needed. A Jewish woman in France, respectably established, felt so fortunate just then that she was willing to do anything for her co-religionists from across the German border, and Sara was so highly esteemed in our street that almost anyone was ready to lend her a hand. Her dependence on Louis, as I saw it in retrospect, was an acknowledgment of his devotion. Nearly always in those days, one-armed Louis seemed reckless and gay. When he had been serving Sara, directly or through her friends, he had been happiest.

"That girl this morning," Louis said, sitting on the bed in that dim hotel room and staring at the wall without seeing the temperance picture. "Fourteen years, from place to place—just drifting. She can't be more than thirty, now."

"A few years less, I should say," was my guess.

"That's no life at all, for a decent young woman. Did you ever try to think how it must feel to be a Jewess?" Louis asked. He did not say "a Jew." All the lure and mystery of womankind, for Louis, was distilled in Jewish femininity. In the smoke of his cigarette he saw dimly bare limbs moving indolently in the gyrations of a near-eastern dance, to the beat of inaudible tam-tams, shells, in the aroma of cinnamon and saffron. Veiled dark eyes peered out of nowhere into nothing, and because the refugee girl from

Cologne had wheat-colored hair and gray-green eyes, he saw a few of those, too, and shapes like the Odalisques of Ingres, chaste coolness, pale satin skins, long shanks, pear-like buttocks.

"I didn't have my wits about me, while that girl was here in the quarter," Louis said.

"What could you do?" I asked.

He told me then that when the refugees had asked about a Moses Bernstein, there had been a vague stirring in his mind, as if a drowsy bird deeply hidden in the foliage of memory had partly awakened, ruffled its feathers, and gone to sleep again.

It seemed that between the summer of 1937 and the outbreak of the war, Louis had taken quite a few German Jews who were temporarily at the Hotel Normandie to a small ground-floor office in the rue St. Honoré. Everything inside the office was shabby, informal and unostentatious. A tall middle-aged Jew with a long brown beard, sharp penetrating eyes, and long expressive hands was always there, unguarded and alone. He wore black broadcloth trousers, extremely high waisted, a plain white collarless shirt with a woolen sweat shirt over it, heelless carpet slippers and a faded gray bathrobe. For furniture he had a high sloping desk, the old-fashioned kind at which bookkeepers and counting-house clerks of the nineteenth century used to sit on high stools. But there was no stool, no chairs, no safe.

That was a private bank, of the simplest kind. As a matter of fact, Wolfe Kaufman had taken me there, in 1928, to cash a check. The Jew had glanced at the check, stuck it in his right-hand bathrobe pocket, taken some banknotes from his left-hand bathrobe pocket, and handed them over. That was all there was to it. The endorsed check was a record. He knew Wolfe, and Wolfe vouched for me. The banking laws of the Third Republic were elastic enough to include private banks, ranging from that small cubbyhole with one man for a staff, to the labyrinths of iniquity described by Christina Stead in her magnificent *The House of All Nations*. The frenzied finance of the Fourth Republic has paralyzed most private banks, because of the reams and volumes of records, receipts, entries and returns now required.

"That banker's name," Louis said, referring to the tall gaunt Jew of the rue St. Honoré, "it might have been Bernstein. Now that I've thought so much about it, I'm almost sure it was Bernstein."

So Louis, after finishing his morning's work as best he could, got on his bicycle and rode over to the rue St. Honoré. Eleven years had passed since he had seen the lean bearded private banker, but Louis could not relinquish the idea of finding him again.

While I had been looking for Victor, in order to locate Old Christophe, Noel, the Chestnut Man, and Gilles Wilf started in one of Wilf's trucks, for the Flea Market just outside the Porte Clignancourt, to buy what was needed for the ragged old man.

All my life I have been fascinated by second-hand stores, bazaars, auctions and junk yards. Having owned so few articles, I have a wistful interest in the personal and household belongings others have used, lost, sold or discarded. If the great central food market of Paris, Les Halles, is like an illuminated night mirage, bustling, kaleidoscopic—the rich, fresh, fragrant produce of the country poured into a city area half a mile square—the Flea Market, so drab on the surface, offers the ultimate in contrast. Around Les

Halles, swarming all over the place, in it, under it and
through it, the dealers are scurrying and shouting, the customers come to buy, with no uncertainty. They go from
meat to fish to lettuce to apricots. Tramps with ladders on
their backs shuffle from tailboard to store and back again.
A few hours ago nothing was there, no trucks, no stallions,
no Mesdames Lafarge, no roustabouts in peaked red caps.
The humans are urgent while the sale is going on; the goods
retain a modicum of vegetable and animal life. In another
few hours the area will be deserted, except for prosaic
plodding types who live and carry on in daylight hours.

What of the great flat community outside the Clignancourt gate? The articles are not alive and never have been.
They represent the creations of assorted mentalities. Some
of the designs were superb; a few are still superb. Others
are in the worst of taste, from all periods ever catalogued or
let slip into oblivion. The buyers do not swarm. None of
them is in a hurry. Each one may find some precious thing
the rest have overlooked, or he may have his pocket picked.
The Flea Market, over which must hover so many of the invisible imps of Satan, is strictly of the day. Nothing is
perishable, in terms of ordinary measurements. What appears to be new is under the strongest suspicion. Here are
the worn, the faded, the obsolete, the antique without distinction: faded fabrics, charred furniture; viols without
strings, bows without viols; cracked cornets, black clarinets
of the period of Albert, harps of lost heavens, hautboys and
seductive flutes of merry hell.

Monday morning is the busy time at the Flea Market,
when goods stolen over the week-end are on sale, before the
detectives get around. If the motif of Les Halles is akin to
nature, the Flea Market has the stale odor and the non-
descript color symbolic of the free will men had who mostly

now are dead. Pristine innocence opposed to ingenuity, guided or misguided, fiendish or serene.

Of the three who went from the rue de la Huchette to the Flea Market that Easter Saturday morning, Noel was the one whose imagination was kindled by the hodgepodge of taste. Gilles Wilf, always the merchant, saw the super-bazaar in terms of deals, the grains of sand that trickle through the hour-glass of profit and loss. What is up must go down.

The Chestnut Man, who stood all day and half the night with the mysteries of seafood, shellfish and crustaceans, sea fragrance, click of claws, protruding beads for eyes, thought mostly about what he and his two fellow Samaritans must buy, and E. Saillens and Sons would pay for: namely, a portable tin bathtub, a pushcart in serviceable condition, and some clothes for Old Christophe.

However bleak and rusty the immense Flea Market looked on dark wet days, under the glowing sun that in mid-morning had raised the temperature to 85° Fahrenheit, with the gilt-edged promise of many more degrees, the area was radiant. No backwash of the holiday tourist throng had spilled beyond the Paris gates that far, but many of the French were "free" and business was relatively brisk. For years it had been difficult for the honest law-abiding Frenchman, and quite a few of those are still extant, to get as far as the Porte Clignancourt, unless he was in some kind of business that entitled him to a truck and gasoline. But two days before the Easter week-end, the Middle-of-the-Road Government had authorized the sale of four gallons of petrol (the nearest thing in France to gasoline) to pleasure drivers, and quite a few of those were in the Flea Market that morning.

In its long questionable history, the Flea Market had

never been stocked so fantastically. During the war years, customers could not get there. Hardships of recovery had bred petty thieves. Notwithstanding all that, the trio from the rue de la Huchette had difficulty finding an old portable bathtub. And in no other way was it likely that they should be able to bathe Old Christophe. Where he was living, there would surely not be a stationary bathtub or any modern convenience within striking distance. No public bathhouse or private bath connected with a barber shop would admit the old man, under any circumstances. The Chestnut Man and Noel had figured that if they brought the tub to Christophe, either he would have to use it voluntarily, or they could strip him and dump him in.

The first tin bathtub our purchasing committee found at the Flea Market was rusty, under its coat of quick-drying white enamel. The second was intended for a child. By that time the word had spread from pathway to pathway that the trio were in urgent need of the tub, so that the only one that would fill the bill cost Gilles 1,000 francs.

The pushcart was easy to find, but cost 2,000 because of the lively demand. Owners of pushcarts are always hard up, and those who need them are improvident. Before handing out the money, Gilles made the dealer swear that it had not been stolen from any quarter within a mile of the *place* St. Michel.

Already the delegation from the rue de la Huchette had glimpsed church organs under tarpaulins, playing cards from Latvia, Syrian ornaments of silver lace, red, white and blue bunting, souvenir corkscrews, primitive radio sets, exhausted storage batteries, bearskin robes, torn tapestries with chunks missing where hearthstones had been, cracked urns for verandas, dented coal hods, bent fire tools, accordions with punctured bellows, medals, war crosses with and without palms, odd rolls of wallpaper, waffle irons, curling irons, U.S. branding irons left over from the first A.E.F., looms out of order, painter's color boxes with palettes, unmatched doors, windows, detached flights of indoor and outdoor stairs, hunting horns, fog horns, marine engines crusted with salt, motor boats without motors and skiffs without oars.

In the bright sunshine, the junk men, the transients, shacks, booths and incongruous objects cast sharp shadows, phalanxes of inertia, infiltration of shadow motion. The moment had come, for Gilles, Noel and L'Oursin, to face a difficult selection. The proper wardrobe for Old Christophe. Gilles, the true "Continental," dressed like Monsieur Bovary without his doctor's bag. Noel, with broad-brimmed felt hat, seersucker jacket and flowing *lavallière,* personified the artistic type. The giant Chestnut Man wore a visored cap, an old sweater, corduroy pants and stout rawhide boots, year in, year out. Each one of the three was an admirable example of a sound Parisian type, but none of their costumes would be suitable for transforming a lousy old hobo into the custodian *pro tem* of Madame Berthelot's flower shop, cash drawer included.

There were rows and rows of shacks, splintered boards, patches of tar-paper, sheet tin or elephant iron, the fronts and interiors of which were filled with second-hand clothes on hangers, pegs and hooks—suits, jackets, topcoats, overcoats, mackinaws, overalls, *monos,* blazers, raincoats, capes, shawls and all kinds of uniforms. As the trio passed one booth after another, resisting the attempts of the salesmen to drag them in or detain them, the infinitely wide choice of goods bewildered them. Luckily, one of the proprietors was reading a copy of *Samedi-Soir,* an illustrated weekly that takes the place of the Paris Sunday newspapers long since suppressed by law on account of the paper shortage and labor's fondness for the six-day week. Noel was first to see the headlines and illustrations of an article about Robert Schuman, and to snatch the paper from the second-hand dealer's grasp.

To those who are not familiar with French post-war politics, a word about Schuman will not be amiss. Robert Schuman, who at present is Minister of Foreign Affairs, was Prime Minister of France before Queuille, who preceded Bidault. Schuman, in whatever capacity he has served or is serving, is the member of the French Government who is the idol of the "average" French. He is bony and rangy, dry in speech, sparing of words and gestures—a homely down-to-earth type of country politician who outsmarts the city statesmen, sometimes, and has a hold upon public confidence that is almost mystical. The moment Noel saw the pictures in *Samedi-Soir* of Robert Schuman in his unpretentious if not meager wardrobe, he realized that Old Christophe, if he were scrubbed, barbered and clothed according to the printed illustrations, would bear a marked resemblance to Schuman and would be perfectly in character as the custodian of a flower shop.

Noel tapped the illustrated article and showed it to Gilles Wilf. The Chestnut Man peered over their shoulders. The bantam-weight dealer, in puce-colored shirtsleeves with pigeon's blood arm elastics, hopped and crackled like a wasp being fried.

"There's what's needed," said Noel. Gilles, never the one to jump hastily at decisions, frowned, tilted his head this way and that, and soberly agreed. Somewhat later the Chestnut Man's unsartorial mind received the gleam of light.

"In effect," the Chestnut Man said.

Gilles, as spokesman in all business affairs, fixed the little
dealer with a penetrating eye.

"Bring me two suits, exactly like those in the paper, for
a man who is built like Monsieur le Ministre—coats, vests,
pantaloons, cravats, four shirts and shoes that correspond.
No nonsense," said Gilles.

Victor, before going into the "sink of Montebello," as
the lost district just east of us was called, had recruited
Fabien to help him search for Old Christophe. Without
much trouble Victor had learned that the old man lived in
the rue Galande, in the back room of a one-woman bordel,
which long before had been abandoned and boarded up in
front.

"That's strange," I said. "I thought he hated women."

According to Fabien, Old Christophe was in his miserable
back room, which he entered through a trash door in the
rear. He was lying on his bunk, tangled in torn soiled blan-
kets, scratching, twisting and moaning. Fabien was quite
sure Christophe was fully dressed, including his old shoes
with holes in the bottom and cardboard inner soles.

"Is he drunk?" I asked.

"I couldn't tell," said Fabien. "If you'll excuse me, I must
be getting back. For orders."

He started away.

When misfortune falls upon a man, all nature's sorrows
combine to increase his burden. Had Easter Saturday been
chilly and wet, like the seemingly endless succession of days
that had preceded it, Old Christophe could have lain in his
dim hovel and let his itch subside. As it was, the sun was

beating down on Paris with unseasonable intensity and the squalor of his filthy interior was dazzlingly lighted, revealing each horrid detail. The thermometers of the Left Bank read 90 degrees Fahrenheit, at 11 A.M., as the unwelcome sunshine through the paneless window fell across his bent legs, arousing him from his torpor into a half-waking nightmare.

So just as Noel and the Chestnut Man were about to rip off the boards from the front window, to slide in the tin bathtub, Old Christophe, blinded by the unaccustomed light, let out an anguished cry, half-crazed by the wild life a-crawling. Entangled in torn blanket and quilt, he clutched frantically, and rolled off the bunk to the cracked tile floor, his numb reflexes too slow to save him.

Alarmed by the yell and the thud inside, the Chestnut Man exerted his strength, tore off the window boards, vaulted in, and pushed open the rotting door to Christophe's back room.

The old man tried to sit up, at the same time waving his thin arms threateningly at the Chestnut Man. Then he saw Noel, and the ungainly tub, just beyond the doorway.

"What right have you here?" Christophe demanded, getting at last into a sitting position, and holding fast to a bump on the back of his head.

"Hold your trap, you old stiff. We've come to clean you up," said the Chestnut Man, gruffly.

The significance of the tub had penetrated Christophe's dazed mind. He began to sweat, shiver and shake in the sunshine. In trying to rise, and escape, he grabbed the rough bunk frame and pulled it over on top of himself, vile rags and all.

"Don't resist," Noel said, soothingly. "We bring you an appeal from your employer. Madame, on your worthless account, has been run down by a truck and gravely injured."

That news was so devastating that Christophe refused to credit it.

"Madame had no right to place confidence in me, being sure I'd betray it. That's my destiny, messieurs. To let folks down, one after another. She's disgusted, no doubt. So am I."

"Madame's in the hospital, you stinking old goat. Get that through your head," roared the Chestnut Man.

"You've got to tend her shop," said Noel.

"Madame requested that?" asked Christophe, dumbfounded.

"Her last words, monsieur," said Noel. "Before she was carried away in the ambulance."

At the word "ambulance," the old man bowed his head.

"A man without britches," he said, and a tear rolled down his cheek.

"Not only have we brought you britches," Noel said, with the soothing authority his words carried whenever he found it necessary to impress anyone, "we have, in addition, procured a full equipment of jackets, vests, neckties and all accessories, the principal garments by the tailor of Robert Schuman, savior of three ministries of France. Perhaps now *you* may rise to the emergency, and listen to good sense. Madame Berthelot has need of what is left of your intelligence."

"She's badly injured?" asked the old man, in awe.

"She will live," Noel said. "Meanwhile her affairs are in your hands."

"And what hands!" grunted the Chestnut Man, disgustedly. He, himself, was always scrubbed clean, his clothes were patched, but he washed and mended them himself, like the sailor he was. The musty odors, the accumulation of dust, dirt and rubbish, the splintered boards, the gallimaufry of unclean insects, the bony old derelict, mangy as a sick sea gull in a driftwood crate, was turning l'Oursin's face pea green.

"The tub," he insisted, dragging in the ungainly apparatus. "I'll get hot water from the *bistro* across the way—if they know what water is, over there."

Christophe knew by that time that there was no escape. On the one hand was his compelling urge to serve Hortense, on the other, his dread of water.

"Man was given free will so he could be unworthy of himself," Christophe said. "A maudlin idea, if you ask me."

"You talk like the Existentialists," Noel said.

The old tramp groaned. "Please leave me," he said.

"When we've got soap and hot water," said l'Oursin. He was as anxious to get out, for a while, as Christophe was to bathe in privacy.

Victor Lefevrais, who had been standing by without getting in anyone's way, told Noel that a boiler of water was heating on the *bistro* stove, and the paint man two doors away had soap in stock. In the "sink of Montebello," soap was a slow-moving commodity on anyone's shelves.

Old Christophe, trapped and coerced, felt his pathological fear of water get the upper hand again. His eyes strayed toward the trash door into the littered back lot outside the wall of St. Julian the Poor. The Chestnut Man read the old man's thoughts.

"Just try any tricks," l'Oursin said. "One false move, and I'll come in and scrub you, myself."

"I have given my word," the old man said, with dignity.

Victor was posted in the trash-covered back lot, as a sentry. Noel and the Chestnut Man retired to the six-foot bar across the rue Galande. There they could hear Old

Christophe splashing, groaning and remonstrating. After a while, Julian the Barber of the rue de la Huchette, by pre-arrangement, appeared with his kit in an old carpet bag, and a flit gun, and entered the old man's den.

"What service!" those outside heard Old Christophe say. "No towels."

Victor was sent on the run for a towel which he tossed through the trash door in the rear.

The suits, shirts and ties were on pegs. The shoes were on the floor. Noel, as an afterthought, had bought a stylish gray Homburg.

"And who's to pay for all this finery?" they heard Christophe ask Julian.

"E. Saillens and Sons, and the Fourth Republic," replied Julian.

"Thus far, none of our republics has taken any notice of me, nor I of them," Christophe said.

There was nothing that would serve as a mirror in Christophe's place. When Julian had shaved, trimmed and dressed the old man, he called in Noel and the Chestnut Man. They could hardly believe their eyes. Even little Victor, who prided himself on his dead pan, made no effort to conceal his amazement. Christophe, himself, was haughty and nonchalant. He still itched, but he felt that it would pass. Julian had removed the old man's stringy growth of beard and soup-strainer moustache, and had trimmed the fringe of gray hair around his bulging sconce. The gray suit fitted loosely, but passably well. The shirt was clean, and not too snug around the collar. The tie was dove colored with a green clover pattern. The shoes were quietly respectable. The Homburg was ministerial. The resemblance to honest Robert Schuman which Noel's keen eye had detected before was now apparent to them all.

"God in Heaven," exclaimed the Chestnut Man. "Some day I'll get rigged out, myself. Who knows what I would look like?"

Washed and dressed, Old Christophe stepped out alone into the rue Galande in the gray summer suit with a five-button vest, the white shirt with detachable soft collar, the dove-colored necktie with the quiet four-leaf clover motif, russet shoes and the new gray Homburg. As he turned toward the rue du Petit Pont, he felt a few eyes at his back and heard a few voices deriding him. Those were soon left behind. Once he had faced toward the south, in the direction of the Cluny, he was halted by a horrid thought. Noel and the others, in equipping him so lavishly, had neglected to give him any money. Christophe felt through his pockets, stitched so neatly by the tailor of Robert Schuman (also the late Stavisky), and found them empty, except for two clean folded handkerchiefs.

Now Christophe had been without money most of the time for years and years, but in the condition in which he found himself that sunny noon he wanted to round out the experience. He longed to sit on the *terrasse* of some first-class café, where he was unknown except to himself, and drink a glass of coffee. Ordinary bar coffee, diluted with ground seeds and chicory, would not do. The beverage must be of real Mocha and Java, well roasted, freshly ground and filtered especially for him, and with it must be served a fresh crisp crescent roll which then brought the fantastic price to fifty francs.

In his weakened condition, following the ordeal of the early morning, the humiliating sequel, the waking nightmare, the compulsory bath, haircut, shave and elegant clothes, Christophe was easily excited or depressed. Even in his calmest moments he had never been phlegmatic. He felt sad, as he stood there on the sidewalk, because, having plumbed the depths of ignominy and been raised to the upper level of respectability and trust, there stood between him and his first wholesome impulse a mere matter of fifty francs in cash.

Noel and the Chestnut Man had jocularly addressed him as "Monsieur le Ministre" and his reflection in windows as he had passed along convinced him beyond a doubt that his likeness to Robert Schuman, at the helm of France's foreign affairs, was discernible. Once he had got clear of that miserable quarter where his identity was all too well known, several gentlemen who had been strolling along the sidewalk of the boulevard St. Germain had bowed to him and raised their hats. From old habit, long dormant, Christophe had responded, in the style of the 90's, lifting his Homburg by the back rim, from the rear, and replacing it with an easy gesture which brought his hand down in front.

"Come what may, I can never return to the rue Galande," he said to himself, with finality.

Across the boulevard St. Michel from the Café Cluny, with a respectable clientèle and a high order of service and refreshments, the old man hesitated. Strange feverish thoughts stirred in his roomy skull. Had those gentlemen who had raised their hats to him actually mistaken him for Robert Schuman, ex-premier and a member of the Cabinet? And, if they had, would not a café waiter, or a manager or proprietor, also accept him as a mainstay of France in time of stress? Supposing, for argument's sake, that he were Robert Schuman. Could not a statesman with so much on his mind stroll out thoughtlessly on a holiday noon without furnishing his pockets with petty cash? In his day, Christophe had

seen innumerable men without change thrown out of cafés,
and too often with sickening brutality. None of those, he
felt sure, had been wearing a well-tailored jacket with five-
button vest, russet shoes and a Homburg that was new and
up to date.

Unwarily, almost resolutely, Old Christophe stepped off
the sidewalk and, eyes blurring, blood roaring in his ears,
found himself caught in an onrush of traffic. In Paris these
days the drivers of cars, large or small, straddlers of bikes
or motorcycles, conductors of buses, truckdrivers, and taxi
men start pell mell with a green signal or gesture from a
traffic cop, feeling no regard for straggling pedestrians who
are distrait or lack agility. Before all is clear in the east-to-
west direction, an avalanche descends from north or south.
In Christophe's case, there were yells, a chorus of horns and
klaxons set up cacophony, one truck tire grazed the toe of
his shoe, a vicious Geugeot brushed his coat-tails. Unnerved
and rattled, Christophe dodged this way and that, clinging
to his Homburg which got dented in the process. The old
man was about to give up and perish when suddenly there
was comparative living space and calm. One traffic policeman had checked the onrush of vehicles and maniacal drivers with his authoritative arm and baton, another had rushed
over to take Christophe by the arm, and escort him safely
to the Café Cluny sidewalk.

The old man was so confused that it took him several
seconds to realize what was happening. When he did regain
his faculties, saw that a cop had him by the arm and was
talking to him, Christophe obeyed an instinct which had
been reinforced through troubled years. He wrenched his
arm away and beat it down the Boul' Mich' sidewalk as fast
as his long legs would carry him. The astonishment of the
well-meaning policemen, waiters, café sitters, chauffeurs and

cyclists, students, promenaders and Left Bank boulevardiers was such that they broke into a gale of laughter and shouts.

As soon as Christophe had put a safe distance between him and the officer, he began to realize that he had made a fool of himself. He slowed down, leaned disconsolately against a tree trunk, and was blackly depressed. And all for want of a good glass of coffee and a crescent roll. The moment he thought about that, the hunger was again upon him —intensified. When he had recovered his breath, he crossed the boulevard St. Michel once more, this time with such extreme caution that a kind-hearted young woman, assuming he was from the country, attached herself to him. In parting, after safety had been reached, she called him "Uncle," which was a terrible comedown from "Monsieur le Ministre." Moment by moment, he felt that he was losing face and self-possession. He needed the roll and the coffee, and badly.

On the sidewalk near the Ciné St. Michel is a public convenience station for men only, built to accommodate six at a standing. Reluctant to pass by the *terrasse* of the Taverne du Palais and crash the rue de la Huchette, Christophe lurked in the shadow of the metal *pissoir*, pretending to read the official admonition that, according to a certain law of the Third Republic, no bills could be posted on the structure. The old man was formulating another tentative plan.

While the bathtub was being filled, Noel had told Christophe that Madame Morizot, of Le Corset d'Art, was tending the flower shop and would stay on guard there until he appeared to take charge. It would be likely, Christophe thought, that Madame Morizot would have sold some flowers, and fitting that she should turn over to him, as the appointed agent of Madame Berthelot, whatever cash she had collected. Since Madame Berthelot owed Christophe a week's pay for pushcart work, amounting to fifteen hundred francs, he would be justified, he decided, in closing the shop long enough to go over to Rouzier's and spend fifty francs for the coffee and *croissant* he craved. Madame Berthelot, with her heart of gold and tender sensibilities, would not want him to go hungry and thirsty, he felt sure. A filtered coffee and fresh crescent roll, served properly in holiday sunshine, would do something for his manhood. He wanted that coffee and *croissant* as he had not permitted himself to long for anything in years.

"Excuse me, monsieur," he heard a man say, and was dimly aware that something smooth was being slipped into his hand. He aroused himself from his reverie, looked at the stranger who was addressing him, and observed that the man was as well dressed, almost, as he was himself, and that his manners were respectful and punctilious. Coincidentally, Christophe understood that the man was in distress and was in some way appealing to him. But it was not until the gentleman had disappeared around the curve of the *pissoir* and entered that Christophe grasped fully that he was holding a leash in his hand and that on the other end of it was a dog of the breed known as Great Dane, an animal that stood as high as a pony and whose massive face was turned his way with deep-set eyes which were regarding him. It was all Christophe could do to keep himself from dropping the leash and making a suicidal dash out into the traffic.

"Holy Saint Pierre!" he exclaimed, and the Great Dane puffed and frowned.

Christopher involuntarily made a movement with the leash which must have been some kind of signal. The huge gray dog, which matched Christophe's gray suit, tie, vest and Homburg so well, sighed again and sat down on the sidewalk. Passers-by could not resist pausing to admire the handsome brute, and the overgrown dog looked back into their eyes with dignity, but paid them no further attention.

Another uniformed policeman approached, glanced, smiled and continued his way. Christophe thought he had never seen the quarter so over-supplied with cops, but he could only stand his ground and wait. The huge dog had taken him on trust, which large dogs for years had signally neglected to do. Christophe was touched, and resolved to respond in kind. Passing gentlemen still doffed their hats, and ladies smiled. With his free hand Christophe responded.

How much time elapsed before Christophe began to feel uneasy because the dog's proprietor was taking such a long time in the convenience station is not certain. The dog showed no signs of restlessness. Finally Christophe glanced anxiously under the rim of the *pissoir* wall to look for a pair of polished shoes and the bottoms of striped-trousers legs. When only two men were left standing inside, Christophe could contain himself no longer. He tugged at the leash. The docile Great Dane rose, and Christophe led him inside, and all the way around. One of the men, who had been drinking freely that morning, felt something brush the back of his legs, looked over his shoulder, let out a yell and dashed into the street without buttoning his pants. The other client blanched and crossed himself.

A moment later, in the open air and sunshine once more, Christophe became aware that he had acquired a dog weighing one hundred and forty pounds, equipped with brand-new leather leash and brass-studded collar.

8. *More or Less in His Image*

WHILE Noel and the others were outfitting Old Chris-
tophe, I started from the Hotel Normandie toward the Café
St. Michel. Parked in front of No. 29, near the entrance to
Rahab, stood a long black low-slung Cadillac I identified as
Carmen's. I had been expecting to hear from her, since our
afternoon at the Independent Show, and also to meet Pierre
Vautier, who, I had been told, occupied the top-floor studio
on the corner of the rue de la Harpe.

As I reached the side of the *terrasse* of the Café St. Michel,
Madame Gillotte, grinning with utter disregard of the absence of one of her prominent front teeth, made a gesture
toward the Cadillac.

"Your lady friend. She's gone up to see the painter," the
baker's wife said.

"Did she ask for me?"

Madame Gillotte shook her head and looked at me, quizzi-
cally. I sat down, ordered a drink, and tried to set aside my
misgivings.

"An unsociable specimen, Monsieur Vautier," Madame
Gillotte remarked, still trying to fathom my feelings in the
matter.

"Just plain crazy, if you ask me," said Madame du Gran'
Chemin.

"I like Pierre's paintings," I said.

Neither of the women could believe that I meant what I

said. Before they could pursue the subject farther, I saw
Bernard Kahnweiler, the famous art dealer and critic, ascend
from the Métro stairway. At the same time, a Hachette delivery man wheeled to the curb on his tricycle and dumped
in front of the newsstand the first bundle of afternoon
papers, placed on sale about noon. Kahnweiler waited for
the benevolent-looking newspaper hag to open the bundle,
then bought a copy of *Le Monde*. He recognized me on the
terrasse and, smiling, joined me, with the paper in his hand.
His career had paralleled the development of modern art.
He had been one of the first dealers to buy early Picassos,
and the work of Braque and Derain. He had launched André
Masson, supported Juan Gris for years before he died, and
encouraged Miro and Gromaire.

Without comment, he spread the newspaper in front of
me and pointed out an article which evidently amused him.
When I read it, I was equally delighted.

François Mauriac, prominent academician and member
of the group of French Catholic writers known irreverently
as "the last pillars of the Church," had attacked Picasso, not
only the recent paintings but the artist's intent. The spear-
head of Mauriac's contention was that Picasso deliberately
had sold his genius to Satan, and had undertaken, at the in-
stigation of the Evil One, to destroy the Christian belief that
God created Man in His own image.

How else could one account for alleged "portraits" of
men and women with three different faces all scrambled together? With eyes at right angles, like those of a flounder?
With breasts, knees, elbows, hands and limbs all out of place,
and out of focus? With plates of herring trimmed with
forks for hats?

When Kahnweiler slipped the newspaper into his portfolio I saw that he had, among other large lithographs, a

copy, numbered 12, of the now notorious Picasso dove which the Communists had printed on innumerable posters, and which even Noel, at Les Halles de la Huchette, had copied with black dyes on pale Easter eggs.

"How many of those were run off?" I asked.

"Only fifty," Kahnweiler said. He smiled again. "You know, perhaps, that Picasso did not draw the dove for the Communist peace meeting. It's part of a series of birds and animals he did for me. Six weeks after it was finished, one of the Communist poets who can't quite leave good art alone, even if it's deficient in propaganda, called at Pablo's studio, saw the dove, and asked if the Communists might use it on a poster. Of course Picasso said 'Yes.' He'll give almost anything away if someone really likes it."

Kahnweiler got up to go down the quai to a little art shop where he often picked up old colored engravings for his personal collection. I walked with him as far as the bookstore of Violet, Aîné. Inside I saw Anatole, the clerk, in his wheelchair. He was alone in the enormous store. He liked to spend long hours, reclining in his wheelchair, reading or looking out over the river. When anyone approached him, he seemed glad to talk.

Anatole was born in 1920, and his mother had died before his clear memory established itself. His father, Alexandre Pillods, had been a coachman employed by one of the de Castellanes, and when his employer's branch of the family went to seed, Alexandre bought himself a taxi with his savings. For several years, until some time in the middle 1930's, Pillods the elder operated from the line of cabs along the curb from the rue de la Huchette back about one hundred feet toward the Cluny.

In 1935, Pillods, senior, was badly injured and his taxi was demolished in a collision with a heavy Rolls-Royce driven by the prominent publisher and bookseller, Lucien Violet, Ainé. The accident was entirely due to Violet's careless driving, while tipsy from champagne, and the wealthy merchant took the matter very much to heart. The case never got to court. Pillods did not sue. Violet, Ainé, made a generous settlement, established a fund to take care of the disabled taxi man and provide a liberal education for Anatole, the cab man's son. To his father's horror and his conscience-stricken benefactor's dismay, Anatole, then fifteen years of age, asked to go to art school. By the time war broke out in 1939 Anatole was at Aubusson, where under Lurçat, Maingonnet and the others who were forming the brilliant new school of modern tapestry designing, he was working with fine concentration and amazing deliberation. He never was idle, and he never hurried. That it required two years, sometimes longer, to execute one of his designs troubled him not at all. He seemed to have been born with an Olympian sense of time.

Like many other promising young artists of France, due largely to the groundwork accomplished by Braque in World War I, Anatole did most of his peacetime military service in the camouflage department. When the call to the colors came in 1939, he was promptly transferred, with the rank of lieutenant, to the infantry and sent into the Maginot line. Later his unit was flanked, decimated and those who survived were captured. While he was away, his father died.

Anatole's first *stalag*, or prison camp, in Germany was in an enclosure that also included a long, low building from which continually came the sound of women screaming. A group of German scientists were conducting experiments there, with gypsy women as subjects, on responses to pain, inflicted in various ways, and of graded intensities and duration. Forced to listen to the sounds from that establishment,

Anatole found himself associating them in his mind with gypsy colors. The illusion became stronger, while at the same time he knew the relationship was imaginary. It was not long before he began trying to weave the gypsy-hued screams into tapestry patterns. His hands began to tremble, his face muscles twitched and his head ached all the time.

Beginning with his nervous collapse, he was ill two years, and was treated not too badly. He was removed to a better camp, where no distracting noises were destructive to his high-strung nerves. Eventually he was sent back to France, was discharged and returned to Aubusson. As soon as he tried working again, he suffered a relapse. When he blocked out a design for a rug, wall hanging, screen or carpet, his eyes blurred with gypsy colors which brought back the sound, inaudible to others, of gypsy women screaming—not loud, but faint, shrill and distant. French army doctors called in American psychiatrists and civilian consultants, and all the medical men agreed on one point. Anatole must give up designing and find another occupation. The way Anatole accepted the harsh disappointment endeared him to everyone who even dimly understood the facts. He sought out Lucien Violet, Aîné, who offered him anything he wanted. All he wanted was a job, living quarters with a view of the Seine, and, within reason, freedom of movement and action. A wealth of books was at Anatole's command, some old, some new, on almost any subject—fiction, non-fiction, belles lettres, history, autobiography, biography, philosophy, science, theoretical and practical, and countless volumes on the arts. His memory, like so many that never have been wrung or strained, was retentive. So, as a book clerk, with all his love of leisure and his mild eccentricities, he sold more books, pleased more exacting customers and incidentally made more money for Violet, Aîné, than any three employees the firm had.

Kahnweiler, that bright Saturday morning, waved to Anatole before he continued to the art shop down the quai, indicating in pantomime that he would stop in and have a chat as soon as he had accomplished his brief errand. Anatole nodded and smiled.

The counters which, on business days were filled with second-hand bargains, constantly marked down, and occupied most of the sidewalk for sixty feet on either side of the broad entrance to the courtyard of No. 27, had been moved inside. While I lingered, glancing at the titles in the windows, Monsieur Busse, looking quite perturbed, entered the bookstore from the rear, hurried to Anatole's side, and implored me, with a gesture, to join them.

"I'm surprised at you," he said to me, as I approached. "I don't understand you at all."

"What have I done, or not done?" I asked.

"You encouraged Monsieur Wilf to buy clothes for that unspeakable old wretch, Christophe. Hortense will be murdered in her bed, some day. You see if she isn't!" Busse said.

"How does it happen that the flower shop is empty?" I asked, accusingly.

"I bought everything! There's no need for that vile old man to come around. There's nothing he can do. When Madame Berthelot gets back from the hospital, I'll reason with her once again," said Busse.

"What have you done with all the plants and flowers?" I asked.

"I'm using them at the hotel, upstairs and down," he said. "I beg of you, Monsieur Paul . . . You seem to be a reasonable man. Back me up, with Hortense. Help me get rid of that fiend."

"I only carried out Hortense's own request," I said.

"We must save her from her impulses," said Busse, more positively than ever. "If we don't, no one will."

Anatole listened to the dialogue, watching Busse's petulant expressions change as if a film were being projected across his mobile face. We all were startled as Pierre Vautier strode in. He had what appeared to be a framed canvas, wrapped in brown paper, under his arm. When he caught sight of me he uncoiled like a Jack-in-the-Box.

"You!" he snarled.

"What a welcome!" Anatole said.

"That woman!" continued Pierre, glaring at me.

"A fine, attractive girl," I said.

"A chump!" Pierre said. "You put her up to that rubbish she was reciting." Pierre changed his voice, and mimicked Carmen maliciously. "A refinement of Miro! But so relentless, Monsieur!"

Anatole tilted his head back and laughed heartily.

"Miro, you said? She didn't mention Derain or Redon?" he asked Pierre.

Poor Busse looked from Vautier to me and back again, as if he were afraid we were coming to blows. As to the reason, he had no inkling whatever.

Pierre continued his devastating imitation of Carmen. "The brick, the gray, the parchment tone. They seem to have ripened together. And that masculine *thing*, the he-entity!"

Anatole burst into laughter again. "She's got you wriggling on a pin, by God she has," he said to Pierre, who turned an angry red.

"I read about your painting, in *Figaro*," Busse said, to Pierre, to soothe him.

"'*La Chasse Spirituelle,*'" murmured Anatole, and laughed more heartily. "What did you expect?"

"I liked the painting. I didn't think you had it in you," I said. "And you needn't be ashamed of the influence of Miro, or Derain, or for that matter, Redon."

"You hoped to collect a commission, I suppose," Pierre said. "She's reeking with her old man's money."

"Her father's money came from selling first-class food. I assumed you'd be broke. In years past you always were."

"Who are you to talk? You never had a dime, not a clean shirt to your name, until you started whoring around Hollywood," he retorted.

Busse was eyeing the wrapped painting, consumed with curiosity.

"Is this the painting? Might I look at it?" he asked Pierre.

I thought Pierre might crown him with it, but instead he had a perverse inspiration.

"Let me loan it to you. Hang it on your bedroom wall, for a while. Then tell me what you think," Pierre said.

Busse was entranced. "Would you, really? I'm anxious to make things right for Madame Berthelot. Might I hang the painting in her room? She was hurt this morning."

"I know," said Pierre. "By all means. Let Hortense gaze at it, too. Perhaps she'll have something to say that's not echoed from some American hack."

"I saw you pussyfooting around the exhibition," Pierre said, turning to me.

"I was aware of that," I said. "Why did you follow me from one end of it to the other?"

"I had an impulse, at first, to speak . . . Then I thought, what's the use. It's disturbing to renew old contacts," he said.

"Yes. Isn't it?" I agreed. "And it wasn't my idea that

Carmen should try to buy the painting. She liked it, and wanted to have it."

"How else could anyone get a Miro, a Derain and a Redon, with Vautier in the bargain, for one price?" asked Anatole.

Pierre turned his guns on the book clerk, with harsh disregard for Anatole's sensibilities. "That stuff you used to do at Aubusson! Lurçat, simon pure. Mostly vanilla and just too colorful for words. You didn't quit designing because of war infirmities. You were fed up with your own insipid folderol. Hoot owls. Shepherds. Butterflies. Antique inscriptions. You used the Boche as an excuse."

Anatole was not at all offended. "We artists never know our own motives," he said. "Remember that, Busse, when you're contemplating Pierre's masterpiece. And keep the Freudians away."

At the mention of Freud, Pierre turned livid, strode to the quai, and out of sight. Busse, with the wrapped painting under his arm, took his leave and went the other way.

9. *Wings of Doctrine*

SANSON-MICHEL MAINGUET, whose saint-like disposition had stood so long between him and his heart's desire, that is, the hand of Madame Berthelot, was in nearly every respect an exception to established rule. Slight and frail, narrow of chest and devoid of robustness, he still had unusually reliable health and in a capital where the common cold obstructs progress and the pursuit of happiness during several months of every year, Mainguet seldom sneezed or even sniffled. His eyes were weak, behind his reading glasses, but no dimmer than they had been when he was a spindle-shanked child in short trousers. His occupation, that of a conscientious government clerk (one of the rarest types extant) had always been cramped and sedentary, thankless and underpaid. No bitterness sullied his soul, and neither did false optimism make him ridiculous. His religion, which meant so much to him, taught that man is frail.

Mainguet's experience indicated that the frailer types, morally and spiritually, spiraled high in French officialdom. Neither the corruptibility of his chiefs nor the sottishness of his subordinates had shaken his Christian humility. The human mind, he believed, could not tune itself with the Divine unless on pure faith the thinker accepted certain postulates. The Arch-Fiend and Tempter could not penetrate the armor of meekness. Mainguet was meek, but not abject. He never neglected a chance to lend a helping hand, that is, to share the only asset he had, not wealth, not influence, not poetry or buffoonery, but factual information.

Of all the laymen in the St. Sulpice congregation, Monsieur Mainguet was the most helpful in liaison between the ordained clergy and the parishioners. Mainguet had changed his place of residence almost as many times as his office address in the various municipal offices and cabinet ministries before coming to the rue de la Huchette. He was known to the priests of St. Séverin and the dignitaries of Notre Dame. For most of his devotions he returned to St. Sulpice, and the authorities of that church called upon him most often for gratuitous services.

About a week before Easter, Mainguet had been sought out by the Very Reverend Léon d'Alexis, S.J., and the assistant professor of ancient Christianity at the Sorbonne, Père F. M. Taillepied, O.P. The two priests just mentioned had learned that Monsieur Mainguet had more than a passing acquaintance with Monsieur Gilles Wilf, who was prominent in hotel circles in the quarter around Notre Dame and who, for reasons of discretion, ecclesiastical celebrities could not approach directly, without risking the appearance of evil. Bishop d'Alexis, in fact, had been named chairman of the entertainment committee to welcome a delegation of twenty-five pious Mexicans who were on the way to Paris, via Rome, bringing a life-size image of St. Felix, the Schoolmaster. The statue was to be presented formally to St. Sulpice, as a token of international Catholic solidarity. The offer had been made and accepted and the pilgrimage had been planned ten years before, in 1939. War and its aftermath had intervened, the voyage and ceremony had been postponed, and in the year of recovery was to be consummated.

The Easter rush of tourists, including 75,000 choir boys from all provinces of France, had crowded the St. Sulpice district to overflowing. Not a bed or a pallet was available there for the distinguished Mexican guests. In the emergency, the Rev. d'Alexis and Père Taillepied had thought of Monsieur Mainguet.

Mainguet's feat in reserving sleeping quarters for twenty-five pious Mexicans, within a few minutes' walking distance of the great cathedral of Notre Dame, the Gothic gem St. Séverin, the ungainly mass of St. Sulpice which was the world headquarters for missionaries of the Jesuit order, and St. Germain des Prés, refuge of the last remnants of Proust's aristocracy, was a remarkable achievement.

Armand Busse, whose loss of his religion was a source of intermittent terror to him, was exerting himself to make the Hotel Mont Souris the delegation headquarters and to extend all courtesies to the Mexican guests.

On Thursday evening before her accident, Mainguet had called on Hortense, in her shop, bringing as a tribute a small second-hand book, quite old and rare, in which was an account of the life and martyrdom of St. Felix the Schoolmaster, whose image the twenty-five Mexicans were having blessed by the Pope, before it was to be installed in a chapel of St. Sulpice in Paris.

Naturally, an admirer could not bring flowers to a woman who spent her days selling them, and Mainguet's own digestion which he had guarded through years of poverty was so precious to him that he would not jeopardize Hortense's by offering her bonbons and chocolates. So he gave her second-hand books, very thoughtfully chosen, and in each one of them, when she read them, evenings, she found something piquant or unusual. She was not one to undervalue Mainguet's modest erudition, or to underrate his inner life.

"He really believes," she said to me, more than once. "How can we place ourselves in that frame of mind, and taste life's flavor, free from fundamental doubts?"

Our conversation, that is, the talk between Hortense and Mainguet did not go very well, that Thursday evening. The rain was suspended for a while, the wind had changed, slightly, so that a certain balm was tempering the dampness.

"Do I understand that the statue of the saint will be flown with the Mexicans from Rome to Paris?" Hortense asked.

Monsieur Mainguet nodded. "They arrive Saturday evening."

"I can't recall that we've ever had Mexicans in the street before. But why not? We have Arabs, Turks, Negroes who speak French, Negroes who speak a dialect of American, Be-Bops, Existentialists, North Americans . . ." said Hortense.

"We mustn't forget the French. Two-thirds of the residents are French," said Mainguet. "Auvergnats, Catalans, Basques, Normans, Bretons, Marseillais, a few from Alsace and Lorraine, the Midi, Mayenne, Burgundy, the Savoy, the Haute Savoy, the Marne, the Haute Marne. So why not Central Americans?"

"You did well to find rooms for them," she added.

"Monsieur Gilles is responsible for that," Mainguet said.

We were silent a moment, then Hortense said: "What troubles me is your saint in the airplane. If that sort of thing becomes the vogue, won't it be disconcerting for pilots and passengers in other airplanes, to pass a flying vehicle high in the air and see a saint's face staring out through one of those round windows?"

"That would depend on how high one was flying," Mainguet said.

"What I'd like to know is how a saint pays his fare . . . How his trip is paid for, I mean—from the company's point of view. Is Saint Felix, for example, considered by the man at the ticket window as a passenger? Surely a saint's image, blessed by His Holiness, could not be stored horizontally, with grips and golf bags in the luggage compartment."

When I saw her for a moment in her room at the X-ray hospital Saturday morning, Hortense was quite repentant because she had gone too far with Mainguet in discussing St. Felix in the plane. Her nerves were tremulous, following the shock of the collision with the truck, and she was faint from hunger. With so many solicitous friends and professionals trying to give her the best of care, no one had remembered to feed her. I went out to a near-by café and brought her back a *saucisson* sandwich, with butter, and a bottle of French tomato juice. While I was watching her eat the makeshift lunch, Dr. Thiouville came in.

By the same ironic process that had bestowed on frail sweet-tempered little Mainguet the name of Sanson, or Samson, who slew the Philistines with the jawbone of an ass, the earnest young doctor, so juvenile and naive in appearance, was named Socrate-Emile Hautecour de Thiouville. And in the same degree that Mainguet was devoted to the principles of Christ, Dr. Thiouville had consecrated himself to the principles of Hippocrates. What stood in his way? He was intelligent, within the limits required for the study of higher medicine and its practice. Like Mainguet, he was healthy and had a deceptively strong nervous reserve which emergencies brought into play. His brain was quick and responsive, his hands were those of a surgeon. His manner, however, was hesitant, and he had the face of a rather timid boy. Even in strong sunlight, it was difficult to believe that he was obliged, now and then, to shave. His cheeks were rosy, his brown eyes fringed with long curved lashes. He lisped ever so slightly when he spoke. His teachers had respected him, the older and wiser ones, but the nurses were more inclined to mother him than obey without question. He had hung his shingle in the rue de la Huchette because it was a live quarter, for those who earned a living and had the spirit to enjoy it. That Dr. Thiouville was a sincere Communist was not due to any detailed knowledge he had of the works of Marx, Lenin and Stalin. Because of his admiration for Frederic Joliot-Curie, then France's High Commissioner for Atomic Research, Dr. Thiouville had followed the great Red scientist into the Party at the age of twenty-one. He was twenty-five in 1949.

The young doctor of the St. Michel quarter, who occupied the former offices of the old reactionary who had retired when Pétain was dispossessed, belonged to a generation of Frenchmen who, generally speaking and for cause, are the most cynical, disillusioned and resourceful among the age groups that make up the manhood and womanhood of post-war France. It is that class of young men and women who strike the observer who has been familiar with France and the French for decades, as baffling and "different." The line or demarcation, or "break" with traditional France is most noticeable in those citizens now between the ages of twenty-five and thirty. Consider for a moment the rough outlines of their experience, thus far.

I can never forget Noel's remarks when one morning we read in the newspaper that Marcel Bernard, France's most promising tennis player, who certainly would have been a contender for the world's championship if his career had proceeded normally, could no longer keep himself in shape for top-flight competition because of the ten years he had lost on account of World War II.

Which ten years of one's life could best be offered the war lords, or one's country defending itself against war lords? Was it better to get it over as a child, from infancy to ten, running the hazards of psychosis, undernourishment and indelible memories of sadness, despair, night flights, explosions, all around the crib, the playpen, the home, or the kindergarten—if any?

Or should one give up the years from ten to twenty, including puberty and adolescence? Or the best military years, between twenty and thirty? Or the years between the ages of thirty and forty, when home life, if tolerable at all, is at its best? Or from forty to fifty, when it becomes possible, if ever, to earn money in quantities beyond the demands of the day? Or from fifty to sixty, when a measure of security, if one is lucky, has been attained? Or could one say to Mars, take the last ten years, the leavings, from sixty to the Biblical limit, and the devil of a lot of good may they do you?

The conscientious Dr. Thiouville, born with the silver spoon and not much else, bearing the names, intertwined, of two fine French families, was one of those who was ten years old in the days of pussy-willow Blum, the sit-down strikes and the Popular Front, the sellout of Abyssinia, Spain, Austria, the Rhineland, and Munich following after. Socrate-Emile was fifteen, and doing well at the lycée, when World War II was declared, and the lack of preparedness and initiative of Daladier, the traitorous hypocrisy of Georges Bonnet, the lack of action against the Nazis and Fascists, the ignoble counter-attack under the guise of patriotism against the French working class—all those events colored his adolescence.

Then came humiliation, defeat, occupation by the Boches, the Black Market obscuring and superseding legitimate enterprise, the Vichy regime, the French Gestapo, Collabos, criminals, Iscariots, and the seething underground and guerrilla resistance, split by the axe of political dissension into Communists and non-Communists and anti-Communists and Catholics, so that loyalties were attached to an almost non-existent France, to republican ideals, to the Vatican, to Moscow, to self-preservation and the Devil take the hindmost.

Dr. Thiouville was twenty at the time of Liberation, and completed his studies under the De Gaulle regime and the first few Middle-of-the-Road makeshifts. He had started to practice in the rue de la Huchette about the time the Marshall Plan got under way. He had become convinced that the Plan was dangerous and unsound. He is of the same opinion today.

The France young Thiouville had known was corrupt and sick, and his boyhood and youth in Paris had not been sheltered from daily contacts with petty graft, profiteering, excesses of brutality and barbarity, torture, usury, denunciations of brother by brother and father by son, acceptance of the vile, forgiveness of the unforgivable, honest block-headedness, dishonest cleverness, wantonness of women and wives, heyday of philanderers, too young or too old. There were no standards, beyond the baseness of individuals. Growing boys and girls, and youth coming into manhood and womanhood, had no illusions or delusions. Money, morals and long-term ambitions had been scrapped in the junk-heap of defeat, and defeat had not been followed by victory, but rescue, that is, liberation. From the French of other age groups, you will hear brave assurances that the French themselves maintained the Resistance, rose up against the Nazis and delivered France. Those young people who endured the war and its sequel from the ages of ten to twenty will say: "The Americans did it, and why? Our continued existence as a buffer nation has become essential to them."

Generalities are always futile and misleading, and it must not be supposed that the individuals in that baffling age group are alike, or that the group is homogeneous. The outstanding examples in the rue de la Huchette, Dr. Thiouville, Anatole Pillods, Be-Bop and the clerk at the Mont Souris, Aristide Riboulet, are as different as young men could be. Anatole is an aesthete and a dreamer; Be-Bop is a Bohemian by nature, with no ambition except to enjoy himself in his own hedonistic ways. He is sold on nearly everything American on account of his passion for jazz music. He imitates the Existentialists of St. Germain who pretend to be profound and are not.

Riboulet is a paranoid type, from birth anti-social and predatory, a natural product of the 1940's. He has no profession, or stable occupation. Neither politics nor ethics has ever come within range of his experience, his capacity for which is narrowly limited. He is a sensualist, whose senses are pitched very low. For him the years when Nazis and French secret police prowled the streets, gaudy women were on the make and modest women at bay and thieving was normal and honesty ridiculous were earthly paradise. In such a state of society boys like Riboulet could thrive.

A student of medicine and surgery like Socrate-Emile Hautecour de Thiouville, with his dark hair, fair complexion, pink cheeks and upturned eyelashes, can fix his mind on his studies, and the glory of serving mankind, to the exclusion of what goes on around him. His people and his class were not republicans, but they were French, anti-

German, anti-Nazi, and, like so many other well-meaning Dodos, sold on old Pétain. For them the old Stuffed Uniform was still the hero of Verdun, and the defender of the Faith.

What was the result? The young student, Thiouville, developed into a specimen as rare as the humble, Christian-like Mainguet—a Communist who was intellectually honest. He could not believe that a society like the one he had passed through, as if it had been an endless contagious war, was fit for reorganization. He thought that a new ideology was needed for man's salvation, and the creed accepted by Joliot-Curie was good enough, in principle, for young Thiouville. He had seen that the profit motive was destructive and vile, that formal religion was habit-forming and deadening to the average human mind. He saw his own class as the average, and acknowledged that its level was too low for safety or sense. A young doctor should help not only those who pay, but everybody, Thiouville insisted. The other-cheek routine, to a former Christian who had lived under Nazi occupation, was beneath a free man's dignity. He did not believe that the United States, however prosperous or dominant, could salvage world capitalism and raise living standards all over the globe. He did not believe that Stalin wanted war, or that Russians wanted to leave Russia. Actually he had accepted on faith almost as many doctrines as Mainguet had.

It must be kept in mind, in trying to understand contemporary France, that more than one-third of the voters are Communists, and that the Communist intellectuals are at least on a par with the Catholic "last pillars of the Church." If, in the United States (leaving out New York City and the motion-picture zone of the Pacific coast in Southern California) one has to walk at least half a day without encountering a bona-fide Communist, in Paris it would be necessary to walk more than half a day in order to get out of the range of vision of innumerable Communists. And they are not all lunkheads or mountebanks. Some work with their heads, and others with their hands.

On Easter Saturday noon, when I was calling on Hortense, nothing was going right for young Socrate-Emile Hautecour de Thiouville. He had chosen the Hospital Dupuy because one of his favorite teachers was at the head of the X-ray department, and most of the staff doctors, internes and nurses were free thinkers, with an inclination toward the Left. It would have been possible for him to have a patient admitted in certain hospitals, where Catholic doctors and sisters of charity were in charge, but a young doctor known to be a Communist would not expect preferential treatment in such institutions.

Dr. Thiouville, so eager to impress his neighbors with his handling of Hortense's injury, was thinking far ahead. The case involved not only the fracture of Madame's funny bone at the tenderest spot. There were also E. Saillens and Sons to be considered. The matter of settlement might be thrashed out in court, and young Thiouville knew all too well that, in the witness box, he, with his pink cheeks, immature voice and hesitant manner, would carry little weight with judges, juries, the press or the public.

A clever lawyer on the other side could make him say that elbows grew on thighs. Any competent operator could take the X-ray photographs that were needed for the treatment of Madame Berthelot's arm. But if they were to be displayed and interpreted in court, Dr. Thiouville wanted to be able to call Dr. Lesserand, his former professor of radiology, who had had lots of court experience and was not identified in the public mind with the Communist Party.

The telephone girl at the Hospital Dupuy, in replying to Dr. Thiouville's original application over the phone, had let it slip her mind that all Paris and all France already was embarked upon the long Easter week-end. So when Dr. Thiouville arrived in the rue Pierre Curie with Hortense, he found the little hospital understaffed, a restless group of patients awaiting their turns in the photographing rooms, and was told that Dr. Lesserand was in Cognac, in the south of France.

Hortense was not in great pain; she was comfortably installed, with the little book about St. Felix the Schoolmaster to read. Once she had eaten the sandwich and drunk the tomato juice she was quite willing to wait all day, and did her best to put the doctor at ease. Hortense knew as well as he did that her case was important to him, and was resolved to say a good word for him whenever possible.

Those who were waiting for news of her, and had expected her back in the rue de la Huchette without delay, were not nearly as easy to satisfy. When Dr. Thiouville got back there, he was bombarded with questions, and could only say that, due to the holiday exodus of doctors, Madame would not be photographed until mid-afternoon.

The doctor's stuffy predecessor had never got used to telephones and for economy's sake had refrained from having one installed in his office. There was a wall telephone in the second-floor hallway at No. 23, the only one in the building. And because of the shortage of instruments, accessories and electricians brought on by the war and aggravated by the demands of recovery, Dr. Thiouville had received no response to his several applications for a private wire. He had to talk out in the hall, within earshot of the Jonquil, the gimlet-eyed and loon-eared concierge, as well as the more curious among the neighbors. Those included the Pigotte sisters of "Rose France," Riboulet, the desk clerk at the Mont Souris, and young David Hatounian from "Rahab." Also Monge, the horse butcher, Noel and the grocer, Vignon. All of them suspected that the young doctor, in spite of his attempt to treat the situation lightly, was more worried about Madame Berthelot and her arm than he wished to admit.

Trying to forget that so many eavesdroppers were listening, Dr. Thiouville went to the wall telephone, a pay station, took the old-fashioned receiver from the hook and, when the operator finally answered, gave her a number in the distant province of Cognac and said he must talk in person with Dr. Lesserand.

The anxious friends of Hortense exchanged glances of alarm. If the young doctor had to consult someone at the other end of France, the case must be grave, they assumed.

"Maybe she sustained what they call 'internal injuries,'" Vignon said. "Those are bad for a woman with tender insides."

Dr. Thiouville was hearing assorted noises from the receiver. He frowned, shifted his stance, fished in his pocket and drew forth what change he had.

"How much?" he asked the operator.

"One hundred and two francs," she replied.

"*Mais, zut, alors,*" muttered Vignon, who with some of the others had approached the instrument. "The slots on this miserable phone take nothing larger than one franc, in metal."

"How could the Government provide machines that would gobble paper francs?" asked the Jonquil, who had come upon the scene.

"I need one hundred and two francs, in metal," Dr. Thiouville said. David Hatounian, Noel, Monge, Vignon and some others scattered up and down the street, to collect one-franc pieces. Meanwhile the receiver dangled at the end of the cord and Dr. Thiouville paced the hallway.

By the time the scouts had returned with two hatfuls of one-franc pieces, the line was dead. Dr. Thiouville aroused the operator again, again asked for the number in Cognac, and when given the ready signal dropped in one hundred and two franc pieces, one by one, while the Jonquil counted grimly, aloud.

The difficulty with pay telephones is one of the innumerable woes of inflation. There are thousands of subscribers in France, and the French under thirty years of age are increasingly telephone-minded. But there is no French coin of a denomination larger than ten francs (although a twenty-franc piece is now in preparation) and so many other articles have to be manufactured before life can be normal again that it will be a long time before the use of pay telephones for long-distance calls becomes feasible.

Once Dr. Thiouville's connection was established he got from Dr. Lesserand the name of an X-ray specialist who was an excellent diagnostician, had a good court presence, and a friendly acquaintance with Dr. Joliot-Curie. Promptly the young doctor got in touch with Dr. Raymond Flandrin de Monique, and the latter, although hard-pressed and overworked, agreed to photograph Hortense's elbow late that afternoon and still later have a look at the negatives.

The whole St. Michel quarter is honeycombed with narrow passageways between buildings, some masked with back doors, others open, and in the days of kings and revolutions, had a network of tunnels connecting various subcellars with one another, the Cluny to the southeast and under the river to the Conciergerie. Years ago the police sealed up the subterranean and under-river passages, but men who know the district can get from place to place without exposing themselves, by making use of the alleys, slits and walled courtyards.

Old Christophe, in his respectable gray outfit, with Homburg and Great Dane, did not enter the rue de la Huchette through the wide end, directly. He led the huge dog down the rue St. Séverin, into a passage not more than two feet wide, through the Jonquil's sheltered courtyard of No. 23, and had only six steps to go in order to reach the front door of the flower shop.

He straightened and swelled with indignation when he saw that the counters and shelves were bare. Not only had Madame Morizot left the place deserted, but all the plants and flowers were gone. Angrily Christophe tried the door. It was locked; the outer handle had been removed and placed inside. Inserting one finger in the keyhole, he rattled the door and thumped until the din brought the Jonquil on the trot from her dim lodge in the courtyard.

"Monsieur!" the Jonquil said sternly. "Do you wish to jar out the window glass?" Then she caught sight of the dog who was standing taut and stiff-legged, awaiting a command. "Jesus, Mary and Joseph," gasped the sallow concierge, and took several steps backward, afraid to turn her flank to such a beast.

"I was given to understand . . ." Old Christophe began.

"Name of God! It's Old Christophe!" the Jonquil said, her Adam's apple stuck in her throat. "That animal, Monsieur. He's yearning to destroy me."

Christophe assumed his haughtiest manner. "Madame," he said, pompously. "Have no fear. My dog, Xavier, does only what I wish. And at present I wish to preserve you, so that you may answer a question. Where is Madame Morizot?"

"She and her husband departed, an hour ago," the Jonquil said.

Christophe, with the Great Dane, led the way back into the courtyard, where the old man tried the rear door which opened directly into Hortense's small bedroom. That too was locked, and the handle was inside.

"Be kind enough to ascertain whether Madame Morizot's harness shop is locked and deserted," Christophe said, and the Jonquil hobbled briskly away. She had got started just as the dog, Xavier, had raised his ears and glared at her again. In a moment she returned, having entered through another back passageway.

"Closed tight, front and back," the Jonquil said.

"Where has La Morizot gone with the cash?" demanded Christophe.

"To the woods outside Montmorency. Her husband's brother has a camp there for boy and girl scouts. In my day respectable children were not allowed to romp in forests and bushes unchaperoned," said the Jonquil.

"And when will Madame Morizot return?" Christophe was addressing the Jonquil as if she were at fault.

"Tuesday morning, most probably," the Jonquil said

"What has she done with Madame Berthelot's flowers, for which I, alone, am responsible?"

"Every last daisy and fern was bought by Monsieur Busse. He had all the garçons and maids from the Mont Souris lugging pots and vases into the hotel," the Jonquil said.

"This isn't the first time Monsieur Busse has tried to ruin me," Christophe said. Then a cunning expression passed over his face.

"Did Busse pay, in cash, for what he took away?" Christophe asked.

"Not a sou. I swear it. He said something about his account. You know the high and mighty way he has," the Jonquil said.

"I shall confront Monsieur Busse. Come, Xavier," the old man said, and the Jonquil watched him start for the Mont Souris. Quite a few of the others in the street saw the figure in gray, and the dog, but no one recognized either of them.

In his room on the third floor, front, just above the chamber he had assigned to Madame Berthelot, Armand Busse was sitting on the edge of a chair, tilting his head this way and that, and gazing almost prayerfully at the painting entitled "La Chasse Spirituelle" which he had propped up on the *bidet* and leaned against the wall. He was trying to feel appropriate emotions, and succeeding only in becoming more confused.

He noted the upper field of gray, the lower ground of dull red, the he-entity with his gesture of despair, the volatile Thing drifting upward. The story had spread through the quarter that Madame Carmen Orey had written and signed a check, with the amount left blank. Vautier, the mad painter who never before had been offered a dime for any work of his, had tossed the check on the floor. His concierge at No. 29 had retrieved it, after Madame and Vautier had gone, and tucked it into a vase on the studio mantelpiece.

Moreover, Busse was aware that respectable newspapers like *Le Monde* and *Figaro* had praised the canvas and its author who preferred to be known as Treves de la Berliere, and not Pierre Vautier.

What was it he, Busse, was missing? Was his taste, after

all, defective? Busse realized that he preferred the works of the Romanticists, especially Corot, to those of the Impressionists, and that the painting of the Cubists, notably Picasso and his frightening three-faced women with fish hats struck terror to his soul. If the priests were right, and Busse, as a card-carrying Communist, was doomed to the foulest mill tails of Hell, he was sure Picasso creatures would abound below and would drop whatever they were doing to torment him. A monotonous refrain kept recurring in Busse's groping mind: "Art must be beautiful. Not ugly, so the flesh creeps. Not pretty, perhaps, so the little finger curls. But beautiful. Is this painting before me beautiful, or is it not? Is someone pulling my leg?"

As he so often did, Busse wished that he had sharper wits, or none at all. Anyway, the painting was worth a lot of money to someone, and the critics had acclaimed it. Was it not just the thing for a convalescent's wall? Hortense could look at it, or turn away. And with her sound sense and innate delicacy, she would help him make up his mind about it. He would not have to pretend. Instead of hanging it on her sick-room wall, before she returned, he decided to keep it until she was in the proper mood. Then he would bring it in, and enjoy her first reactions. He looked forward to that moment of intimacy, to be shared.

His thoughts were scattered by voices, footsteps and other sounds, like nails scratching on hard wood, just outside his room, in the corridor. Riboulet's voice came to his ears:

"He's in there, if you want to see him."

A rapping sounded harshly on the panel of his door.

"Who is it?" Busse demanded, with asperity.

Before there was an answer the door opened and Busse saw, entering, a terrifying animal, enormous in height, indeterminate in color, with mouth sagging open, rows of white fangs exposed, and a lolling red tongue the size of a rubber mitten.

"Xavier! Be seated," commanded Christophe, who followed after. The Great Dane obeyed, while Busse, hands shielding his face, cringed in a corner.

"Take that beast away. How dare you!" Busse cried, hoarsely. Then his eyes, bulging, penetrated Old Christophe's disguise. "You! You filthy old ogre! Leave this respectable hotel, at once."

"When, as Madame Berthelot's agent, I am in possession of the cash, which is due her. You stripped our establishment, depriving us of the holiday trade. I insist on a settlement, here and now," Christophe said.

"Who are you to insist? I'll settle with Madame, as usual, at the end of the month," Busse said.

Christophe tugged at the leash. The Great Dane rose, ears erect, legs and body taut.

"Dogs are forbidden here! Go!" stammered Busse, trying to keep up a front.

"Xavier! Persuade him!" said Christophe to the dog, as he thumbed toward Busse. The Great Dane moved forward, Busse scrambled and vaulted, somehow got around the beast, and made for the stairs, down which he slid and tumbled, with the Great Dane loping playfully behind him.

Busse was squealing, shrieking and imploring.

"Call him off. Help. Restrain him. *Au secours!*"

The huge dog, who in spite of his size was not much more than a puppy, must have thought it was some kind of game. He kept at Busse's heels but did not nip or trip him. By the time man and dog had reached the lower landing and dashed into the lobby, the frantic manager had aroused the whole hotel and neighborhood. Yelling and protesting,

Busse loped out of the main doorway, turned toward the *place* St. Michel and hot-footed along the sidewalk. The Great Dane, in response to Old Christophe's command, stopped chasing his quarry and waited for his master on the sidewalk, which in front of the Mont Souris was always kept spotlessly clean.

"Relieve yourself, if you wish," said Old Christophe to the dog, when he caught up with him. Xavier, as if he understood every word, and to the delight of all the neighborhood, squatted ludicrously, and deposited a steaming heap in front of the hotel doorstep.

Busse, who had discovered that he was no longer being pursued, stuck his head around the corner from the Café St. Michel.

"For shame! How unspeakably foul!" he groaned.

"*Ta gueule!*" growled Old Christophe. The spectators roared with laughter.

By that time everyone had grasped that the distinguished-looking man with the stylish gray Homburg, the dead ringer for Robert Schuman, was the old tramp who that same morning had almost perished from the itch. Christophe, with ministerial dignity, led the dog down the street and sought the shadow of the rue Xavier Privas.

Ten minutes later, after the monkey-faced bellboy, Emile, had ceremoniously cleaned the sidewalk, Busse himself, with all the importance he could muster, tacked up a lettered sign.

"*La promenade hygiénique des chiens est formellement interdit sur le trottoir devant cet immeuble.*"

(The hygienic promenade of dogs is formally forbidden upon the sidewalk in front of this building.)

10. Friends of the Tree

TREES lend their grace to cities. Cities express the characteristics of their people by means of trees—the hemisphere, the zone, the climate, the fertility, the rise or decline, the solvency, the taste. When I went back to my birthplace, Linden, Massachusetts, after many years' absence, few of the houses were intact, hills had been graded, swamps reclaimed, streets paved and widened, trolley wires dismantled, car tracks abandoned. But an incredible number of trees I had known as a child were in their places, larger and statelier, but familiar.

Paris, without her trees, would be lost. There are a few bare streets. One of the widest and barest is the rue de Rennes, which runs from St. Germain to the Gare Montparnasse. And still, along the eaves of the widest, bleakest building, a modern motion-picture house at sidewalk level topped by four stories of office cubicles, grow highly colored flowers, shrubs and languorously drooping vines, high gardens of Babylon.

There are no trees in the rue de la Huchette. Where could anyone have put them? But wherever you stand in the live little street, you see either the trees in the *place* St. Michel or those of the thin oblong parkway and the shaded garden of St. Julian the Poor beyond the eastern outlet. And intermittently, at higher levels, are window boxes with nasturtiums, geraniums and aromatic herbs.

Among the trees of the *place* St. Michel the giant elm
that shades the *terrasse* of the Café St. Michel and the Café
du Départ asserts its seniority. The ancient square is ringed
with plane trees, young, old and middle-aged. It is true
that since I lived in the rue de la Huchette hundreds of
American soldiers and more hundreds of tourists have vis-
ited the quarter. Infrequently, by day or by night, large
rubberneck buses from travel agencies drive through,
packed with sightseers from various States of the Union.
Some stop at the Rahab, and seem to enjoy it. Others are
shunted down cellar in the Hotel du Caveau and, because
of the vulgar trimmings, fail to feel like Robespierre. That
does not mean that the street is lost and dull. Fifteen hundred of the best, the worst and those somewhere between
the two extremes, live, work and sleep there, create their
own diversions, remember and forget, inhale and exhale,
and at dusk are aware of the bats that zigzag in and out.
When trees are needful to complete their mood, trees can
be found along the quai, with their feet in the river, in the
place, or in the churchyards, three of which are within
hailing distance.

Pierre de Gaulle, brother of "Le Grand Charlie," heads
the municipal administration of Paris and is chief protector
of the trees. He loves them, in the way our Franklin Roosevelt loved them, and takes a deep interest in their care and
distribution. He knows how near Paris came to losing the
best of them, when Hitler ordered their destruction in
1944, and somehow von Cholitz and his Nazis failed to
carry out that planned atrocity.

The mayor of the 6th arrondissement, Joseph Faure, and
Monsieur Napier Dacreux, Mayor of the 5th, the former
responsible for the maintenance of the Luxembourg Gardens and the latter for the Jardin des Plantes, think of the

trees in their wards as if they were on their own estates. The Paris Superintendent of Trees, Monsieur David de Largillière, has a small force of experts, and a subordinate in each of the twenty arrondissements. Like all public services in France, the *arboristes* organization is ludicrously understaffed, but, unlike most of the other public servants they enjoy their work and do not spare themselves.

In the 16th arrondissement during the spring of 1949 a large flock of crows built nests in the tall sycamores along the Right Bank near the Pont de l'Alma. Residents of the fine apartments commanding a view of the Seine (and the Eiffel tower) objected to the cawing, very early in the morning. The trouble-shooters of the tree brigade were summoned, ladders were borrowed from the fire department, the high branches in which the crows had built nests were sawed off. Then the other trees along the river had to be trimmed correspondingly. The crows (all city crows whose ancestors had learned how much easier it is for crows to live in Paris than in the country, where farmers take pot shots at them), moved over to the *place* de l'Ecole Militaire. There the army officers and civilian employees of the War College do not seem to mind them. Crows live royally in Paris, on the leavings from the local outdoor markets.

Certain members of the Paris city council have a dislike of pigeons that amounts almost to a phobia. All through the years of unpreparedness, war, occupation and recovery, public buildings have been neglected, as far as cleaning the exteriors is concerned. Pigeons, alas, have multiplied and become more untidy with each generation. Public monuments, fountains without jets, statues, eaves, pillars, temples, palaces and ministries have acquired a *patin* of pigeon crud that looks like the palette of Painter Caligari under a magnifying glass.

At nearly every meeting in the spring of 1949 a measure was introduced into the City Council providing that pigeons might legally be shot by citizens so minded. On each occasion, bird lovers protested, but the main objections came from the police. Communists and De Gaullists were holding rallies every few days, and whichever side sponsored the meeting, the other would threaten, and often attempt, to break it up. Firearms had not been sold to hunters or amateurs of any kind for ten years. Licenses to carry weapons had been held to the minimum. The police officials shivered whenever they thought of what might happen if shotguns, rifles, revolvers and automatics were sold freely to anyone who said he had an impulse to shoot pigeons, in the interest of civic cleanliness.

Not only the carrion crow and the pigeons, alas, alas, have created problems for the tree men. Canary birds and their cousins, the song sparrows and wild finches, threatened for a while to take over the 7th arrondissement, along the elegant avenues like de Bosquet and de la Bourdonnais. Those avenues are lined on each side with files of plane trees, the tops of which reach the level of the third-story windows. Hundreds, if not thousands, of domestic pet canaries escape each year from dealers and private owners. The pale yellow songsters, being gregarious and not helpless, gather into flocks which congregate along the northwestern border of the Champ de Mars, another magnificent park which spans the area between the Trocadéro and the War College, with the Eiffel Tower in between.

The shrubs and conifers in the military park, and the droppings of the sleek saddle horses exercised by the grooms in the shaded pathways, provide in abundance the food canaries crave. The song birds thrive there, and one of the largest flocks roosts each night in the trees of the avenue de la Bourdonnais.

Last spring, while Paris was being trimmed up for American tourists, the tree men of the 7th arrondissement clipped the twigs and branches of the trees. The canaries, wary because many of them already had known captivity, went into a panic. Apartment dwellers near the tree tops opened their windows and many of them placed decoy tame canaries in cages where they would attract the wild birds.

The birds from the outside, hard pressed by the tree clippers, flew in through the windows by ones, twos and threes, and many of them tried to get into the cages. Hundreds of them were admitted, and many of them perished, because canaries have dispositions not as sweet as their songs, and many of the birds, finding themselves locked in cages with strangers, started a struggle for survival of the fittest. Bird stores soon found themselves stripped of their supply of cages. Kids trapped and sold as many canaries as they could, and dyed a few of the song sparrows yellow. Hundreds of birds were given as presents to folks who wanted them, or could not refuse. The wild flock was reduced in numbers, but is growing again, and now that the trees around the Champ de Mars are tranquil, the canaries, sparrows and finches still on the loose are coming back to their old haunts.

Men living in dense forests must feel about trees the way the American Indians felt about quadrupeds when in the midst of a great herd of bison. But in Paris, each tree or group or company of trees means much to individuals, who become aware of city trees at all seasons, from various angles, under changing conditions of light, from personal perspectives. Experts raise them, tend them, transplant, nurse, fertilize and shape them. Men with vision determine which avenues and boulevards shall have majestic horse chestnuts, which plane trees with cordate leaves, plane trees with maple leaves, buckeyes or sycamores, lacy black walnuts, lindens, locusts, elms. Trees resistant to gasoline fumes are placed where the traffic is thickest; brittle poplars are sheltered from the wind; sturdy oaks support the maximum of exposure. Parisians walk among them, beneath them, beside them, in their shade and out. The majority have not noticed the shapes of the leaves, the bark, the trunks, the gestures, the stems or blossoms, if any, the seeds equipped with gliders. But what cold hands would grip their hearts if, some day, trees were non-existent. All seasons would be stale without them.

And yet, one of the women familiar to the dwellers in the rue de la Huchette, and the man she had chosen from all others, cleaving only to him, and he to her, each Saturday night, thought of the trees with fear and loathing, and scarcely could pass one without a shudder of helplessness and rage.

I have already mentioned Achille Ithier, the clerk in the headquarters of the Anti-Alcoholic society, who had occupied during several years Room No. 8 in the Hotel Normandie. In the same way that coffee trees and certain others must grow in the shade of a sturdier, heat- and tempest-loving tree, the characters of some men bloom and bear fruit thanks to the proximity, or dominance, of a stronger personality.

Ithier's disposition and state of being had been developed as it was because of his dislike and resentment of his employer, the Secretary-Treasurer of the Anti-Alcoholic organization. The latter was exigent, overbearing and knew Ithier's weaknesses so well—all except Achille's devotion to the bottle in secret and alone—that each moment of the working day was made irksome and hideous for Ithier. He made mistakes more often than he got anything right—aberrations of judgment, of tact, social, mathematical and psychological. Not one lapse or inadvertence was overlooked by the Secretary-Treasurer.

Actually Ithier had little work to do, except guard the office while his chief was collecting subscriptions, of which no records were disclosed. He had to endure the persecution of his superior, or wait for the latter to return with a cargo of fresh complaints. That was how Achille spent his time from 8:30 until 6 o'clock, six days a week. Six evenings he drank, methodically and steadily, in the silence of his room, from the bottle he kept concealed in his wardrobe. Six nights from midnight until after dawn, he stared at the walls and ghastly pictures, tossed on his bed, fought the pillow and counted the hours, by quarters, as they sounded on the neighborhood bells. The seventh evening and night was as different as salvation is from hell.

I think Ithier in many ways was the favorite lodger at the Normandie with Louis, the one-armed garçon. Louis knew about the job, the bullying superior, the evening tippling, the white nights and the scarlet night. He knew lots about Ithier that Ithier did not know he had disclosed, because late the evening and at all hours of the night, Louis would drop in for a chat and a drink, knowing how lonely Ithier was, and familiar with the woes of insomnia on his own account. Louis was aware of certain changes that had come about in Ithier's routine of existence, and had not inquired about those which were mysterious to him. If the hour was late, Ithier might be expansive, almost gay, and confide a few secrets without remembering afterward that he had talked so much. As a matter of fact, Ithier was fairly cagy even when talking in a jug nirvana, and never surpassed certain boundaries beyond which his manner indicated there were tales to unfold. His interior life had established zones of contact with exterior eventualities. The stuff that dreams were made of had proved to have tangible applications. He lived, in fact, the way surrealists theorized, by intermingling imagination and objective reality. Had he known that, it would have scared him out of his wits.

Ithier was a plain man, medium size, with dark hair pomade could not keep in order, and a pale skin that hotel diets and lack of sleep had left somewhat blemished. He had a stiff moustache. His eyes were too small and set too close together. His nose was sharp, his mouth a crooked line, his ears stuck out like direction finders. He had furrows in his cheeks and across his forehead. His head was seldom clear, and it never ached very badly. Sometimes the crackle of a newspaper sounded to him like musketry fire. Again, the thunder of a loaded wagon drawn by clattering stallions over cobbles, or the backfire of a truck passed unheard. He made motions as if he were washing his hands, which were never spotlessly clean. The Nazis had him up for questioning several times, and never put him on the list for forced labor because they could not decide what such a chap would be good for. As soon as the Boches were gone, Achille told Louis that he kicked himself daily for not having trumped up charges and denounced his chief at the abstinence society. Achille had not thought of that until it was too late.

This is how Ithier met his Antoinette, and the courses of two lives were diverted.

One gray autumn afternoon, in the year of Liberation, Ithier, hunched miserably on his stool behind the anti-alcoholic counter in the boulevard St. Germain, saw that a woman, less than middle-aged and dressed like a poor relation in a play, was sitting on a public bench on the sidewalk a few yards from his window. Her back was turned, so he could not see her face. Her legs were plump and well turned below the knees. Her hands were gloved. She was motionless, but not asleep, and her posture spelled dejection.

A seasonal sound described so aptly by Verlaine as *"les violons d'automne"* whinnied high in the treetops and a small branch with a cluster of fern-like locust leaves was dislodged, just above where the woman was sitting. It tumbled down, through the half-bare skeleton of the tree, and landed on the woman's head, but very lightly. Ithier, inside his window, got his legs entangled with the stool and fell, so startling was the result. For the woman, uttering a pitiful cry, clawed at the twigs and leaves, writhed and cringed until her body and limbs seemed serpentine, and once she got clear was too weak and faint to stand up or even sit erect. When Ithier reached her side, she was limp and sobbing, eyes distended.

Her name was Antoinette de Poitevin, and her aged father was the founder and president of *La Société des Amis de l'Arbre*, that is, the Society of the Friends of the Tree. Her symptoms of fright, when the branch and leaves descended on her head, were due to a recurring nightmare she had had since she could remember. She often dreamed she was alone in a deserted crumbling park, with only ruins, undergrowth and trees of a departed civilization. A whining would stir aloft, a wind would rise to a gale, and the branches of all the trees would thrash and flail, while from the trunks and hollows came gibbering noises. Antoinette would find herself trapped under a dwarf Japanese tree, with gnarled bare branches like the dried tentacles of an octopus. They would drum around her, clutch and pinch her flesh, jab at her eyes and mouth, and close tighter, until she awakened in a cold sweat, entangled in bedclothes and partially exposed.

Of all the remaining de Poitevins, old André, president of the Friends of the Tree, was the only one who still had quite a lot of money, a fortune which had come to him through a long line of de Poitevins so stingy that in spite of wars, depressions and inflations, they had held their own. The bulk of the de Poitevin assets had been deposited for decades in Switzerland.

Old André de Poitevin was so miserly and suspicious that he could trust no servants, and had arranged it so that Antoinette, his daughter, waited on him hand and foot. When she was thoroughly submissive and got him into a good humor, he would tell her that the family fortune would be hers. At times when she showed the slightest reluctance to do his will, he talked about leaving his money in trust for the care of the trees. She had no training, no profession, and the old man had seen to it that no suitor had come near her. That was her condition when she found herself being comforted by Achille Ithier that October afternoon.

Ithier, as deeply moved as she had been, somehow steered her to the Hotel Normandie, upstairs, and into his room. Not long after, the walls being paper thin, other lodgers were regaled with the sound of ecstatic groans, coyote cries and strangled yelps, sighs, soughs, ahs and ah nons and ah ouis, which could not have been outdone by Potiphar's wife, if the prudish young Joseph had lived up to her hopes and expectations. When Louis, for instance, had seen the pair depart, and had realized that the executant of those rhapsodic outbursts was a drab little woman who dressed like a mole and looked like respectability itself, he could hardly credit his eyes. And the possessive self-satisfied way in which Ithier propelled her by the elbow caused Louis to chuckle and cut a brisk caper.

On Easter Saturday noon, while Louis was making up Room No. 9, which had been reserved for a trio of the pious Mexicans who were flying from Rome to Paris with St. Felix in the plane, he was surprised to hear through the wall the voices of Antoinette and Ithier in No. 8.

Antoinette was frantic. "He's made up his mind. He wrote to his lawyer this morning," she said.

"He hasn't made the will?" Ithier asked, alarmed.

"Achille, we've got to stop him, somehow," said Antoinette.

"When will the lawyer come?"

"Tomorrow afternoon," she said.

"Give him a powder tonight. First put the old skinflint to sleep. We'll think of something afterward," said Ithier.

Louis, listening, was puzzled, and frowned, but as he was renowned for minding his own business, let the scraps of conversation he had overheard drift well back in his mind, before he joined us at the Café St. Michel.

We sat looking out across the *place*. The shadow of the spreading European elm fell across the *place*. Its trunk was a shade darker than the pavement; the earth around it had been recently spaded so the branches and new leaves might breathe. Over the sea-food counter spread a young plane tree, a post-Liberation plane tree no higher than the top of the café awning. Shading the *terrasse* of the Café du Départ, with forty customers and three cats, was a larger plane tree dating from the Paris Exposition of 1900.

The dark unglistening fountain with huge shell back, St. Michael, Satan and the sporting dolphins was dry. In front of the famous restaurant of Rouzier, Frères, "La Périgordine," was a straight rank of medium plane trees along the edge of the sidewalk, each with squat shadows beneath them. At the moment when it seemed improbable that leaves could be greener, someone let down two flaming orange window curtains which long had been furled, and the color current flashed between awnings and foliage, positive and negative, direct and alternating, causing volts and amperes to sizzle and recoil.

On the corner across St. Michael's bridge the tricolor flew, dating from the first Bastille Day. The queen of Gothic cathedrals, Notre Dame de Paris, hovered just upstream.

The Big Three and the Big Four, the administrators of the E.C.A., the E.R.P. and the U.N.E.S.C.O., the proponents and adversaries of the Atlantic Pact, had laid off for the week-end. Because of the hot sun overhead, three cases of sunstroke already had been rushed into the enormous gray Hotel Dieu. The pliant shadows, temptresses, were enveloping their objects, their skirts around the base, instead of streaming east or west to political poles.

Celestial impartiality. Terrestrial appetites. Was it Chablis, Pouilly or Riquewihr with the oysters, and were the oysters Marennes or Belons? I chose the spicy scimitar shrimps called Grands Bouquets, who had snapped their last at daybreak, and felt their first warmth in the pot.

Later, lunch with Monsieur Aran, Monsieur Nathaniel, the other Armenians and many of our company, munching cool stuffed grape leaves, hot turkey-liver shish with Beaujolais, sulphur-toasted peppers and tomatoes, more or less Provençal, and some cheese that must have required the co-operation of the fiends Panzouzou, Lambartou and the she-devil Lilit to develop that libidinous flavor.

Dry Anis. Turkish coffee. And ensuing, the Easter Saturday siesta, with little conscious thought, alas, of Him who slept the Three-Day sleep, or those living for the Left or the Right, or salvation, final combat (winken), liberty, equality, fraternity (blinken), or franctuation fluct (and nod).

11. Of Conformity

IN APPEARANCE and manner, there are in Paris today two contrasting types who have developed since Liberation and the second coming of the Americans. The Frenchman of affairs who has been to New York uses American expressions or Americanized French when he thinks he knows what the words mean, dresses in clothes of American cut, of materials tinged with violet, russet, pale green or cerulean, drives full-length American cars with twenty-gallon gas tanks. Such a transformed Frenchman has become known as an "Atlantique." The Atlantique drinks cocktails instead of light aperitifs, smokes what the French call "perfumed" cigarettes, that is to say, the standard American brands, and he is 100 percent in favor of the Marshall Plan or any other handout or guarantee from the Etats Unis.

On the other hand, the "Continental" uses old-fashioned, schoolroom French, writes business letters with all the elaborate salutations and complicated accent marks, wears mourning bands on his arm, smokes a combination of dried leaves and splinters the French Government puts out in the name of tobacco, affects high-waisted trousers and knee-length shirttails, detachable collars and cuffs and dingy neckties. His form-fitting suits are Navy blue, dull brown or conventional black; his hats are of dark felt, with derbies on Sunday. He has never been to America. He does not want to go there. The Old World, in his mind, has no need of influence from over the Western sea or lands where savages roamed in the days when François I ruled France.

Consider French advertising.

I had just crossed the *place* Danton and was making my way toward the St. Michel quarter, via the Café Cluny, when the kind of small shabby man one does not like to bruise or disappoint sidled over and dealt me a handbill, by force of habit from the bottom of a sheaf. Glancing down at it, when he had gone his way, I saw on the paper a line-cut of one of Cézanne's late portraits of himself, after the great French master had grown bald. It seemed odd to me that a furtive little man should be distributing Cézanne reproductions gratis, and then I noticed the text that was printed below the sketch.

"DON'T LET THIS HAPPEN TO YOU"

On the reverse side of the handbill was a blurb about a certain brand of hair tonic.

The French have ideas about advertising, many of them subtle and effective, but none on the grandiose scale now prevalent in the U.S.A. In other fields, the influence of America is creeping into Parisian life, but the bulk of French advertising still holds the Continental tone. Some of it is old-fashioned and ludicrous, and clashes with modern times. For instance, there is a tearoom in the boulevard St. Germain, well north of the Existentialist belt, where chocolate is the specialty. A tall narrow billboard is nailed to the second-story wall, and on it is painted, against a leaden background, the lifesize figure of a fop of the 1890's, steaming cup and saucer in his hand, little finger daintily crooked, hair plastered flat with grease, severely winged and parted, an eloquent slim moustache, gay cravat, spats and high-buttoned patent-leather shoes. The text, in script, reads:

"DECHAUDAT! AH, SON CHOCOLAT!"

Dechaudat is the name of the original proprietor, who died about the time the American Civil War was getting started. It rhymes with the French word for chocolate, pronounced "shock-o-la."

Unfortunately, American sailors on leave in Paris in the years immediately following Liberation were misled by Dechaudat's poster, and thought he was running a sissy's café. In fact, bevies of seamen, at different times, went in to break up what they thought they would find there, and nearly wrecked the place. The incidents did little to foster international amity or understanding.

Old-style autobuses which run along the boulevard St. Germain and the boulevard St. Michel have painted signs which run the length of the vehicle, at the level of the roof, reading:

"VISITEZ LE CAFÉ MONDIAL"

No address is given. In the latest telephone directory about fifteen Cafés Mondial are listed, and none of them is along any of the routes of the buses in question.

On holidays, the police are indulgent and do not inquire too closely into the status of those who set up booths along the sidewalks. A buxom young woman dressed like Marie Antoinette gave me a tiny phial wrapped in printed paper. The scent was very pleasant, and as soon as I got into sitting position, as I do whenever I can, I read the following, and was practically overwhelmed. Here is a restrained translation:

OILS FOR THE BATH
"Secret of Diana"

(The perfumes listed included: Chinchilla, Zibeline
[sable], Antelope, Bambou, Cassandra, and Padisha.)

I think the poet employed by the cosmetic concern had
never smelled a sable or an antelope, but the effect was there.

"Inspired by the traditional customs of antiquity,
bath oils, Secret of Diana, are the modern interpreta-
tions of the perfumed ablutions of the Greeks and
the Romans."

I am equally convinced that the bard has not recently
smelled any Greeks or Romans, in their native habitats.

"Created to reinforce the effect of each extract with
which it is mixed, bath oil develops by means of
bodily warmth an ample effluvium the powerful
symphony of which accompanies mutedly the most
resounding notes of the perfume."

The next heading was "COUNSELS CONCERNING EMPLOY-
MENT."

"In the bath: A few drops judiciously dispersed in
the bath water.
    "After the shower or the toilet: Pour out a few
drops in the palm of your hand and, while your skin
is still damp, rub the oil lightly over your body. Then
spray yourself with your favorite perfume, which
will exalt harmoniously the fragrance with which
the 'Secret of Diana' has discreetly impregnated
you."

Now that the tourist trade has become vital to France's
economy, according to the theories on which the Middle-
of-the-Road coalition is proceeding, a wealth of culture and

entertainment is placed at the visitor's disposal. Officials appointed especially for the purpose arrange each year a series of exhibitions and fairs, gastronomical, scientific, sportive, decorative, artistic, historical and practical. One of the most attractive areas set aside for small outdoor fairs is the beautiful stretch along the Right Bank between the bridge of Alexandre III, with its golden steeds on pedestals, to the Pont de l'Alma, where the famous stone Zouave acts as a water gauge and river traffic proceeds safely until the flood hits the level of his knees. The broad avenue and quai, rich with shade trees and fringed with house boats and river craft for dancing and refreshment, is known as the Cours Albert Ier.

In the spring of 1949 the season opened with a fair for the benefit of ex-prisoners of war, organized by the prisoners themselves. The feature of that show, for me, was the exhibition of modern tapestries from Aubusson, but there were also impressive food specialties from all regions of France. The advertisement that hit me hardest was displayed in the booth filled with delicacies from the maritime province of Finisterre. The prize offering was shellfish, my favorite food, summed up so poignantly by Zola as "liquid fire."

There were two posters, a yard wide and two yards high, revealing, respectively, the innards of an oyster and a mussel, each magnified about one hundred diameters. The diagrams were sketched and tinted vividly, in the minutest detail.

All my life I have been fond of oysters, and more so of mussels, which are so hard to buy in the United States because of the libelous propaganda fish dealers have spread there to discourage the consumption of any sea foods that can be sold cheaply. From earliest childhood I have been reconciled to the idea of eating bivalves alive. I am not squeamish about any good food. Rattlesnake meat à la King I have cooked, myself, and found delicious. I have consumed mountain oysters and prairie dancers that are actually poetic. I relish squid cooked in its blackest ink. Eels stewed or fried, or squirrels in Brunswick pie are to my taste. Nevertheless I got a rude jolt at the Prisoner's Fair when I examined those advertising posters for oysters and mussels. Each organ and part was labeled and numbered.

The mouth of an oyster, so it seems, is near the small hinged end of the shell; just below it, if the oyster is held vertically, small end up, is the stomach. Then come the liver, the intestine, the anus and a pair of small protuberances which may, in the course of a couple of million years, develop into legs like those of a tadpole. The inner organs are enclosed in a cloak, or skin. What sticks out and squirts jets through the parted shells of a clam is delicately called "the siphon."

Europeans were not deterred by those posters from sampling eagerly the oysters, clams, palourdes, cockles, mussels, snails, razor-fish or sea-urchins at the booth in question, but I must confess that I, and other Americans, got out of there in a hurry and contented ourselves with hard-boiled eggs at the Alsatian bar.

An advertisement involving a valuable painting stirred up a scandal at the Foire de Paris. A firm that manufactures and distributes a popular bottled appetizer, within the legally prescribed limit for alcoholic content, featured an oil painting of "Bacchus" in front of its booth in the largest of the food fairs. A few days after the opening, a man employed as footman by a prominent French family attended on his day off. Pausing at the appetizer booth he was haunted by the feeling that the "Bacchus" at which he was gazing was strangely familiar. It was. Before the canvas had been stolen from his employer, Madame Elaine Brault-Sabourdin, grand-daughter of the founder of the first newspaper published in France, the footman had seen the painting time and time again.

He reported his misgivings to an *agent de police* who passed the word along to the local *commissaire*. The latter was puzzled, because of the excellent standing of the appetizer manufacturer, who certainly could have bought and paid for any paintings he needed or wanted. So at first the investigation proceeded in secret, without publicity.

An expert was called in from the Louvre Museum, and he declared, after examining the canvas carefully, that the drink merchant's "Bacchus" had been painted by Rubens, who would have brained any varlet who had offered him a sweetened beverage less potent than rich Flemish beer. Not all of the painting was done by Rubens, the expert said. A loin cloth had been painted over what made young Bacchus so masculine by someone in the art department of the bottling concern, to appease the family trade.

The manufacturer had not stolen the art classic. He had bought it, minus the loin cloth, from a Left Bank antiquarian for 35,000 francs, which then was a little more than one hundred dollars. The antique dealer was innocent, too, but very stupid. He had picked up the Rubens masterpiece, without recognizing it, at the Scrap Iron Fair for 3,500 francs, about eleven dollars. What the painting is worth today in cash will not be ascertained, because Madame Brault-Sabourdin, its rightful owner, will not consider selling it, but a conservative figure would be 7,000,000 francs, about $20,000 at the present rate of exchange.

Although the age-group between twenty and thirty are scornful of historical precedents and French tradition, the past and its relics are always present in French daily life. There are still Royalists, mostly over sixty years of age, who comfort one another and interpret the blunders of republican politicians as hopeful signs of the return of the Bourbons. Bonapartists are rarer than the King's men, and get less comfort from the high clergy, but there are a few of them left. One of the most conspicuous supporters of the Empire lives at No. 20 rue de la Huchette, in the attic above Julian's barber shop, occupying the same room Napoleon used, incognito, at a time when he was in hiding. "Stemwinder," as Monsieur Temeraire is called, because of his huge old-fashioned gold watch, is about fifty years old, but he looks much older. His legs are long, his arms and body relatively short, and he has a neat *embonpoint*, much like Napoleon's. He has a small income which enables him to dress in the mufti of Napoleon's epoch, to drink himself into a dreamy alcoholic haze every day, and pace the bridge or the quai St. Michel as if he were on St. Helena, or was surveying the field of Austerlitz or Waterloo.

A young feature writer for *Le Populaire*, Léon Blum's Socialist newspaper, wandered into the *place* St. Michel one day, saw the brooding figure on the bridge, looking like Napoleon on stilts, engaged Stemwinder in conversation and the Bonapartist permitted the journalist to buy several drinks. Next day there was a third of a column in *Le Populaire* in which Temeraire was described as a *"déhydraté."* That means, in French, one who is dehydrated, in other words, an alcoholic who has burned himself out until he is as dry as a salt mackerel. Stemwinder did not mind the jibes about his old-fashioned clothes, his adherence to a lost cause, or the reference to Napoleon as a dictator. What he resented was the insinuation that he was a chronic rumhound. He prided himself, and with reason, on drinking like a gentleman of the early nineteenth-century school, when weaklings who could swallow no more had their sleeves nailed to the wall and the liquor poured in. So he consulted the Satyr and Monsieur Nathaniel, the handsome tall Armenian, both of whom inadvertently agreed to act as his seconds, strode to the office of *Le Populaire*, found Monsieur Essling, the young reporter, tweaked the latter's nose, and challenged him to a duel.

Essling, who had had a few fencing lessons, accepted the challenge and chose sabers as weapons. The reporter selected two rather fresh young men as seconds and after they had called on the Satyr and Monsieur Nathaniel, the folks along the rue de la Huchette began to worry. They liked Stemwinder, who had never done anybody the least harm. His friends did not want any fresh young scribbler to whack off his head with a saber.

Stemwinder, once the duel had been arranged and announced in the press, drank more debonairly and freely than usual, all up and down the street. He declared that he was second to none with the saber.

The day before the duel, beginning about noon, Stemwinder began to get indignant and angry. He paced up and down, tossing off tumblers of wine the while, and muttering "*Déhydraté*, indeed. I'll dehydrate the young whippersnapper. I'll cut off all his buttons." Once in a while in a café he would seize a broomstick or a feather duster, assume a fencing position and make passes this way and that. Toward evening, in so doing, he lost his balance, fell over, and was carried up to bed.

However, he was up well before dawn, and nothing anyone could say would deter him. He rode in a taxi to the edge of the woods near Longchamps, with the Satyr and Monsieur Nathaniel beside him. Both were murmuring prayers, but the principal began growling and muttering again. The reporter showed up, with his seconds, laughing and joking. A surgeon was on hand. Also about a dozen reporters, all set for a Roman holiday, and a group of anxious men from the rue de la Huchette.

The principals took off their coats, rolled up their sleeves; the seconds selected the weapons, which looked dangerous enough. When the bout began, the young journalist took the offensive, with the utmost confidence, but soon the spectators were astonished to see that Stemwinder, old and out of condition, was parrying with ease all thrusts and sideswipes, while growling softly and narrowing his eyes. Essling caught on, in a very few seconds, and began to shiver and sweat. He lunged, prodded and swatted frantically, until his wind was impaired, and then Stemwinder began swishing his blade within a millimeter of the reporter's ears, nose and throat.

The young man's seconds tried to stop the fight, and were overpowered by the Satyr and Nathaniel, who now viewed the combat in an entirely new light. The Bonapartist, before he got too tired, gave a twist and a flip which sent his opponent's saber flying into a near-by tree top, turned his back, rolled down his sleeves, and put on his coat, with aplomb and dignity.

Now no one in the neighborhood speaks disparagingly in Stemwinder's presence of Bonaparte or John Barleycorn.

Another duel that took place in the course of the 1949 season was fought between a motion-picture director named Jacobi and a critic named Madaule. The *casus belli* in that instance was a screen actress who uses the professional name, Lorraine Ledoux.

Madaule, the critic, in commenting on Mlle Ledoux's performance in a film called *Voici*, wrote that the young star's future was her *"derrière,"* that is to say, behind her. How can I make clear the play on words? The critic was calling attention to the charms conspicuous in profile shots and facing contrary-wise. The director, Jacobi, took exception to the article and slapped the critic, who challenged. Jacobi chose foils, without the safety tips.

The critic had never had a sword in his hand. The director, while he had been an extra, had had about ten easy lessons in order to take part in a mob scene where swords were clashing right and left. The seconds had a lot of trouble with that duel, because Madaule, without knowing it was not good fencing cricket, kept touching the tip of his foil to the ground as if it were a walking stick. Each time he did that, the bout had to be stopped while the tip of Madaule's weapon was sterilized informally with a sulphur match. Finally, the director succeeded in pinking the critic's arm. Honor was satisfied, but the combatants refused to become reconciled.

Of course, as a result Lorraine Ledoux's *derrière* became as familiar to the Parisian public as Sonja Henie's to the wide, wide world.

The most important duel of 1949 was not held in the Bois, as the other two were, and did not involve newspaper writers. The principals were Roger Nordmann, a teacher in a Paris high school (*lycée*) and Maître Jean-Louis Tixier-Vignancour, a prominent member of the bar.

The quarrel began in open court, at the Palais de Justice. Maître Tixier-Vignancour was defending a former Vichy official charged with criminal collaboration. While he was summing up his client's case, the schoolteacher, Monsieur Nordmann, yelled from the front row of spectators:

"You, Tixier-Vignancour ought to know a lot about collaboration!"

Maître Tixier-Vignancour interrupted his plea, confronted his heckler and challenged Nordmann to a duel. Nordmann accepted, and the two men were showering each other with recriminations and abuse when the judge rapped for order, and directed the court officers to quiet the room so that the trial could proceed. Just then it looked as if the duel would take place at dawn the next day.

French law authorizes the police to interfere in a duel if it appears that someone may be injured in the fight, but there is no penalty for the duellists. The judge whose courtroom had been thrown into disorder by the quarrel made an unusual ruling, which no doubt will stand as a precedent. His Honor forbade Maître Tixier-Vignancour fighting any duel, or duels, until the trial was over.

"The ethics of the Paris bar do not permit an attorney to risk his life unnecessarily and willfully while a case is in progress, and thus take a chance of leaving his client defenseless or putting the State to the expense of a new trial," the judge ruled.

As soon as the trial was over—Maître Tixier-Vignancour's ex-Vichy client was found not guilty, as so many well-born and non-Communist members of the Pétain party are in these days—the Paris police, leg men and cameramen from the Paris newspapers began tailing Nordmann and Tixier-Vignancour day and night. The Prefect of Police, in accord with Pierre de Gaulle, had announced that the duel would be prevented.

On the night before the fight, both principals and all the seconds except one of Nordmann's, a Monsieur Pierre Stibbe, a lawyer, slept away from home. The press and police sleuths followed Stibbe, when he rose and started at 7 A.M. in an automobile that wound up within the gates of a country estate at St. Cloud. There the Paris policemen,

who had insisted they would stop the combat, acknowledged that they were outside their zone of authority. Before
the St. Cloud police could be summoned and brought to the
scene of action, the duel was over.

The fight, in that instance, was in earnest. Both contest-
ants were swordsmen, and had a hearty hatred for each
other. In the second round, the lawyer, Tixier-Vignancour,
inflicted a cut an inch deep in the schoolteacher's sword
arm. Blood was drawn, and honor satisfied. But the parties
refused to be reconciled. Careful hostesses will not invite
them to the same parties for quite some time.

Two Americans, both well-known to their countrymen,
nearly got into a duel in the early fall. Art Buchwald of the
Paris *Herald Tribune* saw Ingrid Bergman in the Hollywood
production of *Joan of Arc*. The opening night in Paris was
an international debauch of amity and praise. The new
Archbishop of Paris had been persuaded to appoint a high
church official to attend and publish comment for the faithful. The French Government (then it was Queuille at the
helm) sent top-flight civil dignitaries. Dozens of visiting
American stars trod the red carpet from limousine to theatre
entrance. Everybody was much happier about the whole
thing than Art Buchwald, who, for my money, is a sound
critic.

Anyway, in Art's column in the *Herald* next day, when all
the other papers were outdoing themselves with the hands-
across-the-sea congratulations, Buchwald took the film
apart, historically, artistically, and in other ways. He even
went so far as to suggest that Bergman acted no differently
as the Maid of Orléans than when she was the "little rabbit"
in *For Whom the Bell Tolls* and the lady psychoanalyst
in another expensive picture. He intimated that the more
literate of the French in the audience suffered intensely as

reel after reel did violence to legend, truth, humanity and sense.

Walter Wanger, the producer, was in Paris and published a statement to the effect that Buchwald was prejudiced and incompetent, and hated the movies on principle. Buchwald, having in mind the film director who recently had defended his sweetheart's rear profile, at the risk of life and limb, decided that a man's prose was worth fighting for. He challenged Wanger to a duel, which would have been an all-American affair. Wanger refused to fight, on the ground that Buchwald's challenge was a mere publicity stunt. Buchwald came back with a quip to the effect that Wanger never before had spoken slightingly of publicity. There the matter rests today.

It is significant that in each of the three duels that caught the public's attention, the challenger was a middle-aged man of established pre-war background and his opponent was a young man whose outlook had been shaped by Munich, war and occupation. The struggle, even in the case involving a lady's *derrière*, was between an old conception and a new one. In each instance, the middle-aged man won the decision and his youthful opponent refused to shake his hand.

Nothing is more noticeable in Paris than the flowering by day and by night of the 6th arrondissement, on the Left Bank, which used to be out of bounds for Americans without Bohemian instincts and was invaded semi-occasionally by respectable sightseers who believed they were slumming. It is true that in the days of Hemingway's *Sun Also Rises* painters, models, steady drinkers and hangers-on maintained their world headquarters near the crossroads of the boulevard Raspail and the boulevard Montparnasse. That fantastic cosmopolitan region for the lunatic fringe and the artists who had been driven from Montmartre by playboys, rich widows and increasing rents was not, in the era of the Lost Generation and the notorious expatriates, an integral part of the 6th arrondissement, although the Café Select and the Rotonde, the Hotel Vavin and Notre Dame des Champs, were on the extreme edge of the 6th. The Dome, the Coupole, the Dingo were across the boulevard in the 14th arrondissement, and the sun that caught so many revelers, American and otherwise, still in their cups, rose behind them. In those carefree years before Hitler, when the dog-faced Duce was only a joke in bad taste, the boulevardiers stuck to the Grands Boulevards, and Americans with money to throw around went to Montmartre, and were rooked to a frazzle. On Sunday evenings, the higher-middle-class French who wanted to see how the other half lived, had dinner in Montparnasse and sat on the Coupole *terrasse* until midnight, watching the fantoches, alcoholics and mountebanks. Mid-Western schoolteachers from the United States ventured into that district, in the hope of seeing James Joyce and Gertrude Stein, who had never met, and neither of whom was ever on display. Joyce lived in the rue de Grenelle, in the 15th, and dined at the Trois Trianon near the Gare Montparnasse. Gertrude's famous apartment was in the rue de Fleurus, and she liked to dine at home.

When the Montparnasse district was going full blast, there was no emphasis on music. The Coupole had an orchestra tucked somewhere behind the railing of a balcony, for tea dancing and the insipid stuff known as "standard" music during the dinner hours, and more dancing later. Few customers listened and fewer danced. The drunks were unable, and the tourists were too fascinated watching the drunks. The civilized French, who know about food, have always been against music with meals. The street music around the Dome, the Select, the Rotonde and the Coupole was strictly for panhandling—stray accordion players, atrocious old fiddlers, and half-crazed women with cracked voices and maudlin lyrics.

Today the show place, the rendezvous of eccentrics, Bohemians, playboys, sightseers and international whacks is the St. Germain des Prés quarter, centering around the Café de Flore, and spreading along the formerly staid old avenue to the boundaries of the Latin Quarter on one side and the great gray buildings which house the principal functions of the national government on the other. In cellars and ground-floor fronts and courtyards are innumerable small bars and night clubs. Everywhere American jazz music is the spice of the sound effects. There are so many lively places that each celebrity or group of café-society addicts has a favorite, a second and third choice, and a number of fairly safe hide-outs. The night life has gone underground, although the sidewalk cafés are also crowded—The Flore, Lipp's brasserie for beer drinkers, the Deux Magots which seems to be in temporary decline, and the new Royale, which teems with French who have contrived to prosper under war and recovery and spend more freely than Frenchmen ever did before.

The Mayor of the 6th, Monsieur Faure, has an intelligent interest in cultural activities, especially painting, is a sound gourmet, and is in sympathy with the coalition government's policy of encouraging tourism, especially from the United States.

Each arrondissement of Paris has a Mairie, or district Hall. The Mairie of the 6th, in the *place* St. Sulpice, is a fine old building and in the main lobby is a statue, not of a soldier, politician or churchman, but of the great middle-class painter, Chardin, who lived and worked near by.

The 6th arrondissement has always contained the most tranquil, quiet and soothing little corners of the Left Bank, and now those are interspersed with others, modern, advanced and eventful. One can pass from revelry and brou-ha-ha to seclusion and privacy by taking a three-minute walk. One can rub shoulders with fringe-whiskered Existentialists who babble the latest double talk and provincial nursewomen from the country who have not got used to wearing leather shoes.

On the northern edge, across the Seine, stands the immense palace of the Bourbons, the Louvre, the church of St. Germain l'Auxerrois, the rue de l'Arbre Sec in which stood the first guillotine. Then, at the Pont Neuf, the Seine extends two arms to envelop the Ile de la Cité.

Nearly all quarters in the 6th arrondissement have been respectable, a few dominated by the old aristocracy, the majority middle class. The small corner north and west of the boulevards St. Germain and St. Michel, between the Abbey and the river, is the exception. In an area not larger than one square kilometer vice, art, squalor, vigor, crime, the poor, the rich, all races, remnants of two dozen nationalities and river transients mingle. Those who have money live on the quai, with a view of the Seine. The Dome of the Institut stands guard by the iron footbridge. Near by is Lapérouse, one of the world's most famous restaurants, the Ecole des Beaux Arts that rules the domain of orthodox painting and sculpture, a number of the lowest dives that have survived the reform of 1945, the Buci market which is the choicest of the local sub-centers of food. On the site of the old stables of the Abbey St. Germain is the quaint *place* Furstemberg, where the studio of Delacroix is still intact. Not two hundred yards away stood Molière's first theatre. The smaller and less expensive art galleries are ranged along the rue de

Seine and the rue Bonaparte. Streets are crooked and narrow, traffic rushes through at breakneck speed with a maximum of din. Buildings are old, and from damp cellars to leaking attics are fantastically overcrowded. The millions who have gaped at Mona Lisa, in the Louvre just across the Seine, have had no idea that such a quarter existed, and had they known they would have been scared.

In contrast, the streets bordering the Luxembourg Gardens comprise one of the finest residential districts in Paris, or elsewhere. What it lacks in modern comfort, i.e., plumbing and elevators, is made up in distinction. The gardens around the old Luxembourg palace, which houses the Senate, are superb, with flower beds which feature the late-blooming autumn flowers and trees, pathways and vistas immortalized by Watteau. Old experts play croquet, night workers from factories play cards, parents and nurses bring countless children to play, there is a children's marionette theatre, and the foremost bee-culture school in the world.

The 6th arrondissement has a branch of the Bank of France; the enormous Municipal Pawn Shop known as the Mont de Piété; the Gare Montparnasse; the Diocesaine des Etrangers, the church of St. Germain des Prés, St. Joseph des Carmes, the chapel of the Lazaristes, Notre Dame des Anges, Notre Dames des Champs, Saint Sulpice and the Protestant Temple of Luxembourg.

The headquarters of the French Geographic Society was raided the other evening and a lecturer who advocated free love and promiscuity for students and the youth of both sexes was taken to the local commissariat, but no charges were preferred. He was a respectable married man, he said, and was trying to raise money to cover the expenses of his young wife's third confinement.

A columnist lately gave the opinion that the Anti-Alcoholic Society, just off the *place* St. Germain, has tackled the toughest job in the world, now that the "Zazous" (Existentialists) and North American tosspots have invaded the quarter.

And still, the long hairy arm of world politics has reached into the St. Germain quarter, and influenced the character of international revelry and carousing there, so that it bears little resemblance to the heyday of Montparnasse, in the 1920's and early 1930's.

The French approach to American jazz was from above. That is to say, a few critics whose opinions on art and music were generally respected, were the first to grasp the merits and allure of "*le hot.*" The discerning amateurs caught on, with the result that the French who like or understand jazz at all, have sound feelings about it, select the wheat from the chaff, and spread the gospel to those who are receptive.

The Communists, who in America and all the French colonies are making such a drive to enlist the Negroes in their cause, went all out for jazz, at first, encouraged their industrial rank and file to Lindy-hop and jitterbug, and smiled and applauded in the St. Germain night clubs whenever mixed black and white couples went to town. Then came Zhdanov's pronunciamento in Russia condemning jazz as degenerate and unfit for proletarian amusement. The leaders of the French Communists had to change their tune quickly, and the haunts of the St. Germain "Zazous" were ruled "out of bounds" for earnest French comrades.

I attended the jazz festival at the Salle Pleyel last spring. It lasted a week, with a matinee on Saturday, and was crowded from front-row orchestra to the last row in the balcony. Communists were as scarce as Trotskyists, Titoists and Anarchists at the World Congress of the Partisans of Peace. When the Existentialists took over the St. Germain quarter, and attracted the students and tourists, the Communists began strong-arm tactics to discourage the timid from seeing things at night. In Montparnasse, there used to be little violence. In fact, the area was exceptionally peaceful and safe. Today the small night spots and side streets around St. Germain are somewhat risky. Narcotic addicts and marihuana smokers are infiltrating the cafés. Sailors and soldiers of various nations are involved in brawls with increasing frequency. Homosexuals are often led on, then brutally attacked. The Existentialists allege that the Communists send goon squads to the district, as a part of their anti-American, anti-tourist campaign. Two murders have been committed within two days, and in both cases the victim started out to have a good time in the St. Germain quarter. A young screen actress who had embraced Existentialism, and a fair quota of its prophets, was lured into an automobile, driven to the bank of a canal, strangled, stripped, mutilated and her body thrown into the water with rocks attached. An Englishman who was well to do and had a good job in Paris was followed from a St. Germain night club, and his body was found in his automobile some distance away. Two French sailors and a French soldier were arrested two days later, and confessed. They said the Englishman had made improper advances to one of them, whereupon they put a sack over his head, beat him with their fists, took his money, amounting to 4,500 francs, which they divided equally, stripped off his valuable rings, and returned to duty without being aware that he was dead. They will get off lightly, and no British cruisers will steam up the Seine.

In Montparnasse there used to be plenty of heavy drinking, but not much dope and very little bloodshed. Politics did not exist there, until refugees from Central Europe began to congregate in the middle thirties.

The marihuana fad has produced a few interesting sidelights. The customs officials reported to the police that a pet store on the Quai des Gesvres was receiving extra large shipments of packaged bird seed from North and South America. An investigation revealed that employees of the shop were sorting out the seeds of *cannabis mexicana* and growing the weed in household gardens, for sale.

American students who were in Paris under the G.I. Bill of Rights used to do a land-office business in contraband cigarettes and could buy gasoline in quantities which could be resold, illegally, to the French. Now that the Black Market is dwindling, the boys and girls have hard sledding. There is scarcely a small cheap hotel in the 6th arrondissement that does not lodge a few American service men and women.

The St. Germain quarter is dotted with night spots, including the Club St. Germain, Tabu, the Vieux Colombier, Chez Inez, the Reine Blanche, the Montana Bar and the Civet. For many years, while the French were learning about jazz, no Frenchman except possibly Django Reinhardt, the guitar picker, could play it. Today at the Vieux Colombier the band is led by Claude Luter who plays such hot Dixieland that he cut loose at the Festival with Sidney Bechet and improvised a second clarinet part to one of the Old Master's solos that brought the house to its feet. Even Bechet was surprised and delighted. Pierre Braslavsky could sit in anywhere old-school jazzmen are jamming. The French are not yet playing Be-Bop, but they love it, and after Sidney Bechet, Charlie Parker ran second at the festival with several lengths to spare. French taste in Boogie Woogie inclines more to the light Count Basie riffs than the solid bass and spontaneous inventions of the late Albert Ammons. The slow records of Meade Lux Lewis are in every first-class French collection of discs.

Gone from the boulevard St. Germain is Riess, with his square-cut venerable beard. He was the hair stylist who used to take care of Ernest Hemingway and the late E. Berry Wall. Steinbeck patronizes Riess's successors, René and Marcel.

The "Zazous" quarter surpasses even Oberammergau, as far as beards are concerned. The students wear face decorations in every style, the fringed-gentian, the orang-utan's delight, the Abe Lincoln style, the Reuben Haskins chin whisker, lilacs, spinach, spades, Prince Alberts, les frères Smith, and Rasputins. The hearties have stiff whiskers, and some of the Central and South American boys sport silken Van Dykes.

No district of Paris, before the crusade of 1945 closed the licensed houses of prostitution, had more bordellos than the northwest corner of the 6th arrondissement. In an area no larger than the Yankee Stadium at least forty bordels flourished. On the other hand, streetwalkers were relatively rare. The establishments of joy were not patronized much by tourists. Guides steered the wealthy Americans to more expensive places on the Right Bank. The bordels of the 6th were for middle-class and proletarian French, and foreigners with what is known as "feeble economy." There were a couple of what the madams liked to call "respectable" houses in the rue St. Benoit, two in the passage du Petit Boucherie, three or four in the rue de l'Echaude, five or six in the rue Grégoire du Tours, four in the rue Mazarine, two big ones in the tiny rue Mazet, two in the rue St. Sulpice, and a couple more in the rue des Quatre Vents. No fewer than fifty hotels specialized in renting rooms to couples who did not sign slips for the police and seldom occupied a room more than an hour, unless unusually beautiful friendships were sprouting.

An average of five girls worked in each house, totaling one hundred and sixty. Besides, thirty-two sub-mistresses, thirty-two cooks, maids of all work and chambermaids were employed. The prostitutes, although they suddenly found themselves outlaws, had a less difficult adjustment to make after reform than the employees who remained upright. The cooks are still cooking, most of them, but many of the maids and sub-mistresses, unable to find other jobs, have been obliged to compete with the regulars, and many of them look back on the good old days with regret.

When the quarter east of the *place* St. Michel, where I was at home, was a part of the 6th arrondissement the snug little nest of bordels lapped over the boulevard, into the rue de la Huchette, the rue de la Harpe, the rue St. Séverin and what is now the rue Xavier Privas. It is too bad that everything between the boulevard St. Germain and the Seine, north of the rue Sts. Pères, was never set off from the 5th and the 6th as a separate arrondissement, with local administration more suitable to its low and lively qualities. Certainly it never belonged in the respectable 6th, or the 5th, which is devoted to general learning, the study and practice of medicine, the zoo and the wholesale wine market.

Strangers in cities of Spain or Italy, who want to locate the red-light district, are advised to seek a point equidistant between the principal seminary and the main barracks of the Guardia Civil. As a matter of fact, the same rule, modified for French democracy, would have applied to the little region I am trying to describe. It lies between the clerical and missionary center at St. Sulpice and the barracks of the Republican Guard and the adjacent Prefecture of Police.

It was in the spring of 1949 when the struggle for the proprietorship of peace broke out in earnest between the Communists and the Liberals who distrusted the Stalin dictatorship and Iron Curtain strategy. No sooner had the French Communists plastered all Paris and the environs with Picasso doves announcing their World Congress of the Partisans of Peace at the Salle Pleyel, than the anti-Communist Leftists, Existentialists, Trotskyists, Titoists and Anarchists published plans for a rival meeting in the Vélodrome d'Hiver.

The Communist party is so organized in France that the handful of intellectuals and artists at the top are a source of pride and comfort to the industrial union workers who make up the rank and file. The first-named group, of which Frederic Joliot-Curie, Jean Richard Bloch, Louis Aragon, Paul Eluard and the Abbé Boulier are members, are not to be compared with the "eleven" who make up the Politburo of the American Communist Party. Neither are they anywhere near down to the level of such literary mudhorses as Ilya Ehrenburg, Fadeyev, Simonov and the late high arbiter Zhdanov, in Moscow.

The cultural trimmings offered the delegates to the Communist World Congress against American Imperialism and the Atlantic Pact involved creative and interpretative artists and scientists whose reputations did not rest solely on adherence to a Party Line. Paul Robeson was one of the singers; poems for the occasion were offered by Aragon and Paul Eluard; Joliot-Curie, France's high commissioner of atomic research, was chosen to assure the delegates that French workers and scientists would not make bombs to be used against Russia. It was broadcast far and wide that

Picasso had set aside his work on three-faced females and babies with eyes like flounders in order to do the "tender" dove of peace in a realistic proletarian manner.

The anti-Red rivals could not top Picasso, as a painter, but they promised a telegram from Eleanor Roosevelt, enlisted Marian Anderson, who is several shades darker than Paul Robeson and surely sings as well, matched Joliot-Curie in the science department with Dr. Karl T. Compton, of the United States' "Manhattan Project," and came up with a group of writers quite equal to the French Communist contingent and far superior to the Russians. Those included James T. Farrell, Arthur Koestler, Ignacio Silone and Richard Wright. The Partisans imported from America, Howard Fast and Donald Ogden Stewart, to bolster up Ehrenburg, Fadeyev, Simonov, and Pablo Neruda, the Thrush of Chile.

The Communists claimed that the membership of the organizations who were sending "delegates" to the Salle Pleyel conclave totaled 350,000,000. Their rivals claimed to represent the balance of the world's population. The Communists planned a mass meeting which they described as a popular spontaneous demonstration. In *L'Humanité*, the attendance was 250,000, the police counted 20,000 and the New York *Herald Tribune*, Paris edition, conceded 50,000. Those figures are normal for any outdoor public meeting in behalf of Stalin. I think the various Paris newspapers keep the headlines on the stone, set-up and ready. My own guess, for the Communist affair, was 35,000, at least 30,000 of which had been assigned to duty by their union or organization. Seven out of twelve of the active or avowed Communists in the rue de la Huchette were among them.

Just after lunch, on Easter Saturday, when I was sitting on

the *terrasse* of the Café St. Michel with the American delegate and Richard Wright, who had happened along, there were a half-dozen of our neighborhood Communists, as many "Jouhaux" (left-wing) Socialists, about three Blum followers (Socialists with White Gloves), quite a few who had never bothered voting at all, at least a dozen who favored De Gaulle, and about the same number who supported the Center Government of Queuille. That coalition was made up of Socialists, most of whom were unstable adherents, the M.R.P. (Popular Republican Movement), and the old bumbling Radical Socialists of whom Herriot is the best example and Daladier the worst. Everybody knew how everybody else voted, if they voted or cared. The De Gaulle faction included most of the practicing Catholics, and all the Jewish businessmen.

We formed a happy friendly company of neighbors, more homogeneous than the gatherings had been in the late 1930's, when the line of demarcation was between those who believed in the Republic and those who wanted a dictatorship. The traitors who had struck when the Third Republic was helpless had been dispersed and cleaned out. No one present, except Katya and, possibly, Raoul Roubait, believed that France would "go Communist" in the foreseeable future, and very few saw any likelihood that the United States and Russia would go to war against each other, and use France as a battleground. The more intelligent among the Communists were happy about victories in China, and the untenable position the Queuille Government, coached by the United States State Department, was trying futilely to maintain in Indo-China. They were quite willing to let Western Europe lie fallow for a while. The Communist meetings were merry, and are today. With their millions of allies in Russia and a billion men in the Orient on their side, the French Communist Party, able to muster only about one-third of the votes in a national election, feels secure and optimistic. The Capitalist majority is also feeling fine, but shows less bluster and confidence.

Paul Eluard's "peace" poem was published that day, and when it was read aloud, the local Communists had the grace to look embarrassed. This is the text, in translation:

THE U.S.S.R., SOLE PROMISE

Brothers, we see ourselves reflected in a human mirror
That can never be broken or obscured

Brothers, we see ourselves in an earthly mirror
A large mirror a large country that lights our way

Brothers, all countries believe in her light
Whether they are rebels or friends
The U.S.S.R. enlarges them, improves them.

Behind us fear and hatred and death
Wither the happiness of which we have dreamed
But before us in the East the day is born
The present holds in its strong hands
The germs of a life without worry without boundaries

The U.S.S.R. for herself and for us wants peace
She has known war she effaces its ruins
Working with open eyes upon her victories
She has conquered solitude
United in herself she will unite the world

Brothers, the U.S.S.R. is the only free way
By which we will pass to attain peace
Peace favorable to the sweet desire to live
Might shrinks to a very small size
And the earth reflects a future without stain

"The Thrush of Chile"

In *L'Humanité*, Pablo Neruda, known among his admirers as "The Thrush of Chile," and head of the Chilean delegation to the World Congress of the Partisans of Peace, contributed the following:

MISTER TRUMAN

Mister Truman arrived on the Isle of Puerto Rico

He went to the blue water
   of our pure sea
There to wash his blood-stained fingers.

He had just ordered the death
Of two hundred young Greeks,
His machine guns functioned
Very strictly
Every day.

By his orders, the Doric heads
   —grape and olive—
Eyes of the ancient sea, petals
Of the Corinthian corolla,
Fell in Grecian dust.

The assassins drank of the sweet wine of Chypre
With the North American experts
Between bursts of laughter
With moustaches that streamed
With fried oil
And Greek blood.

Truman came to our waters
There to wash his red hands,
And then pronounced decrees,
Preached and smiled at the University
In his language.
"Shut your mouth, Castilian speech

Extinguish the light of the words
  which meander like a river of crystal.
Death to your language, Puerto Rico."

In *Ce Soir*, edited by Louis Aragon, formerly one of the most imaginative of modern French writers, the lead article read this way:

"The fraternal assembly of our Communist party, in the grave circumstances of today, met in order to hear the calm and clear voice, the beloved voice of Maurice Thorez. How proud one felt to be able to enter, to be able to show one's Communist card to the comrades in charge of the meeting, to belong to this great party which is the guide of our people, and shows to the workers of our entire nation and the world the way of liberty, of honor and of peace."

While we were seated at the café, trying to reconcile the new conformity of formerly distinguished non-conformists, an old man with a beard like Father Time's joined us at the table. He had some papers in his hand.

The American delegate beamed owlishly, and handed the documents to Monsieur Mainguet. The venerable old timer he introduced as Comrade Rappaport, a linotype operator from *L'Humanité*, who had known Jaurès. Rappaport, to accommodate the American delegate, had dug up the information from the "morgue" of the paper, once Socialist, now Communist. The neighbors gathered round as Mainguet read:

"Taravel, Antoine-Paul, called Xavier Privas," Mainguet began.

"It takes our visitors to get to the bottom of things in Paris," said Noel.

Mainguet continued. "Born at Lyon in 1863. Died, 1927.

He was a graduate of the Lycée St. Chamas, a bachelor of science. Xavier Privas organized the entertainments known as 'Evenings of the Pen,' later the Soirées Procope, appeared at the Black Cat, was featured at the Cabaret des Quat'z Arts . . ."

Thérèse began to laugh. "Not even a war hero," she said.

"A hero of the night," said the American delegate.

"Xavier Privas was a founder of the Cabaret des Arts, then of the Noctambules," Mainguet continued.

"Now we're getting somewhere," said Mlle Swallowtail. "The Noctambules is not far from here."

According to *L'Humanité's* files, Privas had for a collaborator in 1903 Madame Francine Lorée, who became his wife in 1913.

"High time," remarked the Satyr.

Privas's inspiration, as set forth in his obituary notice, was "idealistic, charitable, patriotic and sentimental. Among his best known songs were: Les Thurifères, Song of the Hours, Human Songs, Songs Lived, Sentimental Songs, Children's Songs, Sweet Songs, dating from 1897 through the volume called "French Songs" published in 1919.

"Was Privas a comrade?" asked Katya.

"It's never wise or discreet to inquire too closely about that," suggested the veteran from the composing room of *L'Humanité.* "He died in 1927, the year Aragon was admitted to the Party. There's nothing more risky for a man's reputation than having been a comrade too early in the game."

12. The Lost Move in Circles

IN NO. 32 rue de la Huchette, Jeanne Piot and Eugène, wife and son of the fugitive collabo, the Navet, occupied their old apartment. Jeanne rented an extra bedroom to a girl in her early twenties, who taught shorthand in the business college next door. The teacher, Berthe Metalyer de Latouche, preferred to be called simply Berthe Latouche. She had lived there about a year, when I got back to the rue de la Huchette, and still was somewhat aloof from the life of the quarter. She had no callers except young Dr. Thiouville. The neighbors liked Berthe well enough, but no one knew much about her background. She talked little, and not at all about herself. She was tall and svelte, with long legs, dark hair, expressive brown eyes and a natural force of character which enabled her to preserve discipline in the classroom.

It was Berthe Latouche who was the first in the rue de la Huchette to think of using the flat roofs above the wide end of the street for sun bathing, of which she was unusually fond. She was not athletic but liked to be outdoors undressed. Of course, during the weeks of rain and chill preceding the Easter week-end, there had been no sun for any purpose at all.

The institution of sun bathing, like the garage, the auto school, the advance-guard Théâtre de la Huchette at No. 19, the two neon signs, the rubberneck buses, and the brand-new pharmacy, was a modern feature of the street's development. Those of us who had known the quarter in the days of portable bathtubs, itinerant flocks of she-goats to be milked into empty cognac bottles, early morning vendors with their traditional musical cries, had not expected to see the like.

Berthe, in her bedroom, took off her clothes, slipped on adjustable bras and a small scarf down below, covered herself with a robe, eased her slender white feet into mules, and mounted the ladder toward the skylight. Jeanne Piot, so blond, soft and attractive at forty-five, but who never had undressed unless she meant it, watched her lodger with gentle curiosity. Jeanne could not understand why the teacher, who had time on her hands and could do about as she pleased, was alone so much, and knew so few men. It was easy to see that Berthe was well bred, and had been brought up in the strict old French tradition.

The roofs at the wide end of the street were slightly higher than the others, so Berthe, once she gained the top of No. 32, and crossed the narrow gangway, thought she was safe from observation. She had passed on the other side of the broad chimney without seeing Anatole, the book clerk, who was in his deck chair, fast asleep. Their hours on the roofs had never before coincided. She spread her steamer rug in a patch of sunshine, put aside her robe, slipped off her mules, and unhooked the backstrap of her bras. She lay prone, exulting mildly in the warmth of the sun.

Having no reason to suspect that anyone was near by, she rolled over and lay face up, firm breasts pointing skyward, legs outstretched and slightly apart, clasped hands behind her head. She closed her eyes. The sun was stronger than she had realized, and under its spell she fell asleep.

Once she moved, letting her left arm fall by her side, and resting her weight on her right, with her upper arm across a ridge in the boards.

In her apartment above the cabaret Rahab, at No. 29, Helen Hatounian put an Armenian record on the gramophone. The windows were open and the afternoon stillness of the neighborhood was rent with the shrill voice of a near-eastern soprano. The music was less startling to the Armenians than to others within hearing. Its effect on Anatole was catastrophic. The sharp sound reached his ears, and kindled his recollections of gypsy women screaming. Dazed and bewildered, awakened so rudely from sleep, he bounded from his deck chair, upsetting it, and started blindly across the rooftop.

Berthe, aroused by the din of the collapsing chair, the Oriental screaming from below, and the frenzied footsteps, saw what appeared to be a madman rushing toward her. Instinctively, she tried to rise and fell backward with a thud, realizing in consternation that she was as bare as an egg and that her right arm was numb and useless. From her forehead to her toes her skin was angry pink from the sun.

Her plight was so sudden and complete, and had so many facets and angles, that she was unable to scream or protest, but only to gasp, shrink and stare.

Anatole, of the two, was the more startled. What he seemed to see before him dulled the previous panic that had set him a-running.

"*Mais!* Mademoiselle!" he said, almost reproachfully, as he came to a sliding stop.

"Alas, monsieur. My arm," Berthe said, and with her left hand touched fearfully her paralyzed right.

"Your arm?" repeated Anatole. He looked at her right

arm, enormously relieved to have something permissible to gaze at. "Your arm?" he stammered.

"I can't move it," Berthe said. "It's paralyzed."

"I'm desolate, mademoiselle," said Anatole, and at the same time found himself picking up the robe and spreading it over her nakedness.

"Thank you, monsieur. That's very kind," she said, and frowned because she was not making sense. She was not in acute pain, but the loss of the use of her arm was disconcerting.

Each looked at the other. Anatole thought he had seen the girl's face before, and Berthe was almost sure that she recognized him. They had never met, formally.

"You're badly sunburned," Anatole said. "Be careful not to rub the skin."

"I fell asleep," she said.

"Ah, so did I. Did you hear screaming?" he asked. "It may have been my imagination."

"It was a phonograph," said Berthe.

"Precisely," Anatole said. Then he tried to pull himself together. "I should be doing something to help you. What, exactly, I wonder?"

"Could you assist me down the ladder, below the skylight in No. 32?" she asked. She tried again to move her arm and failed.

Berthe was suffering from what is known in the United States as Saturday-night paralysis, several cases of which occur in large cities each week-end, when drunken men go to sleep in gutters, with one arm across a sharp curbstone. Anatole had had no experience with anything of the sort.

"I'm reasonably strong," said Anatole. "May I carry you as far as the skylight? If I can't manage, from there on, I'll call for help."

"I'd rather we got down without help," she said.

A few minutes later, Jeanne Piot, who was as deaf as a post, happened to open the door of her upper hallway. She saw a young man, straining and puffing, barely able to sustain himself on the lower rungs of the ladder. Her lodger was limp and almost naked in his arms.

In the *place* St. Michel, so many new leaves and buds caught the glint of the sunshine that numbers felt the fever of inflation, and touches of green among the twigs and branches, against the fountain and the familiar buildings and the sky soared into the realm of calculus. The bark of the plane trees was freshly mottled and peeled; the elm was stark. The French and the friends of the French were on the *terrasses*. Bookstalls with old paper volumes, engravings and printed music were open all along the quais. Fishermen lounged, stood or sat on all the battlements; tugs, skiffs and barges moved up and down the Seine. No one was flashily dressed. A few small boys had new store clothes, and were conspicuous, half proud, half diffident. What was lacking in *chic*, which was in force before the Taverne du Palais, was gained in wholesome relaxation. There was a priest or two, wearing a beret instead of the comedy flat hat of yore, and, at the other extreme, Algerian peddlers wearing berets instead of scarlet fezzes. Improvement and loss. Some Frenchmen in shirtsleeves or cotton sweaters would have been in senatorial-style white shirts and coats before the war. The *tonnelier* in a leather smock which could be smelled at tables twice removed. The Chestnut Man with a broad red sash around his middle. Noel with flowing tie.

Monsieur Mainguet, without a word to any of us, got up and started for St. Séverin to pray. He loved God and

Hortense. If the Former were to permit any harm to come to the latter, the pious little statistician did not want it written against him that he had failed to bring the matter to his Chief's attention. Mainguet had realized, in crises long past, that without funds or force he had little to offer that was tangible. He wanted to do something for Hortense.

As Mainguet passed through the rue Xavier Privas, on his way to the workingmen's church, he felt the lack of sun. The air in that narrow city coulee was warm, and thick with odors. Heat. but no sunshine could get in. Even the rue Galande had sun that afternoon, because of its orientation. Mainguet felt mildly excited because, moving through the tiny cross street, he was running a gauntlet of illegitimate establishments. The six-foot food shop, Au Petit Vatel, broke laws by the dozen each time five francs' worth of viands were bought or sold. The proprietor of the ten-foot bar at No. 4 rented rooms upstairs for sinful purposes made extra hideous by untidiness. The coal and wine at No. 6 were diluted and bottom grade. The printer was working in the print shop, on a menu where horsemeat was called beef, and all too often rabbit meant cat. The beauty parlor operator and her assistant were occupied, instilling vanity, inimical to God's grace, into females who would use their altered appearance to lure men into violation of the seventh commandment. At No. 9 the herb doctor sold the dried and powdered leaves of one plant that had an aphrodisiac effect, and another to forestall the natural consequences of indulgence. Marihuana was rolled into reefers and smoked at No. 10. Messidor, the locksmith, was beloved of burglars. The stench of the fish store at No. 14 addled a righteous man's pleasure in contemplating Christ's miraculous draft in Galilee. Bawdy women who had been driven from the

large house at No. 18 lurked in the café at No. 13, dressed
as chambermaids without foundation garments. On the corner, the Nest of Vipers nightly harbored jitterbugs and
Lindy hoppers whose antics shamed the praying mantis.

In front of the locksmith's shop sat Christophe on a
camp stool with the Great Dane beside him. Mainguet
spoke kindly to both. Christophe raised his Homburg hat,
tilting it by the back rim and sweeping his hand forward
as he replaced it on his bulging dome. Christophe was hurt
and resentful, which bewildered Mainguet. And the old
bum was right. Noel, Gilles Wilf and the Chestnut Man
were considerate, as men go, but none of them had hit upon
the cause of the strange way in which Christophe, dressed
as Schuman, was acting. Not one of us thought about
francs, or how it was for a man to be elegant and also broke
and hungry.

It was when Xavier, the dog, showed signs of being famished that Christophe was driven to action. He could starve
himself, out of pique, but not a noble animal. Dark thoughts
began to churn in Christophe's mind, and all of them cen-
tered around Busse. Busse wanted to destroy him, and had
taken steps to do so. What were the facts? Christophe was
not insolvent. A week's wages were due him, fifteen hundred francs. If Madame Berthelot owed him that sum, and
Busse owed her much more than that, Christophe was justified, he thought, in collecting from Busse by any means at
all. Busse was manager of the hotel and restaurant, the
Mont Souris. For 1,500 francs a sound meal could be had.
Christophe rose, and the dog whined approvingly.

Leading the Great Dane to the Hotel de Mont Souris,
Christophe passed through the lobby, head held higher than
a Prime Minister's. The huge padded feet of the Dane skidded on the polished parquet. The clerk, Ribou, was absent

from his desk. No guests were seated among the palms and rubber plants. Busse was nowhere to be seen.

Christophe went on into the dining room, which was deserted at that hour. The Great Dane, smelling food from the kitchen, let out one deep resonant bark that echoed through the building.

Busse, two flights upstairs, still staring at the painting, "La Chasse Spirituelle," which was propped on his camouflaged *bidet*, turned pale and trembled. He knew he should investigate and assert himself, and had to admit that he lacked the courage. He wished, as he did so many times each day, that he had been born brave.

The regular waiters in the dining room of the Mont Souris had been excused for a couple of hours and an extra colleague sent by the union was left on guard. When the strange waiter saw a tall man, well dressed and correct, entering with a prize dog on a leash, he bowed and advanced. The dining room was fragrant. All the tables were carefully set. The linen was white, the silver caught glints in the dimness. The curtains of the courtyard windows were slightly parted. There were bouquets of spring flowers at regular intervals, in ranks and files. As their hues and their fragrance assailed Christophe, he straightened and ground his teeth.

"An admirable dog, monsieur," the extra waiter said.

"He's hungry," Christophe said, nonchalantly. "A couple of pounds of raw meat and a bone or two, if you please."

"By all means," said the waiter. "I'll fetch them from the kitchen. . . . And for monsieur?"

"Come to think of it, I haven't lunched today," Christophe said.

The waiter gestured toward the expanse of unoccupied

tables. "Would monsieur prefer to sit by a window?" he asked.

Somehow Christophe preferred not to go too far into the room. He indicated a table near the door which led to the bar, and the waiter installed him there. Xavier, convinced that all was well, stretched out at full length, his huge head on his front paws.

"This will do," said Christophe.

"And what will you have?" the waiter asked.

From somewhere far back in Christophe's memory came recollections of food and wine.

"Have you a plump young guinea hen which could be halved and grilled rather lightly?" Christophe asked.

"We have a chicken of Bresse now being roasted," the waiter said.

"Precisely. A chicken of Bresse. And while I am waiting for the chicken, a rabbit paté and bread, with a bottle of Souilly."

"The paté is excellent. I've tried it myself," the waiter said. He hurried away to the kitchen, returned with the bread and paté, excused himself, came back once more with the wine and a platter on which were raw meat scraps for Xavier.

Christophe was turning the wine bottle in its bucket of ice. "This is cool enough," he said. The waiter started to pull the cork, and showed no astonishment when Christophe forgot himself, grabbed a piece of bread and tore off a huge mouthful which he chewed ravenously.

"It's not often one sees a healthy appetite these days," said the waiter. The old man had tucked his napkin into his collar, and had eaten half the bread and most of the paté. When the waiter started pouring the white wine into a wine glass, Christophe substituted the water tumbler, and when it was filled, tossed it off.

"Is it to your taste, Monsieur?" the waiter asked.

Christophe was on his second tumbler. He swallowed it, and nodded.

The waiter glanced down at the dog, who had cleaned the platter in three gulps. "You're feeding your dog rather early, if you wish a tranquil night."

"I do not want a tranquil night," Christophe said. He had eaten the paté, the bread, the fine aspic jelly, and the lettuce. "More wine, if you please."

"With the fowl, you'll want a red," the waiter suggested.

"Bordeaux," said Christophe.

"Lafitte, monsieur?"

Christophe shrugged assent. "What time is best for feeding dogs, and how much should one like this be fed?" he asked.

"About seven in the evening. Raw meat is best. Five hundred grams for each fifty kilos the animal weighs," the waiter replied.

That caused Christophe to bristle. "With beef at 450 francs the kilo? How much will this dog weigh?"

"About eighty kilos, I should judge," said the waiter.

"In other words, 350 francs for each meal. I shall present him to the Fourth Republic," Christophe said.

"The Government accepts no dogs at the Jardin des Plantes or the Jardin d'Acclimatation," the waiter said.

"One must resort to bribery, I suppose," Christophe said. There was a signal from the kitchen and the waiter went back to get the chicken. Christophe picked up the menu and read the figures. With the wine he had ordered, and the brandy he was going to order, the check would come to well over 1,500 francs. Why not? The old man, warmed inside by the cool wine, figured that Busse, by stripping the flower shop and failing to replenish the stock, had deprived him of the right to work. Was he not entitled to heavy damages? After a period of lean years, a chance to rehabilitate himself had come to him. He had been offered, not a mere temporary job of a menial nature, but the management of an enterprise. Busse had closed out the enterprise. Busse must pay.

Outside, the afternoon was drenched with sunshine, little of which penetrated the Mont Souris dining room. But through the open windows came the scent of spring, the Seine, the budding trees, and those were blended with aroma of cut flowers, false-blue lilacs, mahogany tulips, Wedgwood delphinium, white lilies of the valley, flags, bronze, amber and topaz. The topaz set the tone against the white, stirred by the blue, dimmed by the lavender. In such lone splendor sat Christophe, now tingling with wine. A monstrous hound was at his feet, held in check by his will. From the kitchen he heard the waiter's gay laughter and the voice of the chef. Both were working for him, and none other. He would not be thwarted, least of all by a Busse. Then he was jabbed by reality. The tip! The meal would be so expensive that he would need 1,500 francs for the waiter's tip, alone. He tossed off another glass. The tip money must come from Busse, in cash.

Meanwhile Monsieur Busse waited tremulously upstairs. After the first hollow bark, he had heard no dog noises. But he had to be sure that he would not meet the Great Dane again, so he lingered in his room. The more he thought about Christophe, the more terrified he became. The old miscreant had the glittering eye of the Ancient Mariner. His star was in the ascendancy. Busse had a premonition of disaster, and it made him weak and ill. Eventually, because all was quiet below, Busse took the painting off the *bidet,* wrapped it, tucked it under his arm, and started downstairs. He passed through the lobby, noting that Ribou was not on the job. He strode through the bar, where all was in order. Catlike he stepped into the dim dining room. At first glance it looked to him as if the room were empty, and Busse felt indignant because no waiter seemed to be on duty there. He strode in, and suddenly a huge gray animal lay directly in his path. He let out a little scream, tripped and stumbled forward, then leaped into the air, seeing from the corner of his eye the old man he dreaded most, feasting and glowering at table.

In that split second, while describing a parabola from the floor into the air and down again, Busse experienced all the terrors of fantasy and reality, intertwined. He lost his co-ordination, landed lop-sidedly, turned his ankle and fell hard, sprawling forward and sidewise. His nose hit the polished parquet, and as the waiter and the chef came running from the kitchen and a couple of bystanders trotted in from the bar, Busse lay prone, panting and blubbering. When his rescuers stood him erect, blood was trickling from his nose.

Old Christophe, sitting calmly at his table, showed annoyance rather than concern. He had wanted to see Busse anyway, sooner or later, and there he was.

"In effect," he said, "can not a man lunch in peace?"

The extra waiter, using a clean napkin, tried to staunch the flow of blood from Busse's nose.

"Shall I call the doctor, sir?" the waiter asked. "I think your nose is broken."

Xavier, who up to that time had scarcely moved a muscle, rose to his haunches and surveyed the tableau critically.

"He tripped me, that savage brute!" spluttered Busse, through the napkin.

"What fantasy!" said Christophe. "Luckily there are witnesses. My dog lay still, not moving a muscle, and sat up only at this moment. If you were imprudent enough to leap over him, and in doing so broke your insipid face, so much the worse for it and for you. Am I not right, messieurs?"

Most of those present seemed in agreement. Then all were startled by a heartrending cry.

"My God! What shall I do? The painting. The priceless canvas! My elbow went through it," Busse wailed.

Victor Lefevrais, at the request of Louis, the garçon at the Normandie, spent the first part of the afternoon searching the blocks and streets west of the *place* St. Michel for the refugee brother and sister who had disappeared in that direction earlier in the day. Victor took Fabien Salmon with him.

It seemed impossible to Victor that a man and a woman, looking like Boches, with Boche hats perched on their heads, could walk in plain sunshine through narrow back streets, in a quarter where nearly everyone took a speculative interest in strange passers-by, without leaving a trace. Dozens of men, women and children must have seen the pair, and remarked their timidity. Victor felt sure, as Louis did, that the brother and sister from Cologne had started down the rue St. André des Arts, not because of a fixed destination, but to get away from the crowd in the *place* St. Michel. Their errand in the rue Xavier Privas did not, in Victor's mind, make much sense. He thought it was a blind. He was not willing to believe that Germans ever meant what they said, unless it was vicious and harmful. A banker, Bernstein, if there were any such character, would have lived in a safer locality than Victor's little street.

Victor disliked failing an assignment. Also he shrank from wasting his time. If he were to find the lost pair, for Louis, he would have to proceed some other way. Disconsolately he came back to the *place* St. Michel, with Fabien beside him. Noel, when he caught sight of the boys, understood without words that something had gone wrong.

"Boys. Come have a drink," he said. "It's hot to be trudging around."

"We've been looking for someone," Victor said.

"They were at loose ends, that couple," said Noel, sympathetically.

Victor was chagrined because his errand had proved so transparent. Fabien, feeling as if he might be to blame, dropped his eyes.

"I wonder how it would feel," Noel continued. "Imagine being a foreigner, wherever one went—having no country at all. Me, I've never been out of France, and seldom out of Paris. I begin to feel queer whenever I go outside our quarter."

"Could those people be just plain Germans, and not Israelites?" Victor asked. His tone and manner made it clear that Noel's reflections on the woes of refugees and wayfarers, the homeless, the exiles, had not struck a responsive chord in the boy's mind.

"You don't like them, boy. That's too bad," Noel said. "Whether they're Jewish or German they have troubles enough. When they had to leave Cologne, they couldn't have been more than five years older than you boys are today."

"Perhaps the children of intellectuals," I said.

Victor's eyes were glowing, sulphurously.

"The children of Germans," he said.

Noel caught him up short. "See here, boy. None of that. We don't make war on children."

"I do," Victor said.

"The Boches killed plenty of children," said the timid Fabien.

I have seldom seen Noel more disturbed. "What's the use of being French, if you act like Boches?" he demanded.

Noel, ashamed of his outburst, got control of himself. He patted Victor's shoulder and said, softly:

"The lost move in circles, my boy."

Pierre Vautier, alone in his studio on the attic floor of No. 29, was pacing the floor. His easel was bare, his palette was scraped, his brushes, which he kept meticulously clean, were standing, bristle end up, in glass jars on the mantelpiece. Several canvases on stretchers were leaning against the wall, painted surface inward.

Pierre was in a vile mood. He was often that way.

That sunny afternoon in his studio, Pierre's aversion to women and foreigners was kept active by the Armenian phonograph music, screechingly audible on the top floor, through open windows. Why could France not be for the French?

From where I sat on the *terrasse* of the Café St. Michel I could see Pierre's head and shoulders, crossing and recrossing the window openings. As I watched him pacing I wished that Carmen had not mentioned Miro and Derain. Evidently Pierre was afraid that he had copied those painters, and not merely been inspired by them.

When Anatole hurried across the rue de la Huchette and dashed into the building containing the doctor's office, Pierre saw him, and, knowing Anatole better than almost anyone did, was amazed by the book clerk's show of haste. Something grave must have happened, Pierre concluded. Forgetting himself, and other problems, Pierre trotted downstairs and reached the entrance of No. 23 just in time to meet Anatole and Dr. Thiouville emerging. Without asking permission, and immediately aware that Anatole and probably, the doctor, were wishing him away, Pierre joined them, and went with them back to No. 32. He did not even bother to ask what was wrong, as they mounted the stairs, flight by flight.

Dr. Thiouville, who was in no laughing mood, had gone ahead and pushed Jeanne's doorbell.

In the presence of Jeanne Piot, Pierre Vautier's manner softened. That seemed to be the rule in the neighborhood. There were a few misanthropes, and some others who seemed to dislike only women, but I cannot recall anyone, except the absent Navet, who did not have a tender spot in his heart for Jeanne. It has always seemed to me that the Navet's amiable wife had points of resemblance to the heroine of Somerset Maugham's *Cakes and Ale*. She was always pleasant and receptive, unpretentious and completely feminine. The immense love she had for her only son, Eugène, did not exhaust her capacity. There was more than enough to go around. In pre-war days, she had endeared herself to everyone of good will in the quarter by pinning horns on the Navet, first with a Socialist deputy who was run over by a truck while thinking about it, then with a series of men who seemed to need her temporarily, and lastly with the Turk who took her to Ankara and had the decency to let her return to France, when she seemed to be dying of homesickness.

There was much in Pierre Vautier that seemed spiteful and petty, but he had a wholesome thoroughgoing hatred of traitors, and in years past, when he had been suffering all kinds of frustrations, Jeanne's way of making the Navet perpetually ridiculous had kept alive a small spark of faith in abstract justice.

Dr. Thiouville went straight to Berthe's bedroom, but on entering he fumbled with the doorlatch and left the door ajar, so that Anatole and Pierre, in the living room adjacent, could hear much of what was said. Only Anatole realized that Berthe was being evasive, if not deliberately trying to give the doctor a false impression of what had occurred, so the book clerk was the most bewildered of the three. And Anatole did not know, as Jeanne did, that Dr. Thiouville had been paying Berthe diffident attention for quite a while.

First of all, it was clear that Dr. Thiouville had never seen a case of paralysis at all like the one he was expected to diagnose and cure.

"I fell asleep, with my arm beneath my head," Berthe said. "Both of us were asleep," she added.

The expression of gleeful malice on Pierre's face, as he leered at Anatole, in the living room, was equalled only by the pleased astonishment reflected in Jeanne's lovely face when Pierre cupped his hands and repeated, loudly, in her ear: "They both fell asleep, up there."

Anatole, determined at all cost to be chivalrous, shrugged, somewhat too nonchalantly.

As the dialogue in the bedroom proceeded, Dr. Thiouville lost much of his professional aplomb. If he had never realized it before, he knew then that he was in love with the girl, and for the first time the fearful pangs of jealousy blurred his senses. She must have understood why he had been circumspect, how the Party viewed alliances with those of little faith, that he could not have conscientiously compromised her physically until he had been sure of her politically. He had called on Berthe twice a week, with his heart in his extended hands. And the book clerk, the cynic, the apostle of inaction, the infidel for whom social progress was a false mirage, seemed to have accomplished in one spring afternoon, between two and three o'clock, what he, because of honorable scruples—and an utter lack of knowledge as to how to proceed—had not dared to attempt. A doctor, even an earnest young one, saw enough in the course of his training to make him doubtful about women. It struck him like a blow between the eyes that the one he had adored from a distance was fallible, like the rest.

What the doctor said for a while was indistinct to those listening outside, but Berthe cut in with a remark that brought Pierre to the edge of his chair.

"You must admit that I've had little encouragement, before, to come out of my shell—least of all from you, Doctor," she said.

"Oh, God. The lady's shell," muttered Pierre, so tickled that he could no longer contain himself.

Jeanne touched her lips with a shapely white finger.

Anatole turned shell pink, then a kind of raspberry shade, but he grimly stuck to his policy of passive acceptance. He thought that perhaps Berthe had found the doctor's courtship boring and ˙was using what means she found at hand to discourage him. With his face still flushed and hot, Anatole got up, crossed the room quickly, and closed the bedroom door. Berthe, he believed, was not aware that what she said to the doctor was being overheard.

"The shattered shell," murmured Pierre, as Anatole passed him, and then he let out such a mocking peal of laughter that even Jeanne heard it.

"For a man who's just lost a fortune, you take it very well," Jeanne whispered to Pierre.

"Lost a fortune! How?" asked Pierre.

"The painting!" Jeanne said.

She saw, to her surprise, that neither Pierre nor Anatole knew about Busse's accident.

"You haven't heard?" she asked.

The effect on Pierre, when she explained about the ruined painting, astonished even Anatole. Pierre sprang up, a fiendish smirk on his face.

"Please, Jeanne. Some writing paper. Have you got linen paper? Vellum? Perfumed, if you like."

Puzzled, Jeanne produced some paper. Pierre seated himself at the desk, writing rapidly and boldly in his violent and arrogant script.

Not ten minutes later, Busse, who was moaning and holding cold compresses to his nose, having been unable to find Dr. Thiouville, was handed a sealed note by the concierge of No. 32.

"*Chèr monsieur,*" the note began. "Since our talk this morning, after which I loaned you my painting entitled 'La Chasse Spirituelle,' I have been approached again by a prospective purchaser who now offers me, in the presence of competent witnesses, the sum of one million francs. In spite of my reluctance to part with the work in question, I cannot refuse such an offer. So, if after transmitting my regrets to Madame Berthelot you will return the painting to my studio, I will be glad to let you choose another which, I hope, will serve your purpose as well.

"Accept, dear sir, the assurance of my most distinguished sentiments.

(signed) Vautier"

Left alone, with the dog, in the flower-bedecked dining room, while the waiter and the others were helping Busse make his mournful exit with his broken nose and the painting that was ripped and torn, Old Christophe sized up the situation as a commander would have surveyed a battle which had taken an unexpected turn in his favor. The old man had intended to confront Monsieur Busse with a huge unpaid bill for lunch and demand his 1,500 francs so that he could tip the waiter royally. But now that the meal was eaten, Xavier was replete and content, and the waiter was absent, Christophe began to think in different terms. He had had a strenuous day, what with one thing and another. Madame Berthelot was still in the hospital. He was ready for a long untroubled sleep. The question was: where? He had no intention of returning to the rue Galande. For him, that sordid phase of life was over.

There was a door leading directly from the dining room to the courtyard, from which there was an outlet to the quai. From the quai, he could make a detour and eventually reach the locksmith's shop in the rue Xavier Privas. He felt so good that it seemed to him that he was safe and invisible.

The plan worked well. Messidor, the locksmith, was drunk enough to consent to anything, and not too far gone to accompany Christophe, through a back passageway, into the then quiet courtyard of No. 23 rue de la Huchette. Messidor, with one of the skeletons on his large keyring, unlocked the back door into Hortense's neat little bedroom.

Christophe, alone in the flower shop, made sure that the

front door was locked, and, with Xavier still at his heels, went back into the bedroom. His reflection in the dressing-table mirror reminded him that he was clean and well-dressed. So, instead of stretching out on the floor beside the dog, he lay on Madame Berthelot's narrow bed and soon was blissfully asleep.

At the eastern end of the rue de la Huchette, Victor Lefevrais was leaning against one of the timber props that reinforced the outside wall of No. 1, where the portrait of Amiard, the trussmaker, graced the false window on the second floor.

Fabien Salmon was standing near by, aware that Victor was deep in thought and careful not to distract him.

" 'The lost move in circles,' " Victor repeated, half aloud. "Did Monsieur Noel mean by that that the Boches will come back?"

"That's the way I understood it," Fabien said.

There was not much traffic up and down the rue du Petit Pont. One or two priests walked by, with a hundred out-of-town choir boys in tow, on the way to St. Séverin.

"Those kids must have a rotten time," Victor said.

"Let 'em," said Fabien.

A few Algerian rug peddlers strayed into the Hotel des Hirondelles. Victor had never seen one of them sell a rug, and believed, as nearly everyone did, that the swarthy colonials had some other occupation and carried rugs as a blind. A taxi drove by, slowly, and Victor, because of his preoccupation with the refugees, felt sure that a wooden-faced German in the dimness of the cab had looked furtively into the rue de la Huchette.

"Did you get a good look at the type in that taxi?" he asked Fabien.

"I thought he was an Oriental . . . Perhaps a rebel from Viet-Nam," the butcher's son said.

The afternoon sun was still high and the heat was blistering but not oppressive. In a moment the greenness of the small oblong park, splotched with buff and chrome and violet shadows, was stirred with artificial colors. A bobbing cluster of balloons around a stick, spheres and ellipsoids of ultramarine, vermilion, pale milk and orange rubber, were brought in by a vendor.

"I had a balloon once, with hydrogen. It cost 60 francs," Fabien said. "I liked the feeling of the rubber, tight and thin, but I didn't quite know what to do with the thing. I was afraid it would burst, or get away. So I kept it, and it got smaller and soft and wrinkled. I didn't dare try to blow it up again. Is hydrogen poisonous?"

"If it was, you couldn't buy a balloon full for 60 francs," Victor said. "If poison was as cheap as that, there'd be lots fewer stinkers in France."

Then Fabien saw something that made him catch his breath. The same lean man and woman with foreign hats who had been in the quarter that morning were approaching from the Petit Pont. They looked as lost and uncertain as before, and more dusty and tired. When they paused on the quai, Fabien looked away, quickly. He wanted Victor to be the one to discover them, so he waited, tensely, his eyes on the pavement.

Still watching the balloons, which were swaying and rubbing together, Victor did not notice instantly that Fabien was acting strangely. When he did, Victor glanced around hastily, and stiffened when he saw the refugees. But for a moment, he said nothing. He was figuring that Fabien had spotted the pair, and it did not take Victor long to grasp that his companion was making another sacrifice for him. He felt a surge of unreasonable irritation.

"You saw them," he said, under his breath. "Why didn't you say so?"

"I wasn't sure," said Fabien, but his tone gave him away.

"You'd better go tell Louis," said Victor. "I'll keep an eye on this pair myself."

13. *Citizens of the World*

LOUIS the garçon was standing in the doorway of the Normandie. From the corner of his eye he caught a glimpse of Achille Ithier, the Anti-Alcoholic Society clerk, stealing into the rue Xavier Privas in a manner that showed plainly he was nervous about something in connection with his errand. So Louis sauntered over to the corner just in time to see Ithier turn into the herbalist's musty shop. Trying unsuccessfully to think of a plausible pretext to call on Doc Robinet also, Louis followed and entered.

The aromatic little front room was lined with shelves and old-fashioned wooden drawers in which were herbs, roots and simples, dried, powdered or in solution. Some of the envelopes containing nature's remedies were yellowed with age and disuse.

Before Louis had arrived on the scene, Ithier must have had time to give his order, or it might have been one that Doc Robinet filled for him periodically. At any rate, the herbalist was pottering behind the counter, sifting certain herbs into a beaker, mixing them with a spatula, and pouring the contents onto an oblong piece of blue-green paper which he folded neatly to contain the powder. He then handed it to Ithier.

"Don't you ever get these dried weeds confused in your mind, and give physic to a man that needs lead in his pencil?" Louis asked.

The remark startled and disconcerted Ithier to the point that he dropped the neatly wrapped powder and fumblingly recovered it again.

"Spill any?" Louis asked, grinning.

Ithier, without answering, scurried out of the shop.

"Our famous French politeness," commented the Doc. Louis shrugged, a little annoyed with himself for feeling such curiosity about something that was none of his business. He had heard Ithier and Antoinette talking earlier in the day about giving her father a "powder," but what did it matter to him? He promptly forgot about Ithier when Fabien Salmon came running, to tell him that the two refugees from Cologne were standing near the eastern entrance of the street. Louis went there with the boy, told Victor and Fabien to stand by, and approached them.

"I'm glad you came back," Louis said. "I may have news for you."

The brother looked alarmed. His sister touched his arm.

"Nothing definite, yet," said Louis. "I may have some addresses that will help you."

The sister had been looking at Louis and seemed less startled and afraid.

"If you'll come to the hotel, I'll see what I can find. I knew many refugees in the last years before the war. Some went to New York and wrote me from there," Louis said.

Thus far the brother and sister had not said a word. They had stood, ready to be off at an instant's notice. When Louis made his direct suggestion, the brother looked questioningly at the girl and she nodded assent.

"Hermann Pflantz," the brother said, bowing and clicking his heels, German fashion. "And my sister, Miriam."

"Enchanted," said Louis. "Let's go."

He looked straight into the eyes of the girl, whose lips

parted slightly as she held the fabric of her brother's sleeve between her thumb and fingers.

"You're tired," Louis said.

She nodded again, again gravely.

"We walk every day," the brother said. "In Paris it seems more exhausting."

"You haven't been here long, then?" Louis asked.

"Since this morning," Hermann said.

Louis risked another question, again looking at the girl.

"Have you found a place to stay?"

Both were startled, stepped a few inches apart, and looked at each other. There was no need to reply. It was clear that they had no lodging.

Louis smiled. "This quarter's all right. Nobody's curious. There's a room at the Normandie, just by chance."

"Oh, is there?" said the girl, so palpably relieved that Hermann made no attempt to dissimulate.

"We left our luggage at the railroad station, in the check room," Hermann said. "Having failed to find Herr Bernstein, as we had hoped, we applied in various places for lodgings. No rooms were vacant. Is that usual?"

Louis understood well enough what Hermann meant. Had their appearance been against them?

Having promised them a room so blithely, Louis had to do some quick thinking. He decided that, come what may, he would install the Pflantzes in No. 9, next door to Monsieur Ithier. No. 9 had been reserved for three Mexicans of the St. Felix delegation. The Mexicans were not due until after dinner time, and in the meantime Louis would have to accomplish the impossible and find beds elsewhere for them. He had figured that if the Pflantzes had got into Paris on an early train that morning, in time to reach the *place* St. Michel less than an hour after sunrise, they must have been on their feet at least thirteen hours. He looked at the girl again, and had the queer sensation of identification with her, as if he could feel the texture of her damp clothes against her skin, the weight of dust in the too-heavy tweed, the rough crust of shoes around feet that were capable, still tender. He was breathing as she was, inhaling as her breasts moved under their drab covering, exhaling when she relaxed to that extent. A subtle diffidence took possession of them all, so that Hermann stood slightly apart, waiting to learn how Miriam felt about the one-armed garçon's hotel, and Louis's interest in them, which went beyond what could be explained by events, as Hermann understood them.

Strange things were going on in Louis's mind, and among them one was comforting. Hermann, the brother, who had been wandering the earth with his sister during fourteen years, was utterly unaware of any current or short-circuit or interchange of any kind between her and Louis. Louis could not be too sure, himself, that his own feelings were not playing him tricks.

"In the matter of papers, we're not too fussy. After all, the police on duty have been our friends for years. They accept what I tell them, without nosing around . . . if you know what I mean," Louis said.

The expression on Hermann's face was a study in conflicting emotions. He was relieved, pathetically hopeful, and more than ever alarmed. His sister held herself quite straight, and smiled at him.

"Our passports . . ." Hermann began. "We have passports." He hesitated, and Miriam took a half step forward.

"From Cuba," she said, with a kind of dignity that made her look older. She pronounced it "Coo-bah."

Louis could not conceal his perplexity.

"We were born in Cuba, at a place called Siboney. Afterward, our parents went back to Germany," she said.

"Why, sure. What's wrong with Cuba?" Louis asked.

Hermann bowed his head and looked into the dust, and Miriam, not smiling any longer, looked at Louis. He led the way toward the hotel, and they followed, Miriam in advance and Hermann two paces behind.

Madame Fontaine, since the fall of 1944, proprietress of the Hotel Normandie, was tending the neat zinc bar when she saw the two refugees from Cologne enter the doorway that led directly to the stairs. Whoever went in or out that way had to pass a small window, head and shoulder high, so that anyone on duty at the desk or the bar could see him. When Madame recognized Louis, close behind the odd-looking man and woman in tweeds, she shrugged and would have frowned had she not been warned to be careful about wrinkles in her forehead.

She was a handsome, buxom woman about five feet seven inches tall, with straight shapely legs and a graceful carriage. Her hair was a natural dark red, to which the skillful application of henna lent highlights. Her eyes were chartreuse, her chin willful, her hips relatively slender and her *derrière* trim and flat. Her nature was observant and cynical, smolderingly passionate and coldly practical. She had a rare gift of quick barroom repartee. Across the zinc from her were two of the most disarming and thoroughgoing roués of the quarter, the tall black-eyed Armenian, Monsieur Nathaniel, and the acknowledged Old Master, the Satyr.

The way Madame looked at the German girl's head and shoulders, and just afterward, at the back of Louis' head, caused the two men to smile. They both were aware that the *patronne* had a soft spot for Louis and that the latter, on the theory that employer and employee relationships should not be complicated in reverse of the usual sex orientation, had not responded manfully. Nathaniel assured Madame that he or the Satyr, or both of them, would be happy to serve her, and she took the offer in good part.

"Where does he think he's going with that beanpole?" she asked. "There isn't a room in the house."

"I saw Louis this morning, hopping around her like an adjutant crane," the Satyr said. "He goes wild for the bony type, Madame. You'd do well to take off a few pounds."

Nathaniel volunteered to help Madame go through a course of exercises that would reduce both her weight and her wanton inclinations.

In the meantime, Louis installed the Pflantzes in Room No. 9, which previously he had fitted out with a double bed and a cot, with screen between them, for the use of three pious Mexicans. He had borrowed from the Hotel de la Harpe two framed chromos of the "Bleeding Heart" and the "Christ Child" and two especially harrowing crucifixes, for wall decorations. Hermann seemed uneasy, so Louis left his guests alone for a while and promised to return with the papers to be filled out. The mention of those disturbed Hermann still more. As soon as Louis was gone, the German stepped over to the door to read the placard stating the price of the room. For two, it was 180 francs per day.

"That's possible," Miriam said, and he nodded. Then he walked back and forth, like a water bird. His nose was a beak, there was a pale gleam in his eyes, his knees bent to divide his long thin legs too tightly trousered, and he held his hands behind his back, so the fingers looked like wing tips.

"I drank French beer again," he said, dismally.

"Go to the lavabo and vomit. You'll feel easier," she said, sagely.

Downstairs, Louis had obtained from Madame Fontaine, under the mocking eyes of Monsieur Nathaniel and the Satyr, two printed slips of paper, covered with questions, for the police records. Foreigners and travelers in France are kept under surveillance, to a point, and not permitted to run wild.

"Where have you put your lady friend?" Madame Fontaine asked, more sharply than she had wished.

"With her brother, in No. 9. I've found beds for the Mexicans in the Hotel du Caveau," Louis said. He had not yet made the arrangements, but was taking no chances on establishing Miriam securely before he worried about Mexican priests.

The Satyr laughed heartily at the idea that religious pilgrims should stay at the Caveau, which under its post-war management had specialized in transients of quite another sort.

Louis mounted with his official registration slips.

"You'll excuse the appearance?" Miriam said, as he entered. She was in the act of rearranging the screen between cot and double bed.

Louis opened the table drawer, took out a bottle of thick violet ink and a chewed penholder with a rusty pen, also a desk pad with a blotter on which phone numbers, addresses, initials, names and ribald verses appeared, laterally inverted. Hermann, Louis realized, was gray and trembling, and Miriam's eyes were large and round.

"Shall I precede you, brother?" she asked.

Hermann would not dodge responsibility, although he was limp with fear.

"Nothing to fret about," said Louis, reassuringly. "I'll hand these directly to Benoist, the policeman who collects them. I've known him for years. Nine times out of ten, the slip goes in the files without another reading."

Hermann was scanning the instructions, and began to print his family name: P-F-L-A-N-T-Z.

Miriam stepped nearer to Louis and he looked again into her eyes. They stood facing each other, she questioning without words, he reassuring her. She saw a man who had no treachery in him. He saw a young woman weary of wandering, who had done nothing wrong.

"No one will question our origin . . . in Cuba?" she asked.

"Not likely," Louis said.

Hermann gave his date of birth as March 9, 1919; birthplace, Siboney; profession, teacher of languages. When he came to "residence" he looked at his sister and said, tremulously, "Sweden?" She shook her head. "No. Better Amsterdam."

"Next stop? New York?"

"Havana," she said. He nodded.

"Purpose of voyage?"

Louis prompted him that time. "Travel and education," he said. "That's the best. Nobody bothers tourists with dollars these days."

"Swedish francs," said Miriam.

"Just as good," Louis said. "Dollars, pounds, Swiss or Swedish francs, or guilders. All the other money's risky, including our own, worse luck."

When Miriam sat down to fill out her blank, Louis stood beside her, so that his sleeve was touching the cotton of her blouse. His wrist was an inch from her shoulder, but it seemed to him that he felt the contact through the cloth. He thought she did, too, and did not mind. The brother, he believed, did not notice.

Louis had read Hermann's parents' names. They were Johannes Hermann Pflantz and Brunhilda Storrs Pflantz. When Miriam wrote in the same father and Rebecca Bernstein Pflantz as her mother's name, Louis' grasp of the situation became instantly clearer. Hermann was pure German, Miriam was half Jewish. It was on her account, not Hermann's, that they had fled from Cologne, uprooted, and roamed the earth for fourteen years. The loyalty and sacrifice, then, were Hermann's. Of their misfortunes, the girl was the cause, and the absent father who had married a Jewish woman.

When Louis confided the details to me, I explained the Cuban passports, issued late in 1936 and renewed in Sweden. Fascists caught in Republican territory in the Spanish war, and a few assorted refugees who could pay exorbitant prices, had been sold Cuban passports by the Cuban authorities in Spain. Thus, incidentally, many undesirable citizens and a few good ones got from Cuba into the United States and stayed there.

Once the blanks were filled and Louis was about to leave, Hermann showed more nervousness than ever.

"When, exactly, will your friend the policeman collect, inspect and file our registrations?" he asked.

"Not until tomorrow. You've nothing to worry about tonight," Louis said.

It was Miriam who showed concern, knowing that her brother would not sleep, because of the suspense.

At that moment, Hermann sneezed, and the girl said *"Gesundheit"* and smiled. "Let's be gay, brother," she said. "At this hour, when we were children, we were taken to the Kölnischer Strasse where everyone walked up and down, from the Cathedral to the end of the street, between the stores, shops, offices, banks, insurance companies, government bureaus, places of refreshment and fine residence apartments. Those going west, walked on the right-hand side, and saluted friends going east on the other side. The custom was of no significance, but it was gay, and if one missed the promenade, there was a sense of loss."

"Those times are past," Hermann said, bleakly. "No one walks at twilight in city streets today, for social pastime, in Germany least of all."

He had to stop talking, for his sharp face was contorted and he let out an incredible succession of sneezes, louder and more violent than the first.

"Alas," said Miriam. She looked appealingly at Louis and asked, timidly: "There would not, by unhappy chance, be any feathers in the pillows or mattresses? My brother's allergic to feathers."

Hermann let out another brace of sneezes that shook the house, and left his lean frame limp.

Louis, with a patient smile, proceeded to change the mattresses. Already he had lugged both of them from the fourth floor down to the second, to make his guests more comfortable. Now, with one arm and a stump, he had to remove the two feather mattresses from the beds in No. 9, take them up two flights, bring down the old ones stuffed with hair, and remake four beds.

Just after an ambulance had brought back Hortense from the hospital, and before I thought it tactful to go up to her room, I saw Pierre Vautier come out of Julian's barber shop. He had on a new blue-serge suit, well cut, a new hat, new shoes and a handkerchief in his lapel pocket. I had never seen him approach more jauntily, and when he came abreast he greeted me cordially and asked me to have a drink. We sat down on the *terrasse* of the Café St. Michel.

Pierre was in a most unusual good humor. Of course, in years past I had occasionally seen him like that, elated, seemingly hopeful, and with a good word for everybody. He could be charming, in that mood, if one did not remember the black depression which had preceded it, or fear that the next swing of the pendulum would sweep him too far downward. I had heard about the ruined painting, and assumed that he had not.

"I treated you badly this morning," Pierre said. "Forgive me. I'll confess now that I was pleased and flattered when you noticed my painting, and spoke well of it. What makes us so damned afraid of our emotions? One might expect it of you, with your English ancestry. But a Frenchman—he's supposed to be expansive, even vain, in a pardonable way."

"Could I see the rest of your work, some time?" I asked.

"That's an easy request. Everything I've done is still in my studio, face to the wall. Drop in, if you like, later today. First I've got to do an errand." He looked into my eyes, his own eyes smiling. "A mission you would certainly approve," he added, and, after paying the waiter and tipping him bounteously, he waved his hand gaily and started across the bridge of St. Michel.

"God save us," I murmured to myself. "When he hears what Busse has done, I don't want to be around."

Pierre appeared ten minutes later at Carmen's apartment in the quai de Béthune. The Ile St. Louis was glorious in the sunshine, emerald by topaz by gold. So many fishermen in shirtsleeves were along the platforms and parapets that their bright-colored floats, sharp red and shiny black, bobbed a dotted freehand line. Folks who previously had shivered so long in the damp core of the island were now on the rim, in their holiday clothes, men, women and children. Cafés, shops and restaurants were alive with business, and children's voices came cheerily from the little park, upstream.

As usual, whenever he could get away from business, Monsieur Dassary was on a trip with congenial and prosperous men he had known when they were smart boys. Guy Orey was going out at dinner time, to meet a few friends in the decorative trades, drink, eat, talk and attend the spicy new revue of the Pax Brothers, at the Théâtre de Dix Heures. Guy felt a little uneasy because he was going to have a good time, as usual, and Carmen would be alone and unoccupied. He should have felt still more troubled when she reassured him that she liked things better that way. She had told neither her father nor her husband about the rebuff and disappointment she had suffered at the hands of Pierre. So she was genuinely astonished when he called, unexpected and unannounced, and was engaging and apologetic.

"I've made my peace with Monsieur Paul, and he thought you wouldn't mind my coming," Pierre said. As I heard the story later, butter would not have melted in his mouth. He found the location charming, the island, the river, the view entrancing, the apartment and its furnishings in superb taste, and consented to take tea (in the form of Bacardi cocktails) only on condition that Carmen should dine with him, and see once more the painting she had coveted. He promised contritely that, if she still wanted "La Chasse Spirituelle" it would be hers. Pierre explained, over cocktails, that he had loaned the painting to an injured friend, who would be as well satisfied with another. It was to be returned that evening, he said, and in case it was not sent back promptly, they could call on Madame Berthelot in the Hotel Mont Souris and retrieve it.

Had I been present I would have been warned by Pierre's

tolerance of cocktails, which he had denounced through the years as a barbaric American invention.

Carmen's nature was not manic-depressive, like Pierre's, but she was volatile, and easily lifted out of her habitual boredom. Orey, seeing that she was having such a good time, considerately offered his excuses and departed. The obviousness of his exit could not have been lost on Pierre. In years past I had heard him express contempt for all kinds of unfortunate or presumptuous beings, but nothing had seemed so abject as a subservient, complacent husband.

What Pierre said was: "I honestly wish you could join us, Monsieur Orey. I'd like your opinion, too, as a fellow artist. A painting, I believe, is either worth nothing or a great deal of money. I've offered to give madame 'La Chasse Spirituelle,' because she likes it. She won't hear of that, so I've filled in the blank check she gave me for 1,000,000 francs."

Orey blinked involuntarily when Pierre named the sum, but Carmen seemed pleased that he made no comment.

"Au revoir, monsieur," the husband said to Pierre, and added, to Carmen, "See you at lunch tomorrow, dear. That is if you're not otherwise engaged."

"Dear God," grunted Pierre disgustedly, forgetting himself. He was going to add, "Why not offer this woman on a platter, with parsley around the edges?"

I had just waylaid Victor, after he had got back from the station with the refugees' suitcase and bag, and asked him to find Old Christophe. Stray Germans might wander around without leaving clues behind them, but not a tall old man dressed like Robert Schuman and leading a Great Dane on a leash.

Without much confidence that Mignon, the locksmith's twelve-year-old niece, would tell him anything worth while, Victor asked her if she had seen Christophe. It was then she remembered that her uncle had gone into the Jonquil's courtyard with Christophe and a bunch of keys.

"What do you want him for?" she asked Victor.

"That's my affair," said Victor.

"I haven't seen him," Mignon said, too casually.

As soon as Victor was out of sight, Mignon drew the faded window curtains so that her drunken uncle would not have light shining in his eyes and would be immobilized longer, as a consequence. She stepped cautiously through the inner passageway to the courtyard of No. 23.

Leaning with her ear to the door of Madame Berthelot's bedroom in the back of the flower shop, she heard a long sigh inside, it seemed to her from down near the floor.

"Nice doggie," she said.

There was a low plaintive whine.

Cautiously Mignon opened the door an inch and was about to peer in. A paw about the size of her hand reached out and completed the operation, so the door opened far enough for Xavier, trailing his leash, to emerge.

Mignon was singularly devoid of fear. She had never been hurt, or badly frightened, even while the fighting had taken place at the barricade fifty yards from her home. Many of the soldiers in green had spoken rather wistfully to her, or given her small presents. That was five years ago, when she had been seven. But, imitating the few women of the quarter she admired—Madame Berthelot, Mlle Dominique, Madame Fontaine, and Irma—she had held her head high and moved her skirts away as she passed the Nazi troopers and if they laughed behind her, as many of them did, amused by her spunk, she never turned her head to look around.

And when the Nazis had asked Messidor for keys to fit certain doors, it had been little Mignon who had warned the occupants in time. She had not been afraid, but happy and excited.

Xavier, having relieved himself alongside the Jonquil's trash can, stood looking around. Mignon took up the leash, led him back and eased him into the bedroom. She saw that Old Christophe was lying on the bed, but from the way he was breathing, her experienced ear told her that it would take something drastic to arouse him. Once the dog was inside, and stretched on the floor again, Mignon reclosed the door, and got out of the courtyard before the Jonquil, the concierge, came in the front way.

Mignon saw Victor turn the corner into the rue St. Séverin and watched him as he crossed into the rue Galande. A smile just a shade more enigmatical than that of Mona Lisa passed over her face. Her discovery would be her secret. She wished, as she had so often, that she lived in the tropics, where, according to the Satyr, girls of twelve and a half were grown up, and did more or less as they pleased. The hot afternoon sunshine made Paris like the tropics that day.

Emile, the bellboy at the Mount Souris, was a juvenile delinquent who seemed to have found an occupation that required practically no adjustment.

The telephone rang in the hotel lobby. Ribou was absent without leave; Busse was nursing what Emile irreverently called his *"margoulette"*; Monsieur Wilf, senior, was playing belotte in the rear of the Taverne du Palais; and Hubert was on the quai watching the druggist, Cabat, fish for minnows.

"Ici, le Grand Hotel de Mont Souris," piped Emile into

the transmitter. On the other end of the line was Father Taillepied, O.P., who wished to speak with Monsieur Mainguet.

"He's praying in St. Séverin. Shall I interrupt him?" asked Emile.

That had Father Taillepied stopped for a moment.

"Be kind enough to ask him to phone me when he's finished," the professor of comparative religions said.

Emile hung up and decided to break into Monsieur Mainguet's prayers anyway. He induced Lola, one of the chambermaids, to watch the desk while he sauntered over to St. Séverin. There he found Mainguet alone in the church, kneeling by the altar. Tapping him on the shoulder, Emile said brusquely:

"You're wanted on the phone."

Mainguet, who was deep in prayer, with his eyes closed, was so startled he nearly tumbled off the kneeling platform. He blinked, shuddered and looked at the monkey-faced boy reproachfully.

"You shouldn't call me when I'm—occupied."

Emile made a gesture upward with his thumb. "What's the difference? There's no such thing as time up there, and down here it's costing this other type twenty-two francs for three minutes."

Mainguet sighed and got up off his knees.

By the time he had reached the Mont Souris lobby, Emile, who was as efficient as he was perverse, had Father Taillepied back on the line.

"I'm desolate if I shortened your devotions," the learned priest said urbanely.

"I've been reminded by an Imp of Satan that time on high is eternal, and down here it costs twenty-two francs for three minutes on the phone . . . No bad news of our Mex-

ican pilgrims, I hope." Mainguet could not deny that there
was something in what the boy had said.

"On the contrary, good news. Our co-religionists from
Mexico are not having dinner on the plane, and will not stop
to eat at Le Bourget. Would it be possible for their hosts in
your quarter to feed them, shortly after eight o'clock?" said
Father Taillepied.

"I'll inquire at the hotels," Mainguet said, doubtfully.

"Do your best, because in any event the party will arrive,
and will be hungry, if the journey is smooth. I must confess
I've never traveled by air. I can't help wanting to be intact
for the Resurrection," the distinguished theologian said.

Mainguet decided that he should see Gilles Wilf, since
Gilles had made most of the detailed arrangements for receiving the visitors.

"Where's Monsieur Gilles?" Mainguet asked Emile.

"He told me he mustn't be disturbed," Emile said, in the
tone and manner he reserved for people he considered unim-
portant. Instead of batting the fresh bellboy over the head
with his *en-tout-cas*, and threatening to skin him alive if he
did not take a message to Gilles instantly, little Monsieur
Mainguet, squinting and frowning with indecision, decided
to talk first with the chef. The Abbé d'Alexis had said, in
the beginning, that the Mexican delegation would reach the
rue de la Huchette in mid-evening, after dinner time. No
provision had been made to serve them dinner.

The chef of the Mont Souris was a *prima donna*, like most
cooks who are too good for small restaurants and not capable of commanding the kitchen of a large first-class hotel.
He explained to Mainguet, patronizingly, that meat did not
grow on trees, that milk, butter and cheese had been taken
off the ration list and priced lower than the dairy people
had demanded. Consequently supplies were being held back

and the local dairy shops were bare. Fresh green vegetables had wilted in the scorching sun, to the point that in the afternoon there was little use looking for them. Sugar was still rationed. Coffee was scarcer than it had been since the occupation. The twenty-five Mexicans would have collected a swarm of priests around them before they got out of the airport, and the chef refused point blank to feed a party of fifty or sixty at some indeterminate hour between eight o'clock and the middle of the night.

At the Normandie, Monsieur Mainguet was treated with more respect, but got little encouragement. By the time the Mexicans were ready to dine, there would be nothing left in the larder. Men and women all over the quarter were stuffing themselves, because of the sunshine, the long holiday week-end ahead, and the easing of restrictions. The Normandie's cook might be able to dish up something for the four Mexicans who had sleeping reservations there, but certainly no more.

Thérèse, at the Hotel de la Huchette, assured Monsieur Mainguet that she would lambaste with a hot frying pan any Mexicans or priests who showed their heads around her place. She had been reprimanded by Katya that morning for drinking so much, and had demanded to know why hard-working French proletarians had to set examples when Comrade Stalin, whenever he attended a banquet, drank toasts of vodka until the whole outfit got stiffer than cods and had to be stacked like stovewood all over the Kremlin.

The Hotel de la Harpe, being so close to the Palais, the Mont Souris and Rahab, maintained no dining room. Mainguet began to think hard. Rouzier Frères would be able to handle a party of sixty, and so could Lapérouse, but the bill would look like a statement of the national debt, and Mainguet did not know exactly who was paying. The Palais served good food, but it was crowded with profiteers and gamblers who spent money like water, and the women who ate and frolicked with them were not the kind to give a soothing impression of French womanhood to visiting foreigners with a religious turn of mind. And the floor show at Rahab, with folk songs whose lyrics could not be sent through the mails, and the hootchie-kootchie dance out back, was not typical of austere French living, either.

The sun beat down, the narrow sidewalks and pavements so long neglected because of the war, got warmer and then actually hot, so that Monsieur Mainguet, trudging back and forth, felt the soles of his feet smarting. His shirt was moist with perspiration. For the first time in his life, he, a trained statistician, was beginning to appreciate the complexity of the alimentation problem in modern existence. Had he not, in passing a side window of the Palais, caught a glimpse of Gilles Wilf at a card table there, he might have been buffeted from kitchen to kitchen like a shuttle-cock all the rest of the day. When he appealed to Gilles, the latter left the game and in ten minutes the whole thing was arranged. Gilles simply found Busse, whose face was swollen and discolored then to such a degree that it looked like a crushed eggplant.

"Tell that chef to feed the whole gang, if he has to work all night. Tell him I said so. And if he makes any objections, or gives you any argument, let him know, once for all, who's running this place," Gilles said.

Busse waited for his boss and Mainguet to leave the room and close the door behind them before he started quaking and biting his fingers. He had always been afraid of the chef, and been careful not to cross him. Under normal circumstances he would have approached him gingerly, in making an unusual request. His broken nose, and the million-franc painting he had ruined, had sapped his morale. He could think of only one source of relief. To hurry downstairs and tell his troubles to Hortense.

Before he had got three steps on his way, Gilles' voice came to him from the lobby two floors below.

"Another thing I forgot to tell you," Gilles said. "The Mexicans' baggage. It was sent ahead, by train, to the Gare de Lyon. See that it gets through the customs, so their stuff will be delivered to their rooms before they get in from Le Bourget."

Busse's knees got weak and he sat down on the stairway, where he was. Baggage! Baggage for twenty-five foreigners with long Mexican names which all looked alike. Four different hotels. The customs shed, with only half a staff on a holiday afternoon.

"Did you hear?" called up Gilles.

Busse's reply sounded, from downstairs, as if a sick frog had tumbled down a well.

I had postponed too long paying my respects to Hortense, but I could not bear to face her and admit that all of us, after getting Christophe rigged out like a cabinet minister, had lost him, utterly.

Victor had covered all the places the old man was likely to have gone. He was not anywhere in the "Sink of Montebello." There were few inhabitants of that quarter who could be trusted. Most of them could not have told the truth if they had tried. But, in their predatory and depraved way they were transparent, and every last one of them was curious to know where Christophe was. It was not the day and hour for anyone, young or old, to hide in Les Halles. The central markets were closed, and would remain so until Tuesday near midnight. Among the fishermen along the river banks were so many of our friends and acquaintances that no impressive hoary figure in gray, with a Homburg hat and a dog the size of Xavier, could have escaped unobserved.

Busse, with all of his fears and woes, had one cause for satisfaction. He might have to make good the enormous lunch check Christophe defaulted, but concerning Christophe's reliability, it appeared that he had been right, and the rest of us had been wrong.

I entered Hortense's room, prepared to make excuses and take a cheerful view of things. The sight of her face erased Christophe from my mind. She was suffering, as only a woman as patient and considerate as she could suffer.

"Good God, what's wrong?" I asked.

She glanced over her shoulder to make sure the door was closed.

"My arm has started hurting, just lately," she said.

"Call the doctor. Why haven't you sent for him before?"

She mastered herself with an effort and tried to explain, without incriminating Thiouville.

"I bumped my elbow on the bedstead," she began.

"Have you lost your senses?" I asked, impatiently. It was not like Hortense to act stupidly, or fail to act intelligently. "I'll send for Doc this instant."

Then she broke down, and pausing intermittently when blinded with pain, she told me what had happened. The well-meaning doctor, while adjusting the sling just after she had been brought back to the hotel, accidentally had dropped her arm, which struck the bedstead, and caused the new and painful injury.

I did not wait for anything more, but rang for Emile and sent him on the hotfoot for Thiouville. The young doctor was with us, almost instantly. He entered, glanced at the patient, and turned pale with his hot cheeks burning. He took off the sling, held her arm with one hand and felt around the injured joint. He replaced the sling, and sat dejectedly in the chair by the bedside which I had vacated when he had come in.

"I might have known," he said.

"It wasn't your fault. I struck it against the bedstead myself, after you had arranged it," Hortense said. She must have exhausted all her ability for lying when the Nazis were in power, because no one could have been less convincing. The result was that Dr. Thiouville was hurt an extra degree.

"Please, madame," he said. "You must be frank. So must I."

"It can't be so bad," she suggested. "Perhaps I'm tired, and exaggerate the pain."

"The fragment of bone, which formerly was in place, is now detached, if I'm not mistaken," said the doctor.

"It won't take long to knit together," Hortense said.

"Madame. The X-ray plates, which already have been delivered, along with Dr. Flandrin de Monique's comments in writing, are now worthless. We shall have to return to the hospital and go through the process all over again," the doctor said.

Had Hortense been under rack and thumbscrew torture, she would still have had first thoughts for others. "I beg of you to say nothing, not a word to anyone, implying that you are at fault. I'll tell the story of the mishap, in my own way, and do not wish to be accused of falsehood . . . And, Doctor, since we must make another trip to the rue Pierre Curie, couldn't we take along Monsieur Busse, and turn the X-ray machine on his nose? He's afraid the bones are smashed . . . and so am I."

"By all means. I should have done that sooner. As for you,

I shall have to inject on opiate," the doctor said, and as he fished in his case for a hypodermic syringe, Hortense, trying not to wince, pulled up the sleeve of her nightgown and bared her white arm.

The doctor was preparing himself to face Dr. Flandrin de Monique, and the doctors, nurses and technicians of the Hospital Dupuy, with a case they had already disposed of, and another which had been delayed too long. And later, he would have to treat a case of sunburn extending from the brow he had neglected to kiss to the slender feet that trampled the sprouts in the garden of his heart.

At Hortense's request, I mounted to the second floor in order to ask Busse to get ready. The ambulance was due in a half hour. The damaged painting was again propped on the *bidet*, which now, without its petit-point cover, was a sickly white. Busse was standing in front of it, head thrown back, arms straight and held out from his body, palms forward, fingers tensely extended.

"I'm bankrupt," he said. "The savings I've guarded and defended through the terrible years—all gone. And they won't pay half, not much more than a third."

He saw that I did not know what he was talking about and showed me the note.

"You had no criminal intent," I said, trying to think of something that might soothe him. It was then I understood Pierre's mood of elation.

"How can I recover from an old bum without a cent?"

"Christophe wasn't to blame, either," I said. "There's no law forbidding dogs to enter cafés, and lie still beside their masters. The dog made no move. You tried to hurdle him, and fell. A remarkable Great Dane."

"Won't you intercede with Monsieur Vautier?" he begged.

"That would only aggravate him," I said.

Busse clasped his hands and half closed his eyes, like a tragedian as the curtain goes down. "I lack the nerve to kill myself," he said. "More than once I should have done it, if I could. Twice I bought barbiturate pills, enough to finish anyone, and once I wrote a suicide note. No use. I can't escape that way. Day by day I shall have to work out my indebtedness."

"Don't give up. We'll ask Anatole. He can always think of something," I said.

"You're good. You're kind," he said. "Most people dislike me. Just by being myself I anger them. Why is it some of us are born like that, and whoever sees us wants to bruise our dignity?"

"Whatever you do, don't let Pierre see that you're afraid," I cautioned him.

That took away what was left of his courage.

"He'll fix me with his eyes. He'll see me shake and perspire," Busse groaned.

"Nothing was committed to paper. You didn't ask for the painting. Disclaim responsibility," I urged.

"I'm finished," he said.

I did not enjoy harassing him further, but I had to warn him about Hortense. "She's upset because you closed her shop and drove away Christophe," I said.

"I didn't. I swear I didn't. I'll admit I bought the flowers, but Madame Morizot locked the door and took the key away. If Hortense turns against me I shall die . . . Just now I was about to appeal to her. How many times I've been tempted to tell her everything . . . I mean, everything, about myself? Does she ever speak of me to you?"

There was no mistaking that Busse was in love with her and wanted her to mother him.

"She mentions you, often," I said. How could I wound him deeper in his demoralized state?

"How much does she really understand?"

"I can't say," I answered unconvincingly.

"You're not holding anything back?" he asked.

"I can't tell what's in her mind," I said.

"None of us is ever in communication with another, not really," he said, dejectedly. "That's the reason for sex, I suppose. To give us the illusion of communion even if its reality is denied."

The "do-mi-do" horn sounded as the ambulance turned into the rue de la Huchette. I got Busse downstairs, his face covered with a silken scarf. Hortense, whose pain had subsided because of the narcotic, sat in front with the driver. Dr. Thiouville and Busse climbed into the back. Of the two it would be hard to decide which was the more miserable. The doctor was in dread of going; Monsieur Busse was afraid to come back.

Across the Pont St. Michel, coming toward our café from Ile de la Cité, we saw a group of men and women, mostly women, about fifteen in all. At their head walked a tall, soldierly figure, without rifle, sword or sidearms, holding a briefcase or portfolio under one arm. He wore no cap and no military blouse, but his khaki trousers, olive-drab army shirt and polished boots were in order. He was young, but obviously a leader. Several of his followers were carrying portfolios, too.

He stopped on the bridge, a third of the way over, signaled informally toward the parapet, and a plainly dressed woman, with boots as stout as his, spread her portfolio on the broad stone shelf, made a gesture of good-bye, and stationed herself beside it, pencil in hand.

"Mais, alors! C'est Monsieur Garry Davis," said the Chestnut Man, and wizened little Madame du Gran' Chemin cackled softly and hunched her shoulders gleefully together. She always felt a personal connection with men or women whose pictures appeared in the papers she sold.

The Chestnut Man was right. It was Garry Davis. The American delegate and I recognized our ex-countryman, now "Citizen of the World." Garry paused again, two-thirds the way across the bridge, and stationed another female with a portfolio and pencil. In each portfolio was a large book, spread open like a hotel register, with ruled lines on its pages to guide whoever wished to sign.

Katya and Raoul froze slightly, and the other Commies, Rachelle and the two union steamfitters, looked about the way Queen Victoria must have when she uttered her famous line "We are not amused." I was slightly puzzled by their attitude, because it had been announced in several newspapers that Garry was to address the World Congress of the Partisans of Peace on his pet subject, world citizenship and travel between countries without restrictions or passports.

As Garry came abreast of our *terrasse*, the American delegate, unaware of the displeasure of his fellow Communists, got up to greet him and signed his big book. Nearly everyone in the vicinity was willing, if not anxious, to sign. Members of all political parties, including a few from the extreme Right, stood in line and wrote their names on the dotted line. Most of them had never traveled, and never expected to leave France. They put themselves on record against passport requirements, nevertheless. Had the text of

Garry's pronunciamento extolled the virtues of snake oil for lumbago, he would have won over as many supporters that sunny afternoon. Parisians were in the mood to be agreeable.

I may as well confess that I signed the book, myself.

14. *Double, Double, Toil and Trouble*

I HAD been afraid in the course of my ten years' absence from France that the French might have lost their charming inefficiency, so inconsistent, so inherent in every last one of them and their institutions, as full of reports and surprises as a rocket. Before I had been on the old *De Grasse* an hour, while the seamy old relic of the once magnificent French Line was still in the Hudson, headed for Le Havre, I realized that my forebodings had been in vain. French petty economies still prove ruinously expensive; whatever is easy is made difficult.

There is no unemployment in France. The French are energetic and industrious. They are brave. They try hard, and keep going, in the face of no matter what discouragements. At their worst they can be as arrogant as Hindus, as stubborn as Basques, as taciturn as Finns, but they have guts. You love them for it. It is impossible, more often than not, to imagine how they can possibly succeed. But it is much harder to imagine that Paris will go down into dust, like Babylon, Nineveh, Tyre and Sidon, Sodom and Gomorrah, Athens, Rome, Madrid, Berlin, Vienna, even London, if you like.

The French, although they are not bad at confusing large affairs, do not neglect to hash up the piquant small ones that mean so much to all of us.

I have mentioned that huge trucks bumble through Paris traffic with five-pound loads, while pushcarts which antedate the visit of Edward VII break down under tons of junk. When a little Geugeot which could not win a butting contest with a healthy billy-goat loses a spark plug, eight full grown volunteer mechanics gather around, obscuring it from view and cutting off one another's light. Conversely, if an autobus stalls and ceases functioning, the chauffeur, who is seldom a mechanic and not always a good driver, is left to potter around alone, in the middle of the Opéra or the *place* du Chatelet, and the bus quite frequently obstructs traffic in the busy square during two or three days and nights.

A building job, even if the contractor is honest and the party who has to pay is exigent, would make a smart American boy with a meccano set laugh himself silly. I stood watching a repair crew on a roof in the rue St. Séverin the other day. At first there were only three or four of us, but the number of spectators grew until the street was blocked. Two workmen in patched "monos" (one-piece work suits which button down the front) detailed themselves to try to keep the crowd well back from the area into which chunks of tile or plaster might fall. One man stood on the edge of the rickety roof, in peril of his life, and, clinging to a chimney with both hands, dislodged loose bits of material, with one foot. What was accomplished in the course of a morning could have been done by an energetic squirrel in twenty minutes.

Wherever you go, in the old parts of Paris, you will see elaborate stagings on towers, roofs and against the walls of buildings. Nine times out of ten it takes longer to put up the stagings than to do the repair work. Years ago a building worker fell. His union complained. The Legislature passed a law requiring fantastic staging. The waste is almost incalculable, because private owners of dwelling houses or apartments cannot afford repair work more expensive, measured by the foot-pounds accomplished, than a surgical operation would be. The pulley and the bucket are everywhere. If you saw people all over Paris rendering tallow, molding candles around wicks, and using them for light, it would not seem more incongruous than watching laborers at 100 francs an hour sending single hammers or a few pounds of cement up six stories along the front of a building, with rope and tackle that would not have astonished Vercingetorix.

Why there is no unemployment in France is most evident when one looks into a public office—the baggage rooms at a large railway station, a customs shed, a bank, or any of the offices connected with the government ministries or nationalized industries. It might almost be said that there is no employment, either. Each man or woman on the payroll spends most of his or her time dodging interference, making mistakes or compounding the errors of others. In the airplane factories, for instance, there are now fourteen executives for every six who were hired under private management. Many of the extra ones have been planted there by the Commies, just to obstruct the Government. The Government does not dare weed out the subversives, for fear of a general strike.

Many industrial workers of France act like public enemies. In France there is a cold class war, just as Marx said there would be. Where is there not such a conflict?

Frenchmen are such pronounced individualists that cooperative effort is always difficult for them. I heard (and saw) a wonderful performance by the municipal chorus of Lille of Purcell's *Dido and Aeneas*. The women all wore long full skirts under which one could imagine old-fashioned ruffled drawers. The Carthaginian Queen, as a soloist, was permitted to wear a "Directoire" gown that made her look like Anna Held. The men, young and old, wore business suits, nearly all of them blue. A few iconoclasts, however, held out for brown or gray, and those in mourning—still customary in some of the provincial cities—wore black. The Lille organization was not a chorus, but a throng of soloists.

The performance was staged at the Salle Pleyel, to give tourists a cultural treat. The Republican Guard lined the staircases, in resplendent uniforms to lend the evening an official, ceremonial air. Out in the lobby the spectacle was impressive, dignified and beautiful. I regret to say that few tourists were present. American visitors were spending the evening at the Folies Bergère or in one of the jazz "clubs" of the Existentialist belt, or the expensive booby traps in Montmartre, where New York prices are charged for Yonkers entertainment.

It was heartbreaking to see such magnificent shows, all through the tourist season, so well presented and so poorly attended. Crowds flocked to see a few uninteresting relics of Napoleon, a truly paltry collection, and ignored the "century of hats" at the Carnavalet that offered history and social progress in capsule form for those who lacked time for study.

The race tracks had a banner year. Inflation has played scurvy tricks, but it has brought down the prices at the pari-mutuel windows, so that hundred-franc bets, which were once fairly steep, now cost less than thirty cents, and thousand-franc bets that used to be for millionaires now are automatically marked down to $2.86. Now the rich and poor, and those in between, rub elbows at the tracks.

On many days, the official judges act either like the Marx or the James brothers (not William and Henry), but the public seldom protests. The element of chicanery is always to be reckoned with, in the mind of a sophisticated Frenchman, and its absence would seem like a lack of coarse salt when boiled beef is served.

Mail service in Paris is fairly reliable, but when the post office goes wrong, it stops at practically nothing. A friend of mine, a California man who works for the Paris edition of the New York *Herald Tribune*, has a mother of whom he is unusually fond and who writes him long letters at least twice a week. He has to turn out at least three columns a day for the paper, and cannot force himself to compose long replies to his mother's communications very often. Once in a while, he sacrifices his day off and writes her several pages, being more careful about the omissions than the text. Five months ago he went through one of those letter-writing ordeals, and in addressing the envelope to the California city street and number, forgot to add "Etats Unis," that is, "United States."

One hundred and fifty-six days later, a bellhop from the Hotel California, which is directly across the narrow rue de Berri from the *Herald* building, brought back the letter and handed it to the American reporter. It had been kicking around France all that time and finally had been delivered to the Hotel California, eighteen feet from where it started, because of the word "California" in the address.

Before World War II, in the course of the years when the Popular Front was selling out Spain and the French bankers and industrialists were flirting with Hitler in order to undermine the Popular Front, the suicide rate in Paris jumped. There were no reliable records, since a French census always divorces itself completely from either mathematics or reality. But everyone who read the papers was aware that an increasingly large number of citizens were destroying themselves.

A careful reader observed that most of the suicides were accomplished by the discouraged one throwing himself or herself into the Seine. After further study, the same reader found that a high percentage of the unfortunate incidents occurred between the Pont St. Michel and the Pont Neuf, along the Quai des Orfèvres of the Ile de la Cité.

The newspaper reader above mentioned wrote a strong letter to the Paris *Temps* asking why the city authorities had not stationed police along the Quai des Orfèvres to dissuade those who were tired of it all and deny them access to the Seine. Most of the suicide attempts, he pointed out, not only were concentrated along that short stretch of *quai* but took place between one o'clock and six o'clock A.M. The letter was published, the *Temps* commented editorially, and other letters began to pour in, inquiring and trying to establish why the Quai des Orfèvres and the hours between one and six in the morning proved so fatally attractive to the disconsolate.

A police inspector who fancied himself as a practical psychologist pointed out that the night buses to the outlying quarters and suburbs of Paris nearly all started from the *place* du Chatelet. Most of them were on an hourly schedule. So that if anyone missed a night bus there, he had to wait an hour. The weather was mostly dismal and there was no adequate shelter for those who could not crowd into the few all-night cafés or could not afford the price of coffee or wine. That dreary wait was the crowning discouragement that the desperate and suffering ones could not face. The Quai des Orfèvres was near by, not a block away.

Just after World War II, river suicides became too prevalent again, but all along the Seine as it flowed through Paris, and they were attempted by day as well as by night, due largely to inflation and love affairs which had gone wrong. The municipal officials decided to install emergency life-saving apparatus on the Paris bridges. Wooden cases containing stout life preservers with generous lengths of rope were attached to the parapets. A Sunday afternoon was set aside for a demonstration at various bridges, conducted by the police. The public was urged to attend.

On the Pont du Caroussel, between the Louvre and the Left Bank, a sizable crowd gathered, a strong young policeman lifted the heavy life preserver from its box, wound the rope several times around his wrist, and heaved the stuffed canvas ring over the low stone wall. He had served in the Commissary during his period of military training, and knew nothing of naval affairs. Of course, the heavy weight of the life preserver, dropping several yards before the rope around his wrist drew taut, jerked him over the wall and into the river. Some twenty minutes later he was pulled into a row boat and resuscitated, and had the honor of being the first man saved under the new system.

Some South Americans, Spaniards and Catalans in Paris made the practice of staging cock fights on Sunday and holiday afternoons. In the same wave of reform that closed the brothels some members of the French Society for the Prevention of Cruelty to Animals raised such a protest that the police had to raid the rooster combats. About a hundred fighting cocks were seized, and the captain in charge of the clean-up campaign, figuring that game cocks would be good to eat if subjected to a few days of special feeding, had his men turn the fighting birds loose in an isolated chicken yard on the back slope of Montmartre. The cops threw in some cracked corn and went home for the night.

That must have been an epic night. In the morning all the cocks but two were dead, and the two survivors, too tired for effectual mayhem, were sitting on their beam ends, facing each other and making feeble passes with their spurs.

When the national tapestry works wanted to import angora goats from Kashmir years ago, the Government sent a crew of tapestry experts who were authorities on fine wool with a specially chartered vessel to bring back the goats. The animals, all fine specimens, were driven on board successfully, but they all died on the way back to France because none of the textile experts knew how to feed them.

In the days before the rise and fall of Hitler, young Frenchmen who had strong family or other influence behind them, used to get themselves assigned to the Paris fire department, in order to pass their military service safely and snugly, without leaving Gay Paree. They were asked to do a minimum of wagon polishing and hose testing, and were detailed to stand or sit in Paris theatres and other places of assembly and entertainment during performances, so somebody from the fire department would be on hand if an emergency arose. Practically no emergencies arose, and neither were there any fires worthy the name. Paris is comprised of fire-traps, large and small, that would not be tolerated in Middletown or Skowhegan, but nothing ever burns.

By the way, when the Eternal Flame at the tomb of the Unknown Soldier went out one winter night, it took the combined mechanical geniuses of Paris fourteen hours to get it going again.

Rabelais tells how Diogenes, ashamed because he was the only man idle when his countrymen were preparing for war, and unable to think of any way in which a philosopher could be of use, started rolling and thumping his tub up and down the hill, to keep up the appearance of activity in order not to set a bad example. Some modern Diogenes must have taken charge of the Paris fire department this year. The young men called to the colors no longer try to get into a fireman's *caserne*. Those assigned to duty as firemen do not sit comfortably on their bunks, play French checkers or belotte, serve restless women in all the adjoining blocks with informal consolation, and occupy free seats at the shows. Now even the infantrymen and engineers feel sorry for the *pompiers*.

In the course of the first eighteen years I was in Paris, off and on, I read of only two deaths caused by fires, in peace time, and one of the victims was an American who had just arrived from New York.

During the last nine months I have not seen the fire wagons out once, except for exercise and practice, and we have had very cold weather since October. Electric wiring is done by amateurs, nine times out of ten, and would cause a New York inspector to faint. The gas fittings never were practicable, and have not been replaced or repaired since the outbreak of war in 1939. Steam-heating apparatus which had not been used for years was turned on early in October of 1949; old rusty boilers were submitted to pressure; pipes groaned, wheezed, hollered and croaked. Still no buildings burned. Now and then a curtain is ignited by a match or a candle, and an alarm is turned in. Again a chimney will catch fire. Those occasions are nightmares to tenants and landlords, and a Paris fireman's dream of heaven. He inundates a whole apartment house with water and chemicals and chops down antique oak doors by the dozen, to extinguish a few sheets of paper in a waste basket or a smoldering hole in the upholstery of a chair.

Most of the houses in Paris are built of concrete, of a sort, and finished with plaster. There is not much wood construction. Paper and cloth are so scarce that no waste or oily rags are tossed around. Boilers are so flimsy that when they explode not much force is released. And cigarettes are so scarce and expensive that, vile as they are, Parisians smoke them down so far that what is left could not set off a pile of dry shavings.

It is lucky that there are very few fires because the French could not afford them.

All in all, the French still firmly believe that inefficiency is the law and ordinance of human nature and that, without it, they would become a nation of automatons.

15. An Evening to Remember

FOR ten years the lights of Paris were black, tinged with blood, brown, dimmed with humiliation, gray, drained of hope. Liberation stirred old reflections in the hearts of the survivors, but on Easter Saturday evening, 1949, came the transformation.

The official announcement was undramatic. A few lines appeared in the Paris newspapers to the effect that the coal supply had made available more electric power. Regulations curtailing the domestic use of electricity for lighting purposes were suspended, that is, Parisians could have light in their houses, homes, hotels and little shops every day, and cease to grope in darkness Friday afternoons and Saturday mornings. Hoods were removed from street and bridge lamps, in so far as possible, and permission was given all and sundry to turn on electric advertising signs and illuminate display windows. Individuals read the newspaper items, and decided what to do, without being urged or organized.

In the livelier quarters, like the rue de la Huchette, there was a spontaneous response. No prompting was needed. The lugubrious window of the truss shop at the eastern end was softened by a dim penumbra; Salmon's butcher shop and apartment, and the side windows above, were alight. Each room had one bulb near the center of the ceiling. A tube of white light played on pots and pans, knickknacks and odds and ends in the window of the paint shop. The Caveau was set off with cast-iron filigree lanterns.

All the lights glowed in the Entrepôt, showing counters of green vegetables. Gillotte's bakery was alive, and chocolate rabbits and eggs were ranged on glass shelves which had a prismatic effect. Mlle Swallowtail, to make the Commies squirm, had arranged the window of the "Hard Times" antique shop to feature a large framed oil painting, made from a photograph after death, of Jean Jaurès. Katya, almost across the street, had pictures of Stalin, Thorez and Duclos draped in turkey-red bunting, and beside them a newspaper cut, five columns wide, of French foreign legionnaires carrying by the hair the severed dripping heads of Indo-Chinese patriots who allegedly had been taken "prisoner" in the course of the fighting between the French and the forces of Ho-Minh. It was a retake of the same photograph that had been used to advertise the atrocities of the English in Malaya, some months before.

The Hotel de la Huchette turned on all its lights, drew back the window curtains, and opened all the doors. Monsieur Mercanton had turned some of the brackets so the lights shone directly on the newly painted sign. The pharmacy had large old-fashioned globes of colored liquid, red-pink like Corsican wine and transparent blue-green, with bulbs like the peering eyes of enormous polyps behind them. The Ali Baba Buvette had colored tapers between forty thieves in jars, about four inches high, with rakish heads and pirates' hats.

On the corner where the old police station used to be, which now is used as a warehouse for plumbers' and steamfitters' supplies, the building was dark inside, and so was Mme Mariette's "reformed" establishment. Along with the junkyard, they caught the half-glow from all sides and in front, so that grotesque shapes and shadows offered a pale contrast like the mountain shadows on the moon.

St. Cricq, the shoemaker, at No. 9 across from the drug-store, had, in addition to his meager electric light, a cylindrical kerosene pressure lamp that he pumped up at an incalculable risk of explosion and turned on two large pictures of De Gaulle and Leclerc.

Nowhere was to be seen a single pictorial or other kind of holiday tribute to Prime Minister Queuille, or any of his Middle-of-the-Road predecessors, although the coalition then headed by Queuille, apostle of when-in-doubt-do-nothing, could claim at least one-third of the votes in the quarter. Moderates in politics are not the celebrating kind.

Noel had arranged the windows of Les Halles de la Huchette. He had dyed the light bulbs blue, yellow, pink and green, placed two huge stuffed sea gulls, stained white and fixed up to parody the Picasso doves as the *pièce de résistance*, and found a lot of pre-war price tags, which he stuck into imitation turf with paperweight gravestones he had borrowed from Mlle Swallowtail.

The river end of the rue Xavier Privas was a slice of dusk for bats, but the live wicked stretch was lighted dimly, for purposes largely outside the scope of the Ten Commandments. I saw a few Zoot suits, please believe me, on Negroes headed for the bar at No. 12.

The wide end of the rue de la Huchette, off the *place* St. Michel, was restrainedly resplendent. There was as much light as anyone could wish, but nothing ostentatious. Busse was away when the lights went on, but he had given orders to switch on the neon sign, and for candles to supplement the electric lighting in all the windows. The ivory front of the hotel and the bar gleamed like a wedding cake. Practice Geugeots darted like happy bugs across to the rue de la Harpe and scurried in contrary direction. The fact that Rose France and Au Corset d'Art were dim made the Oriental filigree work of Rahab, and the new neon sign that moved, perversely alluring. Inside, the hautboy wavered and wailed to the beat of the Moroccan drum.

The Café St. Michel and the Taverne du Palais at the western portal were so busy that it was hard to remember that war had been hell. And what caused the most comment were the safety saw horses and four new red lanterns placed on either side of the ditch across the sidewalk in front of the repair job of E. Saillens and Sons.

So the street, from one end to the other, was alight as it had not been in ten years of disaster and recovery. There was also, above and beyond the square of St. Michael, the river and the moon. The Seine was high. The alternate pink and lemon lights, with scarlet and green, trailing colored ribbons alive with river movement, were not as brilliant as in pre-war days. Only a few mellow yellow lamps, still topped with indigo, marked the historic bridges, so that from the high windows above Lapérouse could be seen the Pont Neuf, the incongruous black footbridge to the Louvre, the Pont du Caroussel, the Pont Royal, the Pont Solferino and the Pont de la Concorde. In that impressive circle the fountains were sparkling and playing.

And who, loving our obscure quarter, could fail to face about, and look the other way, upstream, to the Ile de la Cité, the spire of the Sainte Chapelle, the Palais de Justice, the shaded *place* Dauphine, the St. Michel bridge, the Conciergerie, the Prefecture, the Hotel Dieu, and Notre Dame de Paris.

It is there, the Cathedral. Somewhere in astral spaces travel the echoes of men who toiled, the thoughts of the architect planners, the devout who prayed, the élite who approved. After eight centuries the foundations are solid, the stones, arches, windows, doors, transepts, nave and buttresses, aloft the gargoyles, add up to Notre Dame, Our Lady of Paris. She catches the glow and the dimness, the aloofness and interdependence, the rise and fall, and visually exemplifies what spiritually She failed to project—a rich man's church in a poor man's community.

Shall we look farther, to the slum of slums and the central wine market worth a pilgrimage to smell? In the Zoo are the survivors, the beasts too mangy to die. The beasts are sleeping who furtively shuttle by day, in badly kept cages, and those who prowl at night, pacing back and forth, back and forth, gleam eyes, switch tail, pad feet.

That night there was light in the rue de la Huchette.

The Pflantzes, in Room 9 at the Hotel Normandie, as soon as the feather mattresses had been removed and the police cards filled out, started doing methodically what they had learned to do in so many rooms they had shared for economy's sake. The packing had been systematic, so that articles came out of the suitcase and bag in reverse of the order of entry. Hermann undressed and washed, while Miriam, on the other side of the screen, draped clothes on collapsible hangers they had brought with them. They knew the French could not make suitable coat hangers. How right they were!

Later Miriam undressed while Hermann was stowing his stuff and dressing. Before the washstand, the way she stood, hands superimposed across her breasts, head tilted slightly to one side, would have delighted Modigliani. Her face, long and without high coloring, the neutral blond of her hair bleached by the sun, her pale eyes dim with evening, could be, according to the observer, either lovely or plain. But her body, strong, slender and well rounded at the thighs, her knees smooth, her legs long and tapering, was not open to question. It was shapely and unique.

Miriam looked far better without clothes. Her half-brother Hermann appeared to much better advantage with them on.

There was no mirror, and Miriam found that she was looking at herself, bare, wet and gleaming, as if she were a figure in a painting. That startled her. She dried herself more hurriedly than usual, slipped on the simplest of undergarments.

As soon as both of them were dressed, Hermann partly refolded the screen and fitted it around the *bidet*. Only the large front lower rooms of the Normandie had these conveniences. He wasted no time. He polished his boots and started mending some socks. Miriam made ready to wash the underclothes they had removed and not until after she had filled the bowl with water, made suds with French Lux and put in the garments to soak did she notice the hand-lettered sign.

"Alas, brother," she said.

The sign read: IT IS CATEGORICALLY FORBIDDEN THAT CLIENTS WASH CLOTHES IN THE ROOMS.

"Alas," Hermann said. He was faced with the fact that a strict rule already had been broken, before even their Cuban passports, fraudulently acquired, had withstood police scrutiny. Until Hermann was notified specifically that their registration papers had been accepted and filed, all other details were of secondary importance but must be managed in a way that would stir no suspicion.

It did not astonish Miriam that, in the minor emergency, she thought at once of Louis the garçon. Without saying anything she took the partly folded screen from around the *bidet*, placed it, extended, between the beds to isolate Hermann, then removed her gingham dress and selected a peasant blouse and full skirt she had got cheap from a Dalmatian girl stranded in Antwerp. Hermann had felt dubious about the colored embroidery because it was too easy to remember and identify, but he had seen that Miriam liked it, that the costume became her, and had set his fears aside.

"One moment," said Miriam. "I descend."

Louis was behind the bar, and Madame Fontaine at the desk. The clients included Noel, the Chestnut Man, Monge, the horse butcher, the Satyr, Gillotte, St. Cricq, the shoemaker, and Doc Robinet, the herborist. Vignon came in from the W.C., which was of the primitive Ottoman type, still fumbling with an obstinate button on his fly. When the little grocer saw the vision in peasant embroidery standing in the hall doorway, he twitched so violently with St. Vitus dance that he nearly unjointed his neck. Louis scrambled out from under the bar, spoiling his neat fresh hair comb, and Chouette, the guilty truck driver, very drunk for the second time that day, made a grab for the edge of the table at which he was sitting and grunted: *"Bon Dieu!"*

"Excuse me, please," Miriam said.

Louis interposed himself between the girl and the others, but could not cut off the view of Madame Fontaine, who was sizing up her new tenant and trying not to feel the antipathy the ribald steady drinkers were reading into her every glance and gesture.

"May I be of service?" Louis asked.

"If you could mount," Miriam said, apologetically.

"Sure," boomed Madame Fontaine. "By all means, Louis. Mount, my pigeon. Mount. Don't think about the bar, with no one tending it."

"I'm sorry," Miriam said. She was aghast that she had

somehow offended Madame the Patronne, and more so at the thought of confessing about the laundry in soak, where all the men could continue to gaze at her with unanimous approval. She had been stared at, accosted and followed in several countries, but in that district of Paris, where willing women, ready for practically anything, abounded, she had not expected such a spontaneous tribute.

"I am being unfortunate this evening," Miriam said, as Louis followed, two stairs behind her.

Louis heard the statement but he forgot to answer.

"You said, mademoiselle . . ." he asked, on the first floor landing. She paused and faced him, breathing lightly, while he was breathing hard.

"Inadvertently I have broken an ordinance of Madame, and now she is displeased because I interrupted you at your work. She is severe, *n'est-ce pas?*"

"Not if she likes you," Louis said.

"She dislikes me, I think," said Miriam, and Louis could not find words with which to contradict her.

Miriam and Louis, after she had opened the door to No. 9, made a couple of false stops and starts, each desiring the other to go first, or wishing to enter last.

When they appeared, Hermann was looking at Louis anxiously, ready to sink or ascend with his spirits. Was there news of or from the police? When Louis seemed to have nothing to offer, Hermann's disappointment was pathetically apparent. Nothing was more dangerous for anyone in his position than to appear worried. Miriam, understanding, said mildly but reproachfully:

"Monsieur Louis told us distinctly that the collection and acceptance of papers by the police would occur only tomorrow," Miriam said.

"Don't give a thought to it," Louis said. He was gay and did not react to Hermann's fears.

Before Miriam could point out the clothes soaking in the bowl of the washstand, Louis noticed them, caught the troubled glances on the part of the Pflantzes, and laughed aloud.

"That sign's only for folks Madame doesn't like," Louis said. "Pay no attention."

Miriam, without smiling, raised her eyebrows ruefully.

"Madame is not liking me, alas," she said.

"I'll attend to Madame," said Louis. "If she bothers you, let me know. The only thing that really burns her up is an electric iron."

Their sudden woebegone expressions told Louis the story all too clearly.

"You have one, I take it," Louis said.

Miriam nodded her head slowly up and down in assent like a child who had done wrong in school.

He smiled and touched her wrist, lightly.

"Let me see it," Louis said.

"Would it not be better if we deposited it in the safe, with Madame?" Hermann asked.

Miriam took from a drawer an electric iron with a cord neatly coiled.

"Ah," said Louis. "It's one of the kind that hold water."

"Should we leave it with Madame, downstairs?" Miriam asked.

"When you press things, burn some of the incense the Turk up the street has for sale. That covers the smell," said Louis.

"Could we use the iron then?" asked Miriam. "Reliable laundries are so expensive."

"I'll put a stronger fuse in the box out in the hall," said Louis.

Downstairs, at the bar, Madame Fontaine was serving customers. Now and then she set down glasses and tumblers so smartly that liquor slopped over and the regulars grinned.

"Louis's a long time upstairs," said the Satyr.

"With only one arm," said Doc Robinet, "there are undoubtedly inconveniences."

Madame, with storm signals in her eyes, was about to retort when the telephone rang. She grabbed it as if it were Louis's neck and wrenched off the receiver.

"*Alors!*" she said, brusquely, before hearing a word.

Noel smiled beatifically, in her line of vision, not two feet away across the zinc. "Our famous French politeness," he said, and sighed.

"He's not here," said Madame Fontaine into the receiver. "No . . . Not Monsieur Busse. Not Monsieur Wilf, either . . . Monsieur Mainguet? Most likely in church."

She held the receiver against her bosom. Sounds were spluttering, but she ignored them.

"Those imbecile Mexicans," she said. "They've changed their minds. It's a message from some curé, for Monsieur Mainguet. Instead of dining at the Mont Souris, they're all going to the Café Madrid."

She stooped without grunting, stepped through the low slot, strode into the hallway and, cupping her mouth with her hands, yelled up the stairway:

"Louis!"

Christophe, when he awoke, was aware of a spongy pressure inside his head, a noise like a slow leak through his ears, and a taste like fledgling owlets in his throat. Lying flat on his aching back he realized first that the shoes pointing awry from the other end of him did not seem to be his own. The nagging discomfort around his neck proved to be a collar, buttoned tightly, and a four-in-hand tie.

Resolutely he tried to shut those unreal items from his mind and go to sleep again, repeating some words from way back in the past.

"You must not put the vanilla paddle in the chocolate. You must not put the chocolate paddle in the strawberry. You must not put the strawberry paddle . . ."

At that point he lost track of the flavors and had to start over again. Somewhere, some time, he had sat for hours in a damp wine cellar, with three freezers of ice cream he had to stir. There was a wine bottle handy from which he drank —and in spite of himself he had done the wrong thing with the paddles.

Switched back to the present, he sat up. He was awake. No use. A soft squeal of joy sounded near by and the Great Dane, which he had forgotten, stood up and shook himself, stretched, yawned and nuzzled Christophe's hand. Christophe's mind was swaying like a limp signal flag. He reached out with his free arm, touched a drapery, clutched it and in shifting his weight jerked the curtain down, together with its mate and a solid brass rod that rapped him on the sconce. He was silvered with thin moonlight through a window thus exposed. Strange walls shimmered and beyond his outstretched legs stood a dainty dresser.

The Great Dane whined at the door. Christophe let him out. He reassured himself that he was not sick. The food and wine he had consumed had been of first quality. He remembered dimly about the clothes. He knew that it was night, but not which night. He was abominably thirsty.

Spying a small glass-stoppered bottle on the dresser he went for it, and downed the contents at a gulp. The rasping perfume scorched his throat and seethed in his stomach, but when he could breathe again he felt that it had saved him. Details of the day came back. He fished desperately in all his pockets. Not a franc. That made him angry and he growled to himself. He sat back down on the bed, recovered his Homburg which was on the floor, upside down, and began to feel that a commercial career was not for him. He had let Madame Berthelot down. The others had failed to provide him with funds.

The Jonquil, who had been visiting with another concierge, stepped alone into the courtyard, saw the huge dog and stopped short in her tracks. Xavier, having finished at the trash can, walked back to the bedroom doorway and whined. The Jonquil, excited enough to set aside her fears, approached gingerly, turned the door knob and held the door slightly open. She could see Christophe sitting on the bed, in the moonlight, still dressed like Robert Schuman, Homburg and all. Since the whole quarter had long been alerted to find the old tramp, the Jonquil felt a thrill of accomplishment.

"Your dog, monsieur," she said, to make sure Christophe was aware that she was at the doorway.

Christophe came out of his trance, in which he had concluded that soon he must be going somewhere he had never been before. The perfume had restored his aplomb, with interest.

"Madame," he said, severely, "cannot a man guard his employer's premises, unmolested?"

"But of course," the Jonquil said. "I only thought you might be lonesome and dry."

The Jonquil could not have hit upon a suggestion better

calculated to soften Christophe's resistance. No matter about the lonesomeness, but he was drier than a mummy.

"Bring your beast and sit in my kitchen, where no one will see you or be the wiser," she said.

Christophe allowed himself to be led across the moonlit courtyard, and Xavier, on the leash, walked at his heels. The Jonquil, when they were safely inside her kitchen, drew the shades, uncorked a jug, and poured two tumblers of red wine. She drank from hers while she watched him toss his off, and promptly refilled his tumbler.

Xavier, seemingly as content one place as another, stretched himself behind the range.

"You're famished, I have no doubt," the Jonquil said to Christophe. For answer his seamed stomach boiled and rumbled audibly, as perfume and red wine joined in chemical reaction.

"I've been on watch for hours," he said.

The Jonquil chuckled. "I like a man who can keep his business to himself. No one has suspected where you are," she said, to keep him at his ease. "Let me build a little fire and heat my beef Bordelaise, with a few new potatoes, and buttered carrots, if they are to your taste," she added, persuasively.

With the jug in one hand and his glass in the other, Christophe, now perfectly at home, frowned judiciously. "As long as the carrots are not mingled with peas," he agreed. He had wine handy, food was in prospect, no one knew where he was except the woman who seemed anxious to serve him, and would be discreet.

Then both of them were dismayed. Footsteps, soft and surreptitious, caused the Jonquil to replace the stove cover and Christophe to set down the jug, but neither moved soon enough to prevent Xavier from springing up, tensely and trotting to the window, where he nuzzled the curtain aside. Coincidentally the Jonquil peeped out through her Judas window. Christophe sat where he was, like Jupiter, and raised the wine glass to his lips. If anyone entered, he was determined to be discovered in an appropriately dignified pose.

He saw that the Jonquil was relaxing. She saw, crossing the courtyard, Mignon and, beside her, Fabien Salmon whom she was leading by the hand. Mignon went straight to Mme Berthelot's window, now bare of its drape, peeked in, then drew back, disappointed. The Jonquil understood at once that the girl had known Christophe had been there, and had hoped to show the boy where the pushcart man and his giant gray dog were hiding.

Xavier, who had remained silent up to that moment, let out one of his deep reverberating barks.

The effect on the children was instantaneous. Fabien started running and disappeared from the courtyard. Mignon, transfixed, looked first this way and that, trying to determine from which direction the sound had come. But after the first unearthly bellow, Xavier was ordered to be quiet, and obeyed, although the word was spoken in a husky undertone. Mignon walked from the court. She knew that Fabien would tell Victor she had known where to find the old man Victor had been seeking.

"What passes?" growled Christophe, pounding the table in a magisterial way.

"Just some children. They've gone away," the Jonquil said.

The Jonquil poured from the jug, and they both drank, but she only half as much, and half as fast as he did. He was under the impression that his weight was increasing, so that he felt the pull of the earth on his bottom through the chair seat, and sat with feet flat on the floor and knees well apart. He also had the illusion that his strength was growing in proportion, so that he could support more avoirdupois and gravitational attraction.

"My old grandmother used to say: 'Children! When you are comfortable, stay where you are. When discontented, move.' I've found that sound advice," the Jonquil said.

Christophe agreed by raising his left fist and letting it fall twice on the table, but he gave the words a wider application than the Jonquil intended. She was thinking about the cozy kitchen. He had in his mind the cities, woods, rolling country, plains and rivers of France, connected and traversed by French railroads and canals.

"Women," he said, "should stay where one can find them."

"I've a bottle of calvados on a shelf in the cupboard. It gives wine a sound reinforcement," she said.

The smell of the beef Bordelaise filled the room.

"Lunching passably gives one a relish for dinner," said Christophe.

"Ho! Ho! He! Ha!" cackled the Jonquil. "Lunching passably. You're a droll one, all right."

"Mind what you're doing," he said, sternly, because her dry mirth had caused her to spill a few drops of gravy on his napkin. She served him a generous helping.

"What am I doing?" she exclaimed, apologetically, then falling to, she cackled again. "Lunched passably . . . He! Ho! You got into Monsieur Busse for at least ten thousand francs. That's what people are saying. That's passable, all right."

"Busse! Iscariot!" roared Christophe, and Xavier made muffled sounds in his throat.

"He! He! Ho! Hum! Iscariot! Well, I never," laughed

the Jonquil, with fingers over her mouth. "My soul and body! Busse! Iscariot!"

The beef in wine was hearty and the clean new potatoes, hardly larger than pigeon's eggs, were fresh and tender. With plenty of wine, and shots of calvados in moderation, Christophe was inclined to bestow credit where credit was due.

"Madame," he said, leaning back and tilting up his chin, "I am faring well for the second time this day, and in spite of Madame Berthelot's misfortune, and the effrontery of Madame Morizot who absconded with my fifteen hundred francs and more, and Busse's refusal to pay . . ."

"But, monsieur. Fifteen hundred francs. That amount is not what it was, my friend. If Madame Berthelot owes you such a trifle, and those others will not honor your demands, I could let you have that sum."

"You overwhelm me, madame," Christophe said. In his mind he was multiplying 1,500 francs by three, and had almost enough to pay the bill at the Mont Souris, which he had no intention of doing. Fifteen hundred from Busse, 1,500 from Madame Morizot, now 1,500 from the Jonquil, and there was still the original 1,500 from Madame Berthelot, making, in all, 6,000 francs.

"I like to see a man have spending money," said the Jonquil. "It gives him self-assurance."

"You are astute, madame," Christophe agreed. He grasped that his luck had reached a level he had not attained before that day. He saw the Jonquil, mincing and simpering, taking some bills of the Bank of France from a smooth stone crock. With the money in her hand, she began crooning in a rakish voice a Can-Can tune, rotating her bunioned foot, while her pointed knee maintained a rickety counter rotation. She sang:

"Comment veux-tu que je te baise,
Dans un lit, tout debout ou dans une chaise?

Christophe joined in, with a deep bass.

"Comme je veux, je peux,
Tu peux, je veux
La façon que tu plaise."

When later he realized that he was singing and dancing, he frowned and resumed his seat with dignity. He was about to become the holder of some cash, appropriate to his clothes, his cleanliness, his state of repletion, stimulation and well being. He must be involved in some larger plan, directed from without, he concluded. The Jonquil started counting out hundred-franc notes, crisp and unworn. When the silent count of fifteen was reached, she tossed in a thousand-franc bill for good measure.

"What's the difference between friends?" she asked.

"Precisely, madame," said Christophe, picking up the money in self-imposed slow motion.

"And what more can I do for you now, monsieur?" asked the Jonquil, who had not felt so expansive in years, if ever.

"I shouldn't like to ask more of you," Christophe replied but she sensed he had one more request. "There's one detail," Christophe continued, after a pause. "Cigars of Amsterdam, such as are kept below the counter at the accursed Mont Souris. I could not venture there . . ."

"Of course. Of course. I'd love to go," the Jonquil said, almost fluttering with eagerness. She grabbed more money from the crock, bade him wait with a gesture, and started out the door.

And as Christophe saw her depart, slowly he became aware that the perfidy within him was stronger than he was, and must have been with him always. He rose, head bowed, then straightened. As he left the courtyard by a narrow passageway into the back street, two thousand five hundred francs cash in pocket, Homburg perched on head, the Great Dane on leash behind him, he muttered to himself:

"One must not dip the vanilla paddle in the chocolate . . . the chocolate in the strawberry . . . the strawberry in the chocolate or vanilla . . . the chocolate in the vanilla or strawberry . . ."

His footsteps receded, Homburg, dog at heel.

"Oh, strawberry . . . oh, chocolate . . . oh, well.

"Oh, strawcolate, chanilla

"Mocolate . . . Mawberry

"*Merde!*"

And into the courtyard, a moment too late, dashed Victor.

The private hospital Dupuy in the rue Pierre Curie was not quite as crowded and busy when we reached it early in the evening as it had been that afternoon, but the staff was correspondingly smaller. Everybody was anxious to be free that week-end. Of course, the holiday accident cases were coming in, intermittently. They were not as numerous as they would have been in an American city, and the injuries were, for the most part, not as grave as those resulting from the swifter, heavier American cars and the hazards of a mechanical civilization farther advanced than was consistent with the French temperament and the shortage of money in France.

When, in the waiting room reserved for the élite, we were joined by Dr. Flandrin de Monique, I was pleasantly surprised by his attitude. He was the kind of successful Frenchman in a high profession who was also a man of the world, urbane and versatile. As soon as he learned that I was an

American writer, he turned the conversation toward literature.

Dr. Thiouville was on pins and needles. He had permitted Hortense, only because of her insistence, to take the blame for the aggravated condition of her, at first, simple fracture of the elbow. But Dr. Flandrin de Monique, suave practitioner that he was, had not been deceived. The shock to Dr. Thiouville's sensibilities was cruel when it became apparent that Dr. Flandrin de Monique was regarding him with frank admiration. Dr. de Monique addressed the stricken young man as *"Mon chèr collègue"* and evidently had decided that the baby-faced young doctor from the rue de la Huchette had gifts that might carry him far. In short, Dr. de Monique seemed to accept all too easily the fact that the simple fracture of an elbow, in which one of the principal contractors rebuilding France was interested, had developed complications. He had tactfully let Dr. Thiouville understand that the first set of X-ray plates would be destroyed and never mentioned in court, if the case went to court. Furthermore, he had hinted that other simple cases might, in the future, be entrusted to Dr. Thiouville's care.

Busse, because I think Dr. de Monique was anxious to be rid of him, was taken first into the photographing room. The expert did not rebuke the young doctor for bringing in Monsieur Busse after "the nose" had reached an almost unrecognizable shape. Dr. de Monique always spoke of "the nose" or "the elbow" as if the injured members had been detached like bits of ectoplasm from the rest of the body. He assumed that because Monsieur Busse had jumped over the dog of an employee of Madame Berthelot's who had been pressed into service because of her injury, that E. Saillens would pay for that treatment also.

Already sick with apprehension, Busse felt his morale

slump to a new low. It would be weeks, perhaps months, before he had a normal face again, and during that interval, when he would need it most to stand up to Pierre Vautier and face an action for 1,000,000 francs damages to the painting, he would look like an unsavory type in a low carnival. A man in that condition, robbed of whatever dignity his human countenance possessed, would be in no state to defend his rights, or ask for his share of justice.

Leaving Hortense to the medicos, young and old, I went with Busse to the Gare de Lyon, in order to inquire about the heavy baggage of the Mexican pilgrims who were due, we thought, for dinner that evening. The customs sheds in all French railway terminals are dreary and exert a depressing effect before one has asked Question One. That attached to the Gare de Lyon, perhaps because so much stuff came in there from Italy, is more complicated and confusing than the others. There are platforms labeled with letters of the alphabet, from "A" to "Z," and Busse found, to his horror, that the trunks of the twenty-five Mexicans, all of whom had complicated names which might land almost anywhere in the alphabet when interpreted by French baggage smashers on a holiday week-end, had already been separated and tossed into alphabetical mountains of trunks, hampers, boxes, suitcases, duffel bags and packages from Rome, Pisa, Turin, Modane, Chambéry, Aix-les-Bains, Lyon and Dijon.

"Who rearranged your face, old man?" asked a baggage clerk of the more amiable kind, one who was willing to help but knew that there was little use in trying.

Busse resented the man's familiarity and was turned over to another attendant who was hard-boiled and hoped that all travelers would lose everything they had. The second one took Busse into an empty office and told him to wait there.

No one was in the office. No one came. The fourth time Busse went out to complain, he was referred to a freight elevator man.

"What name?" he asked, grinning broadly at Busse's massive beak and two shiners that looked like sketches by André Masson.

Busse drew himself up. "There are twenty-five names," he said curtly.

"Let's take the first one. Probably there's nothing downstairs for any of them," he said.

"I know there's nothing downstairs," said Busse.

"You might inquire at the platforms, outside. But you must know the names."

"I haven't got the names," Busse said. "The men are Mexicans, on official business connected with the Church."

"In that case, to hell with them on both counts," said the elevator man, and turned away.

Busse looked at me with such an appeal in his eyes that I had to choke off my smile. I realized that, returning to the rue de la Huchette, Busse would have to face, besides Pierre Vautier, Gilles Wilf, and tell the latter that the trunks of the Mexicans had been sprinkled like pepper into the fundamental hash of baggage on twenty-six or more platforms, covering a littered half acre.

"Don't trouble Monsieur Wilf," I advised him. "Find Monsieur Mainguet and explain that you must have a list of the Mexicans' names. Then come back with a couple of porters, and sort out their trunks yourself."

When Busse found Mainguet, hanging on the telephone at the Hotel Normandie, he learned that Mainguet had no list of names, and that all the preparations made by the chef at the Mont Souris for the Mexicans' dinner had been a waste of time, labor, fuel and foodstuffs which had been obtained under stress.

"You'll have to tell the chef. I simply can't," Busse said, and meek Monsieur Mainguet sighed. He had been thinking of that.

"The delegation's dining at the Café Madrid," he said disconsolately.

"Well, go on up there, and get a free feed," the Satyr said. Mainguet flushed and could not conceal his hurt.

"No one thought to invite me," he said.

Walking along the sidewalk, Busse made up his mind to undergo a test. Vignon, the wiry little grocer, was approaching. Since Busse could not, because of the narrowness of the sidewalk, turn out to the right, the grocer should have veered to make way. But he was thinking about something or other and did not notice anyone coming his way. Busse, clinging to his determination not to give ground, waited an instant too long, leaped quickly, hit the lower level of the street pavement on a slant, and almost turned his ankle for the second time that day. Vignon, still preoccupied, went on without noticing what had happened, but Irma, the streetwalker, stepped out of a doorway.

"He'd be glad if I broke my neck," Busse said, protestingly, to Irma. "He feels toward me as nearly everyone does."

"Cheer up. Jesus loves you," Irma said, but seeing that the effect of her words had struck deeper than she had intended, she added, compassionately: "You mustn't feel sorry for yourself. People don't care much about other people one way or the other."

"I mustn't be defeated," Busse said. "I must try once again. I started to walk down the sidewalk, as you observed, on the right-hand side to which I was entitled. A man should yield me my place, and step around me. I shall do it again."

"Good luck," Irma said.

Busse started away, and that time met Fabien, the butcher's young son. Evidently Busse did not wish to pit himself against a timid boy, so both of them stepped left, off the sidewalk. We saw Busse, finally disentangled from Fabien, start toward the *place* doggedly. Coming toward him were the Satyr, Monsieur Nathaniel and the Chestnut Man, Indian file, about two yards apart.

Off to the left into the street went Busse, up again he hopped, only to sidestep to the street again to let the tall Armenian pass. Busse, rattled as a rabbit in a roundup, bounced back to the sidewalk just in time to bump into the burly Chestnut Man, who grabbed him and lifted him off his feet by the shoulders to keep him from falling.

"Pardon," said the Chestnut Man in his deep slow voice. "I forget sometimes to look where I'm going."

I was almost as much touched as Busse was by the gentle manners of the strongest man who ever had trod our street.

"My fault. I'm sorry," said the Chestnut Man. "Come in and have a drink."

Busse, although the last thing he wanted was a drink, could not refuse, and was ushered into a bar, his stomach already quivering.

When he came out, five minutes later, still unnerved and pale, he braced himself to enter the Mont Souris, and saw sitting in the lobby, sipping from long glasses of iced green mint, Pierre Vautier, smiling, gesturing and talking a mile a minute to an attractive brunette, dressed in the height of fashion, also smiling and animated, at his elbow. The evening was hot. Pierre and Carmen seemed gayer than if the temperature were a few degrees lower, without a bead on their foreheads or a wrinkle in their clothes. They looked better together than either one separately. One would have said that they had not expected to have such a good time.

There was a screech of brakes, indignant exclamations and an impudent tooting of harsh horn as one of the auto-school Geugeots swerved, skidded and came to a stop without overturning. Busse in his panic had dashed in front of the absurd little car, and already was yards away, headed out of the threatening zone.

The lights! How they made the old streets cozy! And the river, how refreshing and unhealthy! And the moon! Smells of heat, of pavements, of new leaves! Wherever France had been, she was then at the *place* St. Michel. Wherever France was going, so were those Parisians present. Beside the Seine in silvery black. In the aspic of the moon.

On the sidewalk in front of the cobbler's shop, in the street's mid-section, while some of the tardiest eaters were still at table, a few friends were sitting on the curb or on stools and benches which had been brought out by St. Cricq.

Diagonally across, in Room 9 of the Normandie, Hermann Pflantz was trying to read, and Miriam was ironing. Their draperies were closed, but the window was wide open, so they could hear every word that was spoken outside.

"Our shoemaker," Mainguet remarked, "bears the name of the Baron de St. Cricq, who, before the days of radio, free press and the cinema, was a part of Paris's entertainment. Eccentrics roamed the streets in those days. Not in droves, like the Reds, the Be-Bops and Existentialists today, but as unique individuals.

"One night, between the acts on the opening night of a play at the Comédie Française, written by a Monsieur Empis, whose works now are forgotten, Baron de St. Cricq rose from his box and demanded at the top of his voice that 30,000 francs be collected for the author. Most members of the audience, who found the play banal, hooted protests and whistled. The Baron held up his hand for silence. 'If Monsieur Empis had 30,000 francs he wouldn't feel obliged to write more trash,' he said."

The shoemaker was eager to hear more about his namesake. He was a conscientious artisan, somewhat reserved. Like the others, he had dined well, with plenty of wine, so that night he did not mind the limelight.

Mainguet told how the Baron de St. Cricq had sent his servants to all the bath men they could find, and had ordered from each of the latter a tub and hot water to be brought to his house at the same day and hour. His courtyard was filled with bath men and their horse carts and pack donkeys, tubs, jars of water, so that the courtyard and street were jammed with a curious crowd. The rival bath men started arguing, then shouting, then fighting. Heads were broken, animals ran helter-skelter, water was spilled. The Baron and spectators watched, roaring with laughter. Another time the Baron ordered all the carriages from the livery stables in his neighborhood, and rode in the first one, with the others following, empty and in single file. He halted the procession at the Café de Paris, had a glass of coffee on the *terrasse*, then rode back home in the same style.

"Those were the types the Devil made for his own amusement while God was creating the angels," St. Cricq said.

Hermann Pflantz, listening, set aside his book and cocked his ear. Miriam saw that he was getting dangerously excited and was afraid that her ironing, in defiance of Madame's strict rule, was inflaming his nerves.

Below, Mainguet continued. "Pierre Dupuis," he said, "in the time of Louis the Fourteenth, wore a long robe and insisted on being addressed as 'Monsieur l'Arche-Sot' or King of Fools. Anyone else who pretended to be a fool aroused Dupuis' jealousy, and violence, even bloodshed, ensued.

"Vaulesard, mad mathematician and poet, lived in the rue de la Huchette, in the reign of Louis XIII. He used words for figures and numerals for words in his rhymes. And just around the corner, in the rue de la Harpe, Leance, one of the most beautiful women in Paris, was insane. She danced as none of the professionals or court ladies could dance, for any street crowd, and allowed whichever man who took her fancy to go home with her, but never more than one at a time, or the same one twice."

"She was only pretending to be crazy," the American delegate said.

There was a knock on the door of No. 9, upstairs. A pause followed, then Hermann responded. The talk stopped in the street and everyone listened.

"It's me! Louis!" the garçon said, and Madame Gillotte, on the sidewalk, nudged Noel. Someone tittered, and the windows of No. 9 were closed.

Miriam had hidden the iron, and Hermann had tried, unsuccessfully to compose himself before Louis entered.

"Don't be so nervous," Louis said, dismayed by the sight of their panic. "The cop, Benoist, happened in. I gave him your papers. Between us, it's all fixed. Everything's all right. They go straight into the file, nobody sees them, and there they stay. Now will you quit worrying?"

"I was ironing," admitted Miriam, but her heart was beating with joy and relief. "Could I continue?"

"But certainly, mademoiselle," Louis said.

Both were startled when Hermann repeated in a mincing voice: "But certainly, mademoiselle!" He drew himself up, assumed a comical expression, pirouetted on his tiptoes, and toe-danced a waltz measure with an imaginary partner whose stature was indicated by the set of his long arms and hands.

"But certainly, mademoiselle," he repeated to the non-existent partner. "But certainly. Most certainly."

He toe-danced another measure, so lightly that he did not jar the room, in spite of the creakiness of the old parquetry.

Beyond the window curtains and below, on the sidewalk, the group in front of the shoemaker's shop saw Achille Ithier, so pathetically anxious not to make himself conspicuous that he might as well have worn a tag "On Mischief Bent," enter the eastern portal of the street. Pretending to see no one, in order to make believe that no one was noticing him, he sidled into the family entrance of the Normandie.

About two minutes later, Antoinette de Poitevin, almost perishing from embarrassment, entered the street from the narrow rue du Chat qui Pêche, faltering and trembling. Her head was down, her shoulders bent as if the air were cold instead of hot. She must have felt, by a process of substitute magic, the gleeful proddings, nudging, feet shifting, and suppressed comment of those who watched her go.

In No. 9, Louis hung around, first to help Miriam take out the electric iron. Then he sat on the side of the cot to watch her at work, separating a sleeve from a blouse, smoothing it lengthwise on the ironing board, trying the heat of the iron, then moving back and forth, back and forth, rhythmically. Her body swayed, her head tilted and recovered, her hands danced on the horizontal plane like figures in a miniature ballet, approaching, parting, pursuing. Louis' eyes followed. Hermann, reassured, was not afraid of his sister's rule-breaking while the garçon was a party to the infraction. To set the air in motion, if possible, Hermann swung open the windows again, leaving the draperies drawn. Detached from communion with the others, Hermann silently and lightly began waltzing on his toes again, neck stretched full length, head tilted and turned so he was looking over one shoulder at nothing at all.

Mainguet and the group in the street were still talking of odd characters in old Paris.

"There was Zaga . . . Zaga-Christ . . . King of Ethiopia, King of Kings," Mainguet was saying. "And Aotourou, brought from the South Seas by our explorer, Bougainville. The brown man fell in love with a tree in the Jardin des Plantes, went to see the tree daily, talked to it, embraced it . . . so thoroughly he had to be restrained."

"You mean, locked up?"

"It amounted to that. When the homesick animist went out, one of Bougainville's servants stayed with him. Aotourou grieved and moaned, lost appetite and weight. In fact, died, brokenhearted."

"Nature stinks," said Thérèse, the cook.

"Kasangian, the first Armenian in this quarter, was madder than a June bug. He dressed all in black, skull cap, scarf, cravat, suit, long boots with upturned toes, polished black. He lost his mind in the Bibliothèque Nationale, digging like a squirrel for volumes he had dreamed of, and which were never to be found."

"Foreigners were curiosities then."

"Group curiosities now."

"In China, foreigners were devils, forty years ago," said Vignon, the ex-sailor.

"Devils are fallen angels."

"Warmongers. Imperialists."

"Communists and Cubists."

"Goats, owls, ostriches, jackals, wolves. Panzouzou, the southwest wind that brings malaria," Mainguet said.

"The snake," said Thérèse.

"A dose of crabs," Noel suggested.

Mainguet continued. "Scorpions, dragons. Wild dogs and cats. Screech owls and ravens. The son of Hanpa. Datan, Core and Abiron. Belial. Abaddon, Mardouk, Robin. Lambartou, Beelzebub, Lucifer."

"Our California Indians called the Devil 'Coyote,' " the American delegate said. "To St. Thérèse old Nick appeared as a 'frightful little nigger.' To our Algonquians, Arapahoes, Lenapes, and Maidou, he was 'Coyote.' Often he appeared as a man, a red man, not a paleface, but he ended up as a coyote. Coyote didn't bother about Sin, the way the Hebrew Satan did. Coyote didn't invent the sex game we sigh, cry and die for. Our American devil, the wolf of the prairie, did worse. He brought work into the world, along with nits, gnats, flies, mosquitoes, and lice. Also stormy weather, sickness and death. And the Indian's Great White Father did not sacrifice his own son, to be ridiculed and gibbeted. He placed a rattlesnake along the pathway, so that Coyote's only son was fatally stung. So Coyote was the first to be bereaved by Death which he himself had invented."

"Curious," said Mainguet. He liked myths, for a change, in which he was not expected to believe, as an act of faith.

"Why did the Devil want men to die? That makes work for him," asked Mlle Swallowtail.

The American delegate was eager to answer that one.

"Coyote argued that if men died, there would be plenty of funerals. And weddings. He pointed out that men and women who were married would get tired of each other, if neither of them died."

Behind the drawn draperies in No. 9, Hermann, and as

far as he could tell from the preoccupations of Miriam and Louis, only Hermann, heard sounds coming through the thin walls of No. 8 which were disconcerting. No distinct voices, but faint murmurings and unmusical metallic rasping with fragmentary rhythms and no sonority.

Hermann cleared his throat loudly, having in mind that if the occupants of the adjacent room were logical, they might be reminded that sounds carry beyond cardboard barriers.

Louis, intent on Miriam, breathing the air around her with its tang of hot cloth, heard Hermann's "Ahem" and started talking fast, as if he had been as libidinous as he aspired to be.

"Monsieur Pflantz. You're absolutely all right and safe for three months . . . strictly legal, I mean. Then a renewal is possible for three months more. . . . That makes six, and later, an identity card. I can fix that, too," said Louis.

Hermann, drawing up more airily, danced on tiptoes to the window, drew the shades daintily, threw open wider the French doors, and bowed to those down on the opposite sidewalk. He hummed vibrantly, like a swarm of bees, the Waltz of the Flowers, and dancing his amazing tiptoe waltz, each time he passed the windows turning his head over his shoulder to expose his profile, coyly, he murmured: "Most certainly, messieurs. Unquestionably, ladies. St. Cricq, ladies. Zaga-Christ, ladies. Aotourou, tree-lover, ladies. You won't approve of that. Bougainville, messieurs."

The group below were on their feet and others swiftly gathered. Their faces, amazed and amused, were upturned.

"Panzouzou, Lambartou, Hanpa, Robin, mesdemoiselles. Ethiopia. Armenia. Leance, Leance, Leance," he cried. "And Coyote. Whohoohooohoohoo! Vive Coyote, messieurs. Vive flies and mosquitoes. And work. Coyote. Leance. Leance."

"The son of a bitch is crazy," said, in soft English, but completely without malice or disapproval, rather with misty delight, a Negro standing on the corner of the rue Xavier Privas.

When Hermann brought his performance to a close, and made a sweeping bow behind the window railing, there were applause and bravos from the crowd.

"More! *Bis! Encore!*"

Hermann, with an appealing gesture, grimaced to show that he was wilted and exhausted, and begged to be excused. He dropped into a grateful pose and thanked his audience.

"How do you like it here?" called one of the women from the beauty shop. There were in the crowd below a dozen women and two dozen men by that time.

Hermann drew himself up, looking incredibly tall and narrow. He pursed his lips like a camel, and said, pedantically:

"I find it odd, in this community, where the streets are populous and the natives sympathetic, that your quai and river are neglected. Glance up and down, if you please, and you find at all hours the *quai* is almost deserted. Search for a café, between the *place* St. Michel and the *quai* de Tournelle. In vain. For a hostelry de luxe! There is none. For a casino. None. If I am elected, mesdames et messieurs, I will guarantee a passing grade for all French or foreign citizens taking their baccalaureate examinations, and will effect prompt development of the *quai* St. Michel. I ask only that my constituents promenade along the *quai*, from the *place* to the rue du Petit Pont, each evening at twilight, those moving in an easterly direction on the right-hand sidewalk, and those headed west, on the other side, by the parapet. The President of the Republic, Monsieur Vincent Auriol, will station himself at the western extremity, to divert vehicles and direct them away. At the eastern limit will stand the President of the Assembly, Monsieur Edouard Herriot, for a corresponding purpose.

"I thank you, and await the results with confidence!"

And Hermann, as his hearers cheered and uttered incredulous comments, stepped back, drew shut the French doors and closed the draperies.

16. Before the Easter Music

THE lives of Madame Fremont and her daughter, Yvonne, had lost their natural continuity when Fremont, the former postman, had set out to join De Gaulle in 1940. He had been an understanding husband up to a certain point, and had loved Yvonne, and she him, so devotedly that no criticism had been possible between them.

In the course of the year following Fremont's heroic gesture, the daughter had started coughing and losing weight. An American hero once said: "I regret that I have only one life to give for my country." Fremont, listed as "missing," has, to all intents and purposes, sacrificed three.

On Easter Saturday evening, lame Jacqueline, who worked with them, and to whom walking was painful on account of her short misshapen left leg, suggested that they all—Madame Fremont, Yvonne and she—take a walk along the quai. As they passed through the rue du Chat qui Pêche, Madame realized that she had not seen, at close range, before, the entrance of that street, the narrowest and shortest in Paris and only twenty yards from her doorway, since it had been widened and improved in 1946.

Yvonne, walking between the others, coughed as she breathed the river air. It did not seem to matter. She felt that she was too far gone to think of precautions or treatment, and while she helped her mother do the work that brought in money to feed them, the girl realized that she was an extra worry and expense. On the whole, when she died, the results would more or less balance. It was the final collapse and "agony" of death she dreaded, and the inability to work up to the finish. Would the time be long or short? Must it cost too much, the burial and all? How deeply would her mother grieve? The shock and protracted suspense her mother had endured, when and after her father had gone away had absorbed, Yvonne thought, most of her mother's capacity for suffering. But one day followed another, Monday became Tuesday, holidays occurred, soiled clothes were brought in, washed, ironed and delivered, and the reserve of strength and resistance in Yvonne was dwindling ever so slowly. Her nerves might give way, as her mother's had. Nervously, Yvonne was the stronger.

Lame Jacqueline was trying to decide whether she was glad or sorry that her husband was elsewhere, with another woman. She liked, on the whole, being busy and lonely, and helpful to the Fremonts. That was better than being a twisted disappointment to the man she had loved. He was vigorous and gay. He did not take away her money. She liked the way he smiled when he felt good, the way he hurried off before he grew too uneasy or bored. What was it between them? If she should get hit by an auto and was taken to the Hotel Dieu, Albert could come to see her, and sit on the cot, talking gaily, and the other patients would wonder what such a man saw in a cripple with Eleanora Duse's eyes. Once in a while, when her husband had been pleasantly drunk and rather absentminded, she had been able to respond to him, and feel like a woman shaped normally, with legs just alike.

What did she do for such a man? She was always where he could find her. She never disapproved of his behavior if she knew about it, and never asked questions, if she did not know about it. She supported herself, in the laundry, and had saved a little, one way or another. He knew that whatever she had was at his disposal. Lots of men who had got married could not truthfully say that they were glad, but Albert said that, now and then. In fact, he let her know that he would be jealous if she as much as looked at another man. That was not likely, and if she did, who would look at her?

Mrs. Fremont could only remember the quarrels she had had with Fremont, in particular the final one that ended in his departure. The tender moments were slipping away. She was haunted by the fear that if he were alive, he remembered the unpleasantness, too, and that what they had enjoyed was losing all reality.

So the three women, one deformed, one morbid, one tubercular, paused in their walk along the *quai* to lean on the parapet. They were units of a whole called France. They were paying a kind of taxes never entered in the books of account.

What did they do, on the evening of national recovery, the first real night of spring? Madame Fremont reproached herself for not having rallied, for her daughter's sake, to face her situation squarely. She was thinking what she might suggest to please Yvonne. Nothing came to mind. On other occasions, when Yvonne had been a lovely little girl, as pretty as Hyacinthe across the street, Madame Fremont's efforts to please her had gone wrong. Whatever Fremont did, the girl had relished and shared. Madame Fremont thought further back, and could not remember that she had responded lovingly to her own mother, who had tried to please her. Why was it that time washes away first the happiness but the pattern of frustration persists?

Lame Jacqueline had seen Easter cakes, in the form of nests, with chocolate lumps in the shape of eggs, in the windows of Gillotte's bakery. Why not a pastry, with coffee at the Café du Départ? She offered the suggestion because the Fremont women needed a diversion. Madame Fremont consented for the sake of Yvonne. Yvonne, without appetite, made no objection, so as not to disappoint the others.

So, for the first time in years, Madame Fremont and Yvonne ordered cakes and coffee on the sidewalk of an outdoor café. Two hundred and seventy francs, about seventy-five cents, U.S.A.

In Room No. 8 of the Normandie, Antoinette de Poitevin and Achille Ithier were meandering across the acres of brandy, strewn like garlands on branches swayed by woodwinds. Intermittently they could hear, through the drapes and open window, a muted phrase from a jazz trumpet, the steady Dixieland support of Be-Bop's drums, an ear-sip of sax, clarinet, jug-pug, turoo. The French jazz band at the Nest of Vipers was wishing it could shimmy like its sister Kate, and winging the Wang Wang Blues. What might to an outsider have proved visually comical—Antoinette in her store chemise, Achille in honeysuckle-colored pyjamas—was to them rhapsodic.

He leaned over and whispered in her ear: "Zuzu."

She. "Lamby."

He. "Swallow."

She. "Robin."

He. "Mon coeur." (My heart)

She. "Mocqueur." (Mocker)

Next door, in Room No. 9, Hermann was reading, to the lovers' accompaniment, *The American Presidency* by Harold Laski. And Miriam was ironing.

Since the scarcity of eggs from the country prompted the

French to keep hens in the city, the old schedule of rooster crowing had lost its regularity. Cocks did not signal for ghosts to walk at midnight, and for dives to close at two A.M. They crowed in all the arrondissements whenever a flash of light awakened them, between eleven and dawn.

While the jazz band of the Nest of Vipers took a recess for brandy and reefers, and the sweating jitterbugs, male and female, white and black, tall and short, French and foreign, took a breather on the sidewalk or sat on the steps of St. Séverin, Hermann thought he heard a rooster crow, and frowned, but he was right. A rooster had crowed in the back yard of the Hotel of the Swallows, which is of a category so low that Algerian rug peddlers can afford to room there.

The inhabitants of the rue de la Huchette are not the kind who dance in the streets on a hot night, when rest and recovery are in the air. They were sitting on doorsteps, *terrasses,* curbs, or in chairs at windows, or in alley entrances, or strolling up and down, grouping, regrouping, and listening, thinking or talking. Many were drinking, and a few were eating between meals.

"It is early for roosters to be crowing," Hermann said to Miriam.

"There are fewer regulations in Paris—even for birds," she said. "*Gott sei dank.*"

They heard a rustle and a stirring outside, in the street, and Hermann, opening the draperies and leaning over the window rail, saw that several large black limousines were driving into the wide end of the street and stopping in front of the Hotel de Mont Souris.

Busse, after walking the back streets trying to calm himself and get up courage to return to his work, had approached by way of the quai St. Michel, and saw the cortege of limousines when they crossed the bridge. He ducked through the passageway into the courtyard behind the hotel, entered the back door, and glanced from the back hallway into the lobby. There was no sign of Pierre, who then was sitting with Carmen on the *terrasse* of the Départ, near the table occupied by the Fremonts and Jacqueline.

When Busse went over to the hotel desk, trying to act as if nothing had happened, Ribou and Emile greeted him sulkily.

"The boss" (which always meant Monsieur Gilles) "is hot under the collar. Where you been?" asked Ribou.

"I've been attending to the baggage," Busse said, haughtily, but he was like jelly inside.

"It isn't here," Emile said.

Monsieur l'Abbé d'Alexis entered at that point at the head of the first carload of Mexicans, who appeared to have enjoyed their dinner with gusto and seemed well disposed toward everyone, although few of them spoke or understood the French language. Four or five other abbots were on the sidewalk, counting the Mexicans as they descended from the autos, with a view to taking some of them across to the Hotel de la Harpe, a group of four to the Normandie, and two to the Hotel de la Huchette. The street was alive with people again, all anxious for a look at the visitors and, if possible, the traveling wooden Saint.

Somehow, instead of the twelve who had reservations at the Mont Souris, thirteen were ushered into the lobby.

Busse, in terror for fear that Pierre would pop in to confront him at any moment, passed out the registration slips with trembling hand and tried to aid the nearest Mexicans to fill out the blanks. Each one had to print his family name and given name, but since most of them had names like Leon Gerardo Luis Gomez y Gutierez (that one being addressed as Don Luis and less formally as Señor Gomez) the confusion began to get fantastic. Each slip had to show where the registrant had come from, where he was going, his address in Mexico, his address in France, the length of his proposed stay, and its purpose, also his passport number, date, and the place of issue.

About three slips had been completed and signed when all the lights went out, and cries of protest, glee, derision and dismay filled the quarter.

In Room No. 9 at the Normandie, Hermann was clinging to Miriam, demoralized. He felt sure that the electric iron had caused the blackout, and at first assumed that only the Normandie was affected. The din outside, and a furtive glance through the drapes multiplied his misgivings. The whole street, and everywhere as far as he could see, was in darkness, except for a few feeble candle flames and St. Cricq's kerosene lamp.

Miriam, although less shaken than Hermann, was frightened enough. She hid the freshly ironed clothes and the ironing board with its stand as best she could in the dark, wrapped the hot iron in a newspaper, placed it in a shopping bag, and followed Hermann out of the room. Both cowered against the thin wall as they heard, from No. 8, a ritual groan, low in a woman's throat, transcending dark or light, and rising, a rocket cry of winner take all, at its crest. The trembling refugees, startled out of their remaining wits by the lovers' sound effect, slunk through the hallway, whisked past the Judas window, and into the street, where they made their way to the rue du Chat qui Pêche and thence to the *quai*; their hotel haven was no longer secure, and no longer theirs. Madame would turn them out or, more probably, have them arrested. Even Miriam felt sure of that.

"It is not for us to break rules," she said, miserably. Hermann gulped and shuddered.

In his wheelchair in front of the bookstore, Anatole was enjoying the shank of the evening. Olympe, the grandmother of the brood of cats of the Café St. Michel, weary of the long day's activity around her, and liking the feel of the moon on her fur, had stepped cautiously through the maze of chair legs, table legs, trousers legs and legs in socks and stockings, and, with a purr from deep in her throat, had hopped into his lap. Soon she was as relaxed as he was.

Anatole was still musing over the behavior of Berthe Latouche, and the way she had let the implications rest about their encounter on the roof. He still felt that a gentleman should not make denials of omitted commission. He had made polite inquiries of Jeanne Piot as to how Berthe was, had been reassured with knowing smiles that Berthe's arm was much better, in fact quite normal, and that the sunburn was much worse. Berthe would blister and peel from forehead to toes. Jeanne had hinted that Berthe might like to talk with him, but Anatole had demurred.

As he reclined by the river with the cat he comforted himself with the reflection that nothing had to be done about anything until another day. If only he had not carried the girl, and registered the firm elasticity of her flesh, the smoothness of her limbs and back, her forehead and front, her breasts in bras, and hind cheeks, all warmed by the sun. He tried to remember the verses of the Song of Solomon about women's parts. Women's charms were not like fruit, and love was not the red red rose.

Around the corner came the boy, Victor, who had watched Hermann's dance from a darkened doorway and

wished for a rifle with a silencer and a telescope sight. He
thought of the German as an evil bird and himself as the
hunter, wet, famished, worn with waiting, until the prey
had come into sight and range, with waterfowl legs and scav-
enger's beak, to be shot but not retrieved.

"Victor," Anatole said, and the boy, who liked a word
from a man who had fought and been in prison camps, said:

"Yes, *mon capitaine*."

"I am no longer a captain, not even in the reserve," said
Anatole. "I am unfit for service. I always was unfit, but the
authorities were late in finding it out."

"Was there torture, sir? Did you witness anything like
that?"

Anatole, unnerved, almost heard faint screams, and found
himself saying, for no reason he could grasp:

"Christ is risen."

"Do soldiers believe that?" asked Victor, accusingly.

"Not many of them, unless they are dying and a chaplain is at hand, or they think they are dying, and no chaplain
is near. But some are able to believe, and it does them no
harm," said Anatole.

"And the torture?"

"There was no torture, boy."

Victor looked hurt and disappointed, knowing much
about what Anatole had suffered. Anatole, unable to be dishonest at such a moment, was stung, and relented.

"You're an honest boy. There was torture."

"Yes," Victor said, tensely.

"Stop thinking about torture. There is no more justifi-
cation for dwelling on it than administering it. Don't talk
about it. Let torture be."

"Forget what you like, sir," Victor said. "I won't forget.
If I'm the last one in France to remember, I won't forget."

He went along, down the *quai*, and Anatole, sickened, said sadly to Olympe:

"Suffer the little children to come unto Me, and forbid them not, for of such is the Kingdom of Heaven."

In Hortense's room, which Busse had so carefully prepared for her, sat Hubert Wilf and Monsieur Mainguet, talking quietly of this and that while the café crowd was sitting and the street crowd was strolling. Hortense was no longer in acute pain but she was not sleepy. She and her two admirers were aware that confusion reigned elsewhere in the Mont Souris, on account of the arrival of the Mexicans and the lights going out. She understood that Mainguet was holding himself aloof from the pilgrims and their escort because he had been overlooked in connection with the dinner at the Café Madrid. And on other occasions Hubert Wilf had refrained from taking part when there was a rush of work because ordinarily he was not encouraged to share in the management of the hotel. Hortense wondered about Busse, but assumed that he was too busy to sit at her bedside. That a painting had been borrowed for her room and that Busse had put his elbow through it, she had been told. She had not seen Pierre's letter to Busse and had no idea that the ruined canvas was being quoted at 1,000,000 francs.

The thirteenth Mexican, for whom no sleeping provisions had been made, had solved his own problem. At dinner he had drunk heartily of the excellent French wines and liqueurs, had tossed off a few at the Mont Souris bar, and then had wandered upstairs. The first door he tried and found unlocked had been that of Busse's room. He had entered, stretched himself on the bed, and was sleeping as soundly as any peon in his native land.

On the *quai*, Victor Lefevrais had recognized the Pflantzes and, when he found they were acting strangely, had watched and followed them. That something suspicious was in the shopping bag the sister was carrying seemed all too apparent, also that the couple were afraid to return to the Normandie. Whatever the object might be, Victor felt sure that they were at a loss as to how to dispose of it, and that it was incriminating to them. They crossed the bridge to the *place* Notre Dame, looking furtively behind them from time to time. The lights of the district were out. No one knew how to explain that. Some thought that the Seine, running fairly high, had flooded a conduit. That had happened before. Others had concluded that the Communist leaders of the union of electrical workers had selected the gala evening for a strike demonstration, in order to upset the Government's plans for a recovery celebration.

Miriam and Hermann had no doubts whatever on the subject. By some unlucky miracle, their electric iron had caused a short circuit which might involve criminal prosecution and incalculable damages. They could not decide what to do or where to go, and in those circumstances acted peculiarly. They could not bring themselves to drop the valuable iron into the Seine, or leave it in a trash can. And until a consultation with Louis was possible, they dared not be found in Room No. 9 of the Normandie.

Just then Louis was doing his best to take care of the six Mexicans who were billeted on the eastern section of the street. For one, he had an attic room under the eaves of the Normandie. That one was a priest, but, like the other Mexicans who were ordained members of the clergy, he wore a conventional black coat and trousers, with only the high-cut smooth vest and collar turned backward to distinguish him from his lay companions.

The pair who were left at the Hotel de la Huchette, from which Thérèse the cook, roaring drunk, had been decoyed in order to avoid an international incident, also were priests. But the three who were slated for the disreputable Hotel du Caveau were men of Mexican affairs, most amiable and courteous, but wide awake and of contrasting temperaments.

No. 1, addressed as Don Fulgencio, was lean and taciturn. He said almost nothing unless one of the others asked him a question, which was seldom. His prosperity, Louis understood, depended on sound Church relationships. He might have been a statuary and vestments merchant, a dealer in expensive gravestones, or a banker with shares in Jesuit public-service enterprises.

The second member of the trio, Don Jaime, talked a great deal, but inconsequentially. He was like a salesman who had relatives in a higher category of some going concern. Louis had come in contact with that type from every European nation. They were practicing Catholics by expediency but without theology or piety.

Don Primitivo was a jolly sprightly little man who talked sense, as Louis understood it, and made himself clear without too many words, in spite of the language barrier. Don Primitivo was an instructor in Spanish literature at a Mexican University, an authority on the works of Cervantes and Lope de Vega. Unless Louis was badly mistaken, Don Primitivo wanted to make the acquaintance, without delay, of a sympathetic Frenchwoman of the roguish kind. So Louis lingered downstairs at the Caveau bar while his charges were being shown upstairs, and arranged with Oudin, the proprietor, that Don Fulgencio and Don Jaime share a double room, while Don Primitivo was assigned to the small hall bedroom on the top floor, off the stairway.

Within a few minutes, Don Primitivo was downstairs

again. He and Louis tossed off a few drinks of *marc* and went, by means of back passageways, to the rue de la Harpe where Louis tapped on the door of the ladies' shoe store and was admitted by the Madame.

In all the hotels where the Mexicans were being received, they tried to explain, when they learned that their baggage had not been delivered, that they had been traveling light for several days and were in urgent need of their trunks before they had to appear for the Easter mass at St. Sulpice. Naturally, inquiries about baggage were most insistent at the Mont Souris, where the Abbé d'Alexis, J.C., and Père Taillepied, O.P., were deeply disturbed by the flaw in their arrangements. The Abbot sent for Monsieur Mainguet, who, when Emile the bellboy found him in Hortense's room, sighed meekly and followed the boy downstairs.

Almost anyone else would have passed the responsibility to Busse, who was trying to copy a list of the Mexicans' names from the garbled registration cards. It had slipped Busse's tormented mind, if he ever had known, that a Mexican inscribed as Gomez y Gutierez is really Señor Gomez, and that another named Gutierez y Salzedo is actually Señor Gutierez. In fact, Busse had to simplify the whole process by copying only the last name, farthest to the right. Ribou, meanwhile, had been sent to the Hotel de la Harpe, the Normandie and the Hotel de la Huchette for a list of the Mexicans there.

About half the Mexicans were priests, and those who were not were soon scattered throughout the quarter. A group had been drawn by the jazz strains from the Vipers' band and were seated on benches in the cellar of the Nest. Others were at Rahab, watching the Irish houri performing the hautch dance.

None of them took advantage of the opportunity to visit

by candlelight the gem of small Gothic churches, St. Séverin, and none of the priests from St. Séverin had been included in the welcoming committee organized by the Abbé d'Alexis.

There was a first-class row going on between the higher Paris clergy and the St. Séverin priests. Relatives of a former Vichy official named Henriot, who had been tried and shot as a collaborator and traitor, had applied to the head abbot at St. Séverin for a memorial mass on the anniversary of the execution. St. Séverin, the church with the workers' congregation, had refused to stage masses for convicted and executed Collabos. Eventually, after much discussion, the mass was celebrated in Notre Dame, where proletarian worshippers are seldom seen and never heard. The prevailing theory was that any sinner, whose relatives had the price, was entitled to a memorial mass, whatever his politics.

Ribou, who hated Busse and knew he was in trouble, took no pains with his supplementary lists of Mexican names. He wrote down almost anything, and just after he had turned them in, Busse, trapped behind the desk, saw Pierre Vautier entering the lobby with Carmen, so lovely and animate, on his arm. They had just had their fortunes told by Madame Niska, who had seen in the cards that adventure was at last coming to Carmen, and that Pierre was in danger of losing his immortal soul. Both were pleased with the prospect.

When Pierre saw Busse's eyes bulge like those of a frog, from a face that was all bandage, swelling and discoloration, he beamed. The effect, by thin candlelight, was worthy of Goya or Doré.

"Don't interrupt your work, old man," Pierre said. "I know how much depends on you. Madame Orey and I are not in a hurry."

Carmen squeezed his arm impulsively.

"We'll be around most of the night," continued Pierre, turning to smile down into her eyes.

"I can't wait to see the painting," Carmen said. "But I've promised to be patient."

"The secret is out. Madame is the purchaser," said Pierre.

He led Carmen away, toward the bar, with a wave of his hand to Busse, who was sweating like a shoat. Gilles Wilf came in, frowning darkly, deepening the crepuscular gloom.

"Now what about the baggage?" he grunted to Busse.

Mainguet, having been chided by the Abbé d'Alexis and consoled by Father Taillepied, approached the desk, somewhat flustered.

"I'm on my way to the Gare de Lyon," Busse said, defensively, to Gilles. "After all, they couldn't find anything on those littered platforms without knowing the names of those to whom the trunks belonged."

Gilles thumbed over toward the Abbot. "His Nibs should have given us the list in advance," Gilles said. "I'm sick of this whole business."

Pierre, long cool drink in hand, waved again at Busse through the barroom doorway.

"Here's to '*La Chasse*,'" he called, and Carmen looked up at him admiringly.

"I'll be the first one to own a Vautier," she said.

"I'm the first one for sale," he said.

"The Pursuit of the Spiritual," she said, pensively. "I can see with my eyes closed that He-Entity."

Pierre had been thinking that the He-Entity had been placed in a likely spot on the canvas for an elbow to penetrate.

"That may be lucky," said Pierre, but she did not try to fathom his cryptic remarks. She believed she would develop and learn.

I saw that Jeanne Piot had a light in her window, and walked up the long flights of stairs in the hope that I might have a talk with her. Passing the doorway of the apartment where Hyacinthe had lived, I tried to feel nothing, or, rather, to set aside what I was feeling in order to deal with it from a distance and at another time. The hallways and stairs were dark but my legs remembered them and guided me. I had never mounted the last flight while the Navet was in residence there.

There was nothing vacillating about Jeanne. What she had experienced would have disfigured another face, or twisted a lesser, or even a stronger, character. Jeanne was Eve, Mary Magdalen, Moll Flanders. She had never had an enemy one would not have chosen for one's self. She was alone in the salon. Eugène, exhausted, was asleep in his bedroom. Berthe Latouche, in her room, was burning with fever and racked with semi-delirious dream-fantasies. Her skin, that morning so satiny and lovely, was inflamed and blistered under its coating of sulfa ointment.

"How long has this been going on, with the teacher and Anatole?" I asked, knowing how Jeanne liked to dwell on amorous intrigues. I had to speak clearly, with my lips close to her ear.

"At first, I was way off the track," Jeanne said.

"You thought she liked the doctor?"

"No. Not as far off as that," she said.

"What's wrong with the doctor? I like him," I objected.

"Who can make love according to a Five-Year Plan?" she asked.

"There's no one around I like better than Anatole," I said.

Jeanne was doubtful. "A man can be too nervous," she said. "Berthe's still a virgin."

"Are you sure?" I asked.

"She's going to be hurt," Jeanne said. "It's her own fault. She got herself into a trap."

"You mean that miserable bookworm turned her down, when she offered herself? He's a cad."

"Don't say that," Jeanne said, coming to Anatole's defense. "He didn't pass her up. She was hurt long ago, not by anyone in particular. Men were afraid of her, because she said more or less what she meant, and seemed to have brains."

"You should explain about Berthe, to Anatole," I suggested.

Jeanne was solemn. "You think so?" she asked.

"Tell him that, since the girl's so sensitive about her appeal, he ought to set her mind at rest. He's a tender-hearted fellow."

"She's lucky, about that. If she'd made a bluff about some *salaud*, and he took advantage, she'd suffer, and no mistake. The book clerk'll be considerate and kind. I'll be surprised if she doesn't love him in the end."

"You'll try to fix it, then?" I asked.

"When I was younger," Jeanne said, blushing, "I tried to arrange things for some girls I knew who hadn't had much luck."

"What happened?"

Her embarrassment was genuine and charming.

"The men wanted me, instead."

The wicked Gilles Wilf, soon after the lights went out, had a rather fanciful impulse, the kind that seldom had come to him of recent years. He was wearing, as usual, the Continental black suit, with senator's white cotton shirt and black four-in-hand tie, black patent-leather shoes and a black derby hat. On the hat rack in the dim lobby of the Mont

Souris he noticed a black felt hat, rather broad, which belonged, most likely, to one of the French church business-men who had entered with the Mexicans. In the semi-dark-ness he borrowed the black felt hat, replacing it on the hook with his own *chapeau melon*, sauntered unnoticed through his own busy bar and just outside the doorway was ad-dressed pleasantly by a couple of Mexicans. Prompted by another sudden whim, Gilles pointed to his mouth and let out a few assorted noises which led those standing around to believe that he could not speak.

In the street, the lobby and the higher windows puny flames of makeshift lights appeared and disappeared, having no more general effect than stray fireflies in a swamp. Gilles as he wandered eastward felt like a character from the Ara-bian nights, with money in his pocket and responsibilities abandoned. The Government was vacationing in the South; the nation was still bankrupt; the left hand of business and commerce was quicker than the right; his hotel was at sixes and sevens; the illegally rented midget cars of the auto school were afield, like woodchucks at night. Recovery, to Gilles, would mean that a smaller proportion of his acts would be illegitimate, but he cared little about that. As Frenchmen go, Gilles was patriotic. Throughout difficult years he had done much to keep afloat the principles of individual initiative and the private-profit motive.

He knew his brother Hubert was hanging around Mad-ame Berthelot and that nothing would come of it. Already he had fired the chef, for complaining too loudly about the dinner he had prepared for the Mexicans and which had been by-passed so cavalierly by the pilgrims and the priests. He should have told Busse about that, but Busse seemed to be out of his depth already. What was the matter with him?

Why such crises of nerves? There was no baggage for the Mexicans. Well and good. The night was warm. Let them sleep in their pelts, and go to mass in wrinkled clothes. Gilles decided to go to the Caveau bar and have five or six cognacs.

As Gilles passed through the dark mid-section of the street, Madame Fontaine, standing in the dimness of the Normandie hallway, was stretching for a delicious yawn. Her movements were sensuous and concerted. Gilles was aware of the firm slender hips and full breasts, as she rose on the balls of her feet, arms outspread, flexed the muscles of her limbs, and let out a faint sigh.

"What the devil," muttered Gilles to himself, as he plodded along, now with a strange reluctance. "I not only want a woman, which is bad enough, but a specific and particular one, which is the depth of folly. I must be losing my mind."

Gilles argued with himself. After all, he was a businessman well known in the street. The woman whose silhouette he had seen, in solitary gesture, might be anyone's sister or wife. Men became unstable when the lights were out, he thought. Just because it was a holiday night, and France was getting her head above water, what likelihood was there that if he approached a strange woman in a hallway she would not take a swing at him, or yell for help. Where would he be then?

He turned into the Caveau bar and his mood was improved when he found that Oudin was too drunk to recognize him. There were a few stray Mexicans, and a couple of Moroccans who spoke both Spanish and French in such a way that the languages sounded very much alike. Everyone was talking, except Gilles, and no one listened to what another was saying.

It was not long before Gilles slipped away.

"This is silly enough to be done by Brother Hubert," he admitted, as he overcame his better judgment and started back toward the Normandie. His step faltered, and his heart, gone youthful for the night, did a hop when he saw the statuesque Lady of the Yawn and Stretches turning alone and leisurely into the rue du Chat qui Pêche. At the corner of that tiny street, Gilles, reproaching himself, nevertheless turned right and followed her toward the river. The woman did not hear him, or if she did she gave no sign. The *quai* was vacant for fifty yards in either direction.

Gilles saw the woman halt and lean on the parapet, looking pensively down at the moving river surface, ebony and indigo. The moon, coming out thinly from behind a cluster of cirrus clouds, contributed platinum.

"That is all that was lacking," Gilles sighed. "I am cooked."

He leaned against the parapet, a few feet downstream from the woman. He had almost got up his courage to say "Good evening" when he decided that he must not talk. So he gesticulated at the moon, the river, Madame's figure, and emitted subdued weird sounds.

"Another original," said Madame under her breath. She had thought all of the odd types had been in her own hotel that night. But she was touched, for it was evident that the man who was accosting her in such an unusual manner was almost pathologically shy, in his heart, and sadly inexperienced.

"You may speak, if you wish," she said, in an encouraging way, and stepped a little nearer.

Again he pointed to his mouth.

"You can't talk?" she asked. "Then you never boast about your conquests, unless you're addicted to writing."

Gilles made her understand that he abhorred putting anything in writing, which was true, and therefore convincing. He stepped a little nearer her, but misjudged the distance, so that his hip was touching hers. Now it comes, he thought, the slap in the face or the call for a *flic*. For that he was prepared, but what happened disconcerted him more than a rebuff. She snuggled against him, not too boldly, but frankly, looked him in the eye, not too coyly, merely as if she and he were similarly minded.

Swallowing hard, Gilles took her arm, escorted her furtively along the narrow *quai* in the shadow of the buildings, and turned into the snug passage. His movement was so unexpected and the alley so dark that a less adventurous woman would have shrunk back. Instead, she preceded him. The passageway brought them to the back courtyard of the Mont Souris. There were no candles in the rear windows. Madame had never been in the courtyard or known of its existence. Neither was the hotel familiar to her, except for its aspect from the front. She assumed that she had been appropriated by one of the visitors from Mexico, and felt the additional thrill so many women have when they think they are about to upset something relatively holy.

The darkness still held, and she remembered afterward a glimmer of surprise because the mute foreigner seemed to know his way around so well. Gilles unlocked a bedroom door, on the second floor. She sidled in without a murmur. In the darkness garments were removed, in her case without undue haste. Still, Madame was the first who was completely undressed. She lay on the crisp fresh sheets, face toward the ceiling, and stretched again. Gilles, one leg still tangled in his trousers, lost his balance, upset a chair, and, when he was in the most ridiculous state conceivable, abjectly exposed, the electric lights went on full blaze.

The night shift in the baggage and customs sheds of the Gare de Lyon had little to do after midnight, and when French public employees have almost nothing to do they are more reluctant to stir themselves than when they are overworked.

Before the war there had been two of what might be called minor executives in the customs department of that railroad station. Today there are five. The ranks of the clerks have been doubled, and the number of working porters reduced by a third. All of them loathe travelers.

The largest group was loafing in the shed, discussing an item from *Figaro*. Butter had been placed on the "free" list and could be bought and sold with no regard for price ceilings or ration cards. The dairy producers in the country had held back a large part of the Easter supply in the hope that a higher price could be obtained later, if the Black Market survived. While butter had been scarce, oleo-margarine was more in demand. Whoever had struck butter off the ration list had neglected to do the same for margarine. *Figaro* had "discovered" that 8,000 employees were being paid by the Government to distribute about a quarter of a pound of margarine per day. Even worse, the clerical force consecrated to margarine occupied two entire floors of a large building in the rue St. Denis, while hospitals, schools and public institutions were overcrowded and there existed generally throughout Paris the most acute housing shortage in its history.

More than half the employees in the Gare de Lyon, in the lower categories, belonged either to the Communist Party, the union under the influence of Communist leaders, or both. Most of the rest were Socialists, whom the Commies regard as neither flesh nor fowl, and first on the list to be liquidated.

"It's all very well to talk about reducing the margarine force of 8,000 employees to two or three employees, but what would become of the 7,997? There isn't room for them in other offices. They would all become 250-francers, and nearly starve to death," said one of the clerks in the shed.

A 250-francer is an unemployed Frenchman on the dole, which amounts to seventy cents a day.

A telephone rang in an office some yards distant from the platform on which the conversation about margarine was taking place, and one of the clerks reluctantly shuffled off to answer it. He took his time, spoke gruffly, and did not hurry on his way back.

"Those damned Mexicans, again," he said.

The baggage had been scattered through the sheds marked "A" to "Z" and mixed with tons of other luggage. The consignment was numbered 72, and a porter, seeing a trunk with a sticker bearing that number, on the "L" platform, looked it over and started growling.

"This one has no customs mark," he said. The senior clerk of the night shift was on his feet, immediately bellicose.

"Those bastards," he said, meaning the Mexicans he had never seen, and the busybodies who had made so many inquiries and complaints about their stuff.

A few trunks were snaked from near-by platforms from the alphabetical piles, bearing stickers numbered 72, but there were twenty-six platforms and most of the trunks of the consignment were buried under others with stickers bearing other numbers. None of the No. 72 consignment, belonging to the Mexicans, had passed the French customs at the border. They must go back into the basement, by means of the freight elevator, to be left until called for by the voyager in person, with the right keys. Then they would be taken up to the ground floor room, dumped behind the horseshoe counter, and examined by a customs man who would afterwards mark them with chalk, according to the orders of the day, and the porters would take them wherever the voyager directed, either to the check rooms or the taxi-cab stand.

So Busse, who had driven to the station in the small sedan he occasionally used from the Wilf garage, steering with difficulty on account of his nose bandage and swelling, found a truly chaotic situation. The head clerk had ordered the subordinates to take down into the basement all the trunks numbered 72 that could conveniently be found and pried loose. When Busse, protesting and imploring, presented his list of Mexican names, the clerks and porters merely laughed at him, and continued slinging trunks around and wheeling them away.

Although Busse was too low in energy or spirit to assert himself, the head clerk took the initiative before Busse would have had a chance.

"You were here this afternoon?" he asked.

Busse admitted that he had been.

"And you reported that the baggage of these Bible-thumping turnips from Mexico had passed the customs inspection at Modane," the head clerk said, accusingly.

Busse drew himself up. "They have passed the customs," he said.

"Where are the keys to those trunks?" the functionary demanded.

"The keys?" Busse repeated in horror.

"Shall we use crowbars?" the clerk yelled.

The *place* St. Michel, in the old days, was dim and quiescent at 2 o'clock in the morning. Paris "night spots" were elsewhere—at the famous crossroads in Montparnasse, on the inner slopes of Montmartre, along the Grands Boulevards, the Champs Elysées, on the edge of the Latin Quarter. Very few autos rattled through and even fewer silent bicycles. Traffic was practically suspended.

No tourists were brought by the American Express and Thomas Cook into the rue de la Huchette. New Orleans jazz and Chicago Be-Bop had not invaded the cellars, to supplant the Bal Musettes on the ground floors. At 2 A.M. the fountain of St. Michael with its huge shell background, the warrior saint, the dragon and the dolphins, exerted its bronzed plastic force, in an almost empty square.

The trolley tracks were crisscrossed, and no tramcars rolled over them. The pens for waiting passengers were ranged in skeleton order, and no crowd packed itself into them. The young plane trees now standing along the western border were doubtless in some tree nursery awaiting transplantation. The older trees were not as tall as they are today, but were, perhaps, more luxuriant. The franc, which before the war fluctuated between 15 and 50 to the dollar, was discussed as voluminously in the press and everywhere. Some of the politicians were promising to stabilize it, to balance the budget, and nothing constructive was done. Today, with the franc at 350 to the dollar, the politicians are still doing nothing.

On the Easter week-end of recovery, at 2 A.M., the *place* was neither dingy, deserted nor dark. Nor was it garish, boisterous, congested or in any kind of whirl. The newly revived street lights were reflected in the somber bronze of the fountain, at the base of which, on either side, were new plaques commemorating those of the quarter who, in the August, 1944, uprising against the Boche, had offered their lives, and whose offer had been accepted. The *terrasses* of the cafés were not crowded at that hour. There were just enough customers who meant to stay a while. Others were saying good night. The soft laughter of the street girls from the rue St. André could be heard, the lap of the river, the tread of the neighbors in the rue de la Huchette, along the quai St. Michel, the rue Xavier Privas and the rue du Chat qui Pêche. Others were asleep in hotels, apartments, hall bedrooms, back rooms of shops, go-downs adjacent to kitchens, concierges' loges, on cots, beds, stuffed chairs and bunks. Nobody was uncomfortably hot. Much more important, no one was cold.

Thérèse the cook, on a roving drunk, had grabbed from the driver's hearty hand, as a Hachette truck passed by, an early copy of a weekly newspaper, printed mostly in advance but with a few columns of news or last-minute comment on page 1 and page 6, the front and back. She barged across the Pont au Double, balanced herself under a street lamp and tried to read the headlines, in front of Notre Dame.

As hard as she tried to focus, the letters of the headlines got confused and scrambled.

She saw a man and a woman sitting on a bench in front of the dingy city hospital. They saw her lumbering toward them, too late to make a getaway. Expansive and filled with friendly feeling, she gestured in a way that parted them, and sat down heavily between them, spreading the Paris *Dimanche* in front of all three.

The two were Hermann and Miriam, who had settled on the bench some time after the lights of the quarter blazed again in unison. The sack with the electric iron was in Miriam's lap. Victor, who had followed and watched them so long, had stationed himself inside the iron fence of the park around Notre Dame and, in spite of himself, had fallen asleep.

"I can't read what the paper says," Thérèse told Hermann. As drunk as she was, she sensed that he was quaking with fear.

"The devil, comrade. You can't think Thérèse would do you any harm, or your lady comrade, either. I only want the news. To tell the truth, I've drunk too much to read it for myself."

Hermann tried to speak, and could only stammer:

"We weren't afraid of you, madame."

Thérèse patted the top headline. "Now what does that say?"

Obediently Hermann read aloud: "EUROPE RELAXES OVER LONG EASTER HOLIDAY."

"That's fine. Go on. Europe and Thérèse. We got two more days to go, but never mind. Continue."

"To an extent that has not been possible in the past ten years, the people of Paris, and with them those of Western Europe, let themselves go in the celebration of Easter today. The weather, if unseasonably hot, was welcome. The bright sun, the clear sky, the new leaves all fitted the gala mood. The Government terminated many of the war-time restrictions.

"Yesterday there were the usual holiday accidents, a record death toll, but to be expected when French motorists, after a decade of prohibition against pleasure driving, were issued gasoline. After sundown, the street lights, many of them unhooded, blazed forth and the illumination was swelled to pre-war proportions by the advertising signs and brilliant shop windows. For a short time yesterday evening, beginning about 11:30, certain quarters of Paris were thrown into darkness . . ."

"Alas," murmured Miriam, weakly, and started to rise.

But Hermann's voice was jubilant, and suddenly his impish mood of the early evening possessed him again. He got up, and revolving in waltz time on tiptoe, the paper spread before him, quoted, as follows:

"Certain quarters of Paris were thrown into darkness by the failure of two conduits leading to one of the large power plants. The damage, due to a rupture of overhead wires, was repaired and by one A.M., all lighting was normal again."

Thérèse, stirred by the dancing and the festive behavior, tried to rise and join in. She slipped, tottered and fell, and, unable to rise without help, asked "comrades" Hermann and Miriam to take her home, to the hotel six doors from their own.

Miriam, clutching the iron to her breast, looked at Hermann, and nodded. Together, they got Thérèse to her feet and three-abreast they crossed the bridge toward the rue de la Huchette. They made a pleasant commotion and passed within a few yards of Victor, but he was sound asleep.

When Busse left the customs shed the second time, faced with the problem of the keys and each Mexican in person, he drove the sedan aimlessly, around the Gare de Lyon, nearly losing his life, and endangering a few others, half a dozen times. He parked again, within three hundred yards of the station, having his eyes on the enormous café across from its main entrance. He could not go back to the hotel, be speared like an eel by Pierre, with the eager millionairess on his arm, and tell Gilles Wilf and the Abbé d'Alexis that all the arrangements had failed. The trunks had not, after all, passed the customs at Modane. Each one must be opened in the presence of a customs officer at the depot, and each voyager must sign an individual return or statement.

He was still a member of the Communist Party, and party

policies had been applied to the case. Busse knew all too well
what happened to French Communists who showed dis-
loyalty, or even who failed to "militate." The superintendent of the station had ordered the head clerk to set aside
formalities and clear Lot 72. Backed up by his Party comrades, the head clerk had said:

"You cannot order me to break the law."

His nervousness was so acute that Busse parked the Wilf
sedan in a spot where parking was absolutely forbidden. He
went into the huge café, more dead than alive, asked for a
jeton, waited in a ragged line to use the pay telephone, and
got Mainguet on the line. Busse's voice had such a quality of
despair that Mainguet could not turn down the request. The
little man said good night to Hortense, and indeed it was
time, looked in vain for Gilles Wilf, then found a Mexican
who could speak French, after a fashion. Mainguet explained
that those Mexicans who had gone to bed must be aroused,
and those who had found other attractions to their taste
must be found, if any of them were to have their trunks in
time to dress for the Easter mass and presentation ceremonies.

Busse, at the café across from the Gare de Lyon, sat down,
back against the wall, in a corner of the spottily occupied
terrasse. All the people around were strangers to him, and
mostly to one another. They were going, waiting, coming.
Nearly all of them were drowsy and tired.

He felt sick and ineffectual. The day before, that morning, even, he had had a good position, a few friends, some
associates who were obliged to respect him, a bank account
of 330,000 francs. He had seen his way clear out of his political involvements. He had, at every turn, shown weakness. And if a dreamer weakens, what becomes of his dream?

In the middle distance Busse saw a truck without brakes bump into the back of the borrowed sedan, causing it to hop forward, hind wheels too far from the curb. Let that, too, be destroyed

The Mont Souris was out of the question. Where else should he go? He felt his collar—wilted. His tie—lop-sided. He was alone.

He saw a police officer approach the sedan, observe that it was improperly parked and dented in the rear, make note of its number, and saunter away. A traffic charge!

A fly or moth fluttered into his coffee and, although Busse was sorry, he lacked the initiative to rescue the insect. He suffered as the creature died. He would regret not having saved it. He was living to grow old.

Busse had ordered a Suze. The waiter brought a Dubonnet, and failed to take away the coffee cup.

"I want my mother," Busse moaned, and the waiter, thinking that his client was asking for the *addition*, said:

"*Parfaitement, monsieur.*"

Of the thirteen Mexicans in the Hotel de Mont Souris, only twelve of whom had been registered, eleven were found either in their beds, the barroom or at Rahab. The Hotel de la Harpe produced four of their six. The Mexican priest in the attic of the Normandie responded, and so did the two in the Hotel de la Huchette.

Five taxicabs were secured from the *place* St. Germain des Prés by Emile, who rode his bicycle there and led the empty cabs back to the rue de la Huchette. The first four cabs were loaded, and the fifth one reserved for Don Fulgencio, Don Jaime and Don Primitivo from the Hotel du Caveau. Little Monsieur Mainguet, who seldom had been afield at that hour of the morning and seldom had been able to afford a taxi, was to ride in the last cab.

At the Hotel du Caveau, Don Jaime was unable to find his passport. His companions, and then Oudin, the proprietor, searched the room, but all were too nervous to do a thorough job. A Mexican passport, with a photograph of a medium-sized, fairly dark and ordinary-looking man stamped on it, was worth a great deal of money. Unhappily for Oudin, a few other foreign passports had disappeared while the possessors had been guests of that hotel.

Louis, of the Normandie, when he heard what had happened, and feeling responsible for the Mexicans in the Caveau, confronted Oudin with blood in his eye.

"I didn't do it," Oudin said.

"You'll wish you had, when I get through with you," Louis said.

"Figure it out for yourself. I couldn't risk a scandal with these specimens, protected by the Archbishop, and God knows who else." Something in Oudin's manner made Louis inclined to believe him. At that moment, two *agents de police* came in with Chouette, the drunken truck driver for E. Saillens and Sons, between them. They were looking for a place to dump him, and had used Oudin's coal cellar for similar purposes before.

Don Fulgencio, the most impressive of the Caveau Mexicans, and Don Jaime, babbling, braced the two policemen, and tried to tell them about the passport they insisted had been stolen. The Mexican priest, from the Normandie, acted as interpreter.

The officers, who had had dealings with Oudin before, dropped Chouette so suddenly that he almost slumped to the floor. Every officer at the Commissariat of the 5th had been itching to get Oudin, on any charge at all that could be made to stick.

"Well, well," one officer said, and looked at Oudin, smiling with satisfaction. "A brand-new passport, eh?"

"Please. I didn't do it," Oudin said. He wished at that moment that he had stolen the passport, so that he could return it. In that case, his medicine would not be so severe.

The senior officer looked at Oudin again, more pleased. "Don't keep us waiting. Hand it over," he said.

"Search the place yourself, I beg of you," Oudin said.

Reluctant to exert themselves, the two policemen followed the Mexicans, the priest, Oudin and Louis upstairs.

One of the officers found the passport, which had slipped from the tilting table of the *escritoire* into an empty space behind the drawers. The line of taxis got started for the Gare de Lyon as the clock struck three.

At the Gare de Lyon a porter who had been sleeping most of the evening, in an empty cubbyhole used in busy hours as an office, joined the group of Communists on the platform. He saw the stack of baggage comprising Consignment 72, from Rome via Modane, and the head clerk, now rather proud of himself for having stood up to the station superintendent, told him what was happening.

"But, comrade," said the porter. He was an exiled Spaniard, a Catalan who had adopted the papers and personality of a deceased Catalan cousin who had lived on the French side of the Pyrenees. He had fought against Franco, and since had taken an interest in international affairs. "But, comrade," the Spanish porter said to the head clerk. "Mexicans are not North Americans. It is the tourists from the United States we've been instructed to harass. During our war the Mexicans helped us. They defied the United States, and the British, and your Señor Blum, and sent us arms and money to fight Franco."

The head clerk's face showed dismay. "Come to think of it, you may be right. We shouldn't have got these Comrade Mexicans out of bed."

So when Mainguet, more than usually timid, led the chattering delegation of pilgrims into the customs shed, he and they were received with apologetic cordiality, and found that the trunks, and even a few extra ones which had got into the consignment by mistake, had been chalk-marked and O.K.'d.

Louis the garçon, the two policemen, Noel and Monge were leaning against the Caveau bar. Oudin, still awed by his narrow escape from trouble, was behind the zinc.

As happened so often, Louis felt a slip of paper in his vest pocket and took it out to examine it. It was a blank form he had picked up from the floor when he had swept No. 8 that morning. He glanced down and read the heading: "Société des Amis de l'Arbre." (Society of the Friends of the Tree.)

"That's funny," said one of the cops.

"What's funny?" asked Louis.

"The old duffer who runs that society was found dead tonight," the officer said.

Louis, whose head was ringing slightly from the long day of sociable drinking, caught on to himself and waited.

"Dead?" he repeated.

The officer told him that old Monsieur Poitevin had died in bed, apparently, some time after having eaten his dinner. A fire had started in a pile of rags in the apartment below, smoke had filtered upstairs, the firemen had rung, then entered to see if everything was all right, and had found the body in the bed.

"He had died . . . all by himself?" Louis asked, feeling queer inside.

"There's always something to hold up the certificate," said the officer, bored. "They found a slip of green-blue paper, the kind druggists use to wrap up powders. Until that's been examined . . . who can tell?"

Louis controlled his agitation, left his drink unfinished, and started back toward the Normandie. He calmed himself, and shook his head. After what had been heard through the walls, he could not believe that the couple in Room No. 8 were guilty of anything grave. Impossible! A man like Ithier! A respectable middle-aged woman!

Still, he reflected, perhaps he ought to notify Antoinette that her father had been found dead.

But as he neared the Normandie, entered and mounted the familiar stairway, he asked: what concern of his? Who had invited him to know them, to pick up a bit of paper, to listen to what a *flic* had said? Let them sleep, if they could. Let them find out everything or nothing. Later. In the morning.

He listened outside Room No. 9. Apparently Miriam was safe.

Louis, in his own room two floors higher, undressed partly. He was tired. Soon he was asleep.

And about this time, Monsieur Gillotte was aroused by his alarm clock, awakened his wife, and they prepared to roll out, shape and bake the *croissants* for another busy day.

The sky was streaked with light behind Notre Dame.

Two bats zigzagged up and down the rue de la Huchette.

Paris
December 20, 1949

Blackstone Studios

Books by Elliot Paul which are included in his continuing series, ITEMS ON THE GRAND ACCOUNT.

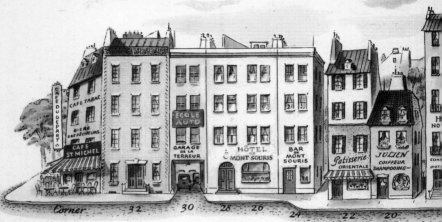